Course	Engineering Problem Solving I
Course Number	**59:005**
	The University of Iowa
	College of Engineering

http://create.mcgraw-hill.com

ISBN-10: 1121259707   ISBN-13: 9781121259706

Contents

Credits

CHAPTER **3**

Introduction to Engineering Design

Chapter Objectives

When you complete your study of this chapter, you will be able to:

- Identify and explain the key steps in the design process
- Explain the importance of the customer's role in the design process
- Apply the design process to solving an open-ended problem
- Understand the importance of the engineering design process in development of engineering solutions to society's needs

3.1 An Introduction to Engineering Design

What do you say when asked why you are planning to be an engineer? One possible response is, "I want to become an engineer to design . . . ." It might be to design a water-quality system for a developing country, a new spacecraft for NASA, the tallest building in the world, an auto-guidance device for automobiles, new and improved sports equipment, or even synthetic blood. The key is that engineers design devices, systems, or processes to help humankind.

So what is engineering design? Engineering design is a systematic process by which solutions to the needs of humankind are obtained. Design is the essence of engineering. The design process is applied to problems (needs) of varying complexity. For example, mechanical engineers will apply the design process to develop an effective, efficient vehicle suspension system; electrical engineers will apply the process to design lightweight, compact wireless communication devices; and materials engineers will apply the process to design strong, lightweight composites for aircraft structures.

The vast majority of complex problems in today's high technology society do not depend for solutions on a single engineering discipline; rather, they depend on teams of engineers, scientists, environmentalists, economists, sociologists, legal personnel, and others. Solutions are dependent not only on the appropriate applications of technology but also on public sentiment as executed through government regulations and political influence. As engineers we are empowered with the technical expertise to develop new and improved products and systems; however, at the same time we must be increasingly aware of the impact of our actions on society and the environment in general and work conscientiously toward the best solution in view of all relevant factors.

The systematic design process can be conveniently represented by the six steps introduced in Sec. 3.2.

1. Define the problem to be solved.
2. Acquire and assemble pertinent data.
3. Identify solution constraints and criteria.
4. Develop alternative solutions.
5. Select a solution based on analysis of alternatives.
6. Communicate the results.

Building on an Engineering Degree

Nick Mohr

Nick Mohr received his BS in mechanical engineering and then went on to obtain his medical degree. He is currently a resident physician in emergency medicine, caring for patients in the emergency departments of two trauma centers and on a helicopter transport service in Indianapolis, Indiana.

Once he finishes his residency, he plans then either to look for a faculty appointment at a university or to pursue further training, perhaps in a postgraduate aerospace medicine program offered by Johnson Space Center (JSC) in conjunction with the University of Texas. Recently, he spent some time at JSC working with the flight surgeons in space medicine, which he found to be "incredible."

Dr. Mohr was involved with numerous student organizations and activities while pursuing his engineering degree, including Team PrISUm (Iowa State University's solar car team), the Cosmic Ray Observation Project, and the Ames (Iowa) Free Clinic. He feels that his involvement outside the classroom was one of the most important aspects of his undergraduate training. It provided him experience in learning how (1) to solve novel problems and make decisions without knowing the right answers; (2) to succeed and fail when the stakes for failure are high; and (3) to identify what consequences are worth fearing, and using those consequences to choose risks worth taking.

Dr. Mohr recalls that as a student, he had no idea how many doors an engineering degree could open and offers the following advice to students just beginning their engineering education:

"There is no harm in being uncertain about what path your career may take, and in fact, many people change their direction along the way—that's not bad. The important part is to have dreams, and to follow them wholeheartedly until they change. If we do that, we will solve some very interesting problems in our lives and can improve the world in which we live. A strong and diverse educational foundation in engineering has opened doors that I never could have imagined when I was in college."

A formal definition of engineering design is found in the curriculum guidelines of the Accreditation Board for Engineering and Technology (ABET). ABET accredits curricula in engineering schools and derives its membership from the various engineering professional societies. Each accredited curriculum has a well-defined design component that falls within the ABET guidelines. The ABET statement on design reads as follows:

Engineering design is the process of devising a system, component, or process to meet desired needs (Fig. 3.1). It is a decision-making process (often iterative), in which the basic sciences, mathematics, and engineering sciences are applied to convert resources optimally to meet a stated objective. Among the fundamental elements of the design process are the establishment of objectives and criteria, synthesis, analysis, construction, testing, and evaluation. The engineering design component of a curriculum must include most of the following features: development of student creativity, use of open-ended problems, development and use of modern design theory and methodology, formulation of design problem statements and specifications, consideration of alternative solutions, feasibility considerations, production processes, concurrent engineering design, and detailed system descriptions. Further, it is essential to include a variety of realistic constraints such as economic factors, safety, reliability, aesthetics, ethics, and social impact.

Figure 3.1

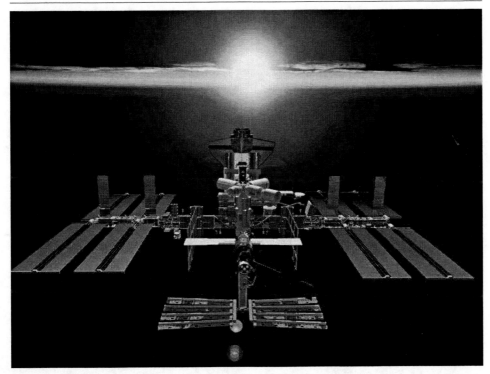

The engineering design process was very critical in the design of the international space station.

3.2 The Design Process

A simple definition of design is "a structured problem-solving activity." A process, on the other hand, is a phenomenon identified through step-by-step changes that lead toward a required result. Both these definitions suggest the idea of an orderly, systematic approach to a desired end. The design process, however, is not linear. That is, one does not necessarily achieve the best solution by simply proceeding from one step in the process to the next. New discoveries, additional data, and previous experience with similar problems generally will result in several iterations through some or all the steps of the process (Fig. 3.2).

It is important to recognize that any project will have time constraints. Normally before a project is approved a time schedule and a budget will be approved by management.

For your initial introduction to the design process, we will explain in more detail what is involved at each of the six steps above. Simply memorizing the steps will not give you the needed understanding of design. We suggest that you take one or more of the suggested design problems at the end of the chapter, organize a team of two to four students, and develop a workable solution for each problem selected. By working as a team you will generate more and better solution ideas and develop a deeper understanding of the process.

The process begins with a definition of the problem (Step 1) to be solved. In many cases the engineering design team does not identify or define the

Figure 3.2

Environmental engineers used the engineering design process to maximize the efficiency of this recycling system without causing damage to the environment.

problem. Instead customers, field representatives for the company, and management will provide the initial request. The team must be careful not to define a solution at this step. If it does it has not satisfied the design process. For example, assume company management asks a team to design a cart to transport ingots of metal from one building to another, the buildings approximately 200 meters apart. The solution to this problem is already known: a cart. It is a matter of seeing what is available on the market for handling the required load. It may be to the company's benefit to find a "new system" that effectively and efficiently moves heavy loads over a short distance. This would open up the possibility for a rail system, conveyor, or other creative solution. Usually a simple problem definition allows the most flexibility for the design team. For example, the initial problem could be defined as simply "Currently there are ingots of metal stored in building one. We need a way to get the ingots from that building to building two."

The team next acquires and assembles all pertinent information on the problem (Step 2). Internal company documents, available systems, Internet searches, and other engineers are all possible sources of information. Once all team members are up to speed on the available information, the solution constraints and criteria are identified (Step 3). A constraint is a physical or practical limitation on possible solutions; for example, the system must operate with 220-volt electricity. Criteria are desirable characteristics of a solution; for example, the solution must be reliable, must be easy to operate, must have an acceptable cost, and must be durable. You might think of a constraint as a requirement—all possible solutions must meet it—while a criterion is a relative consideration, in that one solution is better than another ("durable" is a criterion, for example).

Now the team is ready for the creative part of the process, developing alternative solutions (Step 4). This is where experience and knowledge, combined with group activities such as brainstorming, yield a variety of possible solutions (Fig. 3.3). Each of the alternatives is now analyzed using the constraints and comparing each to the specified criteria. In many cases prototypes are built and tested to see if they meet constraints and criteria. Computer modeling

Figure 3.3

The brainstorming of new ideas for solving an engineering problem is important in the design process.

and analysis are used heavily during this step. Then, using a device such as a decision matrix, a solution is selected (Step 5).

The last step of the design process often involves the most time and requires resources outside the original design team. Communicating the results (Step 6) involves developing all the details and reports necessary for the design to be built or manufactured as well as presentations for management and customers.

Although the systematic design process appears to end at Step 6, it really remains open throughout the product life cycle. Field testing, customer feedback, and new developments in materials, manufacturing processes, and so on may require redesign any time during the life cycle. Today many products are required to have a disposal plan prior to marketing. In these cases the original design needs to include disposal as a constraint on the solution. Although a six (6) step design process is outlined above, other more expanded steps are in common use. For example, Figure 3.4 illustrates a nine-step design process.

To further illustrate the iterative nature of the design process, study Figure 3.5 for a typical industrial activity. The process begins with a conceptual design and proceeds to preliminary design, detailed design, prototype design, and the final design. Note that design evaluation is conducted frequently during the process. Also note that the design is optimized at the detailed design stage. Optimization is beyond the scope of this introduction, but suffice it to say that it occurs after the solution is determined and is based on the analysis of alternatives (Step 5).

Figure 3.4

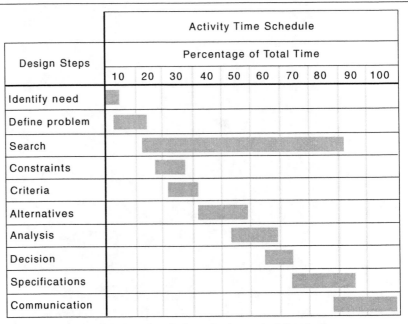

A time schedule must be developed early in order to control the design process.

Figure 3.5

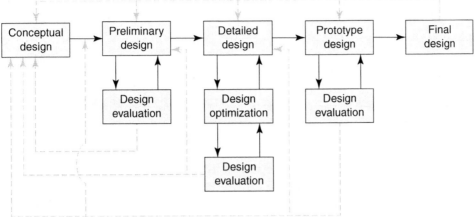

A flow diagram for the categories of engineering design.

3.3 Design and the Customer

Often customer requirements are not well defined. The design team must determine, in consultation with the customer, the expectations of the solution. The customer therefore must be kept informed of the design status at all times during the process. It is likely that compromises will have to be made. Both the design team and customer may have to modify their requirements in order to meet deadlines, cost limits, manufacturing constraints, and performance requirements. Figure 3.6 is a simple illustration of the Kano model showing the relationship between degree of achievement (horizontal axis) and customer satisfaction (vertical axis). Customer requirements are categorized in three areas: basic, performance related, and exciting.

Figure 3.6

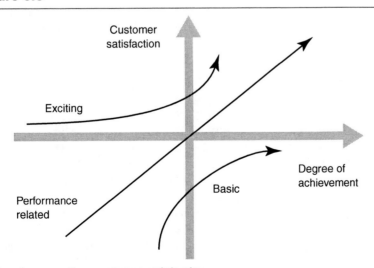

Factors in generating customer satisfaction.

Basic customer requirements are simply expected by the customer and assumed to be available. For example, if the customer desires a new electric-powered barbeque grill, the customer assumes that the design team and the company have proven their ability, with existing successful products, to design and manufacture electric-powered barbeque grills.

Performance-related customer requirements are the basis for requesting the new product. In the example of the barbecue grill, cooking time, cooking effectiveness, ease of setting the controls, and ease of cleaning are among the many possible performance-related items that a customer may specify. As time goes by and more electric powered grills reach the marketplace, these requirements may become basic.

Exciting customer requirements are generally suggested by the design team. The customer is unlikely to request these features because they are often outside the range of customer knowledge or vision. The exciting requirements are often a strong selling point in the design because they give the customer an unexpected bonus in the solution. Perhaps the capability of programming a cooking cycle to vary the temperature during the cooking process would be a unique (but perhaps costly) addition to the solution.

Figure 3.6 indicates that the basic requirements are a must for customer satisfaction. The customer will be satisfied once a significant level of performance-related requirements is met. The exciting requirements always add to customer satisfaction, so the more of these features that can be added, the greater is the satisfaction.

3.4   The Nature of Engineering Design

In the first half of the 20th century, engineering design was considered by many to be a creative, ad hoc process that did not have a significant scientific basis. Design was considered an art, with successful designs emanating from a few talented individuals in the same manner as great artwork is produced by talented artists. However, there are now a wealth of convincing arguments that engineering design is a cognitive process that requires a broad knowledge base, intelligent use of information, and logical thinking. Today successful designs are generated by design teams, comprised of engineers, marketing personnel, economists, management, customers, and so on, working in a structured environment and following a systematic strategy. Utilizing tools such as the Internet, company design documentation, brainstorming, and the synergy of the design team, information is gathered, analyzed, and synthesized with the design process yielding a final solution that meets the design criteria.

What do we mean by a cognitive process? In the 1950s Benjamin Bloom developed a classification scheme for cognitive ability that is called Bloom's taxonomy. Figure 3.7 shows the six levels of complexity of cognitive thinking and provides an insight into how the design process is an effective method of producing successful products, processes, and systems. The least complex level, knowledge, is simply the ability to recall information, facts, or theories. [What was the date of the Columbia space shuttle accident?]

The next level is comprehension, which describes the ability to make sense of (understand) the material. [Explain the cause of the Columbia accident.] The

Figure 3.7

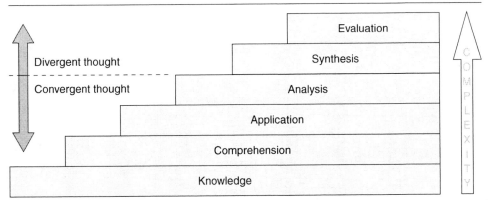

Bloom's taxonomy on learning aligns with the engineering design process.

third level is application, which is the ability to use knowledge and comprehension in a new situation and to generalize the knowledge. [What would you have done to prevent the Columbia accident?]

The fourth level is analysis, which is the ability to break learned material into its component parts so that the overall structure may be understood. It includes part identification, relationships of the parts to each other and to the whole, and recognition of the organizational principles involved. The individual must understand both the content and structure of the material. Figure 3.7 shows that analysis is the highest level of convergent thinking, whereby the individual recalls and focuses on what is known and comprehended to solve a problem through application and analysis. [What lessons did we learn about the space program from the Columbia accident?]

Levels 5 and 6 on Bloom's taxonomy represent divergent thinking, in which the individual processes information and produces new insights and discoveries that were not part of the original information (thinking outside the box). Synthesis refers to the ability to put parts together to form a new plan or idea. Everyone synthesizes in a different manner. Some accomplish synthesis by quiet mental musing; others must use pencil and paper to doodle, sketch, outline ideas, and so on. [Propose an alternative to the Columbia fuel tank insulation design that would perform the required functions.]

Evaluation is the highest level of thinking. It is the ability to judge the value of material based on specific criteria. Usually the individual is responsible for formulating the criteria to be used in the evaluation. [Assess the impact of the Columbia accident on the U.S. space program.]

To help your understanding of the levels of cognitive thinking, review several exams you have taken in college in mathematics, chemistry, physics, and general education courses (e.g., economics, sociology, history, etc). For each question, decide which level of thinking was required to obtain a successful result. You will find while moving along in your engineering curriculum that exam questions, homework problems, and projects will reflect higher and higher levels of thinking.

3.5   Experiencing the Design Process in Education

The design process, although structured, is an iterative process with flexibility to make necessary adjustments as the design progresses. The emphasis in this chapter is on conceptual design. At this stage of your engineering education it is important that you undergo the experience of applying the design process to a need with which you can identify based on your personal experiences. As you approach the baccalaureate degree you will have acquired the technical capability to conduct the necessary analyses and to make the appropriate technical decisions required for complex products, systems, and processes. Most engineering seniors will participate in a capstone design experience that will test their ability to apply knowledge toward solving a complicated design problem in their particular discipline.

3.6   Design Opportunities and Challenges of the Future

The world continues to undergo rapid and sometimes tumultuous change. As a practicing engineer, you will occupy center stage in many of these changes in the near future and will become even more involved in the more distant future. The National academy of Engineering has identified 14 "Engineering Grand Challenges." These include: 1) make solar energy economical; 2) provide energy from fusion; 3) develop carbon sequestration methods; 4) manage the nitrogen cycle; 5) provide clear water; 6) restore and improve urban infrastructure; 7) advance health informatics; 8) engineer better medicines; 9) reverse-engineer the brain; 10) prevent nuclear terror; 11) secure cyberspace; 12) enhance virtual reality; 13) advance personalized learning; and 14) engineer tools of scientific discovery. (Source: National Academy of Engineering of the National Academies, "Grand Challenges for Engineering," www.engineeringchallenges.org, viewed 8/16/2010.) The huge tasks of providing solutions to these problems will challenge the technical community beyond anyone's imagination.

Engineers of today have nearly instantaneous access to a wealth of information from technical, economic, social, and political sources. A key to the success of engineers in the future will be the ability to study and absorb the appropriate information in the time allotted for producing a design or solution to a problem. A degree in engineering is only the beginning of a lifelong period of study in order to remain informed and competent in the field.

Engineers of tomorrow will have even greater access to information and will use increasingly powerful computer systems to digest this information. They will work with colleagues around the world solving problems and creating new products. They will assume greater roles in making decisions that affect the use of energy, water, and other natural resources. Engineering design solution considerations for energy, the environment, infrastructure, and global competitiveness are addressed in the following sections.

3.6.1 Energy

In order to develop technologically, nations of the world require vast amounts of energy. With a finite supply of our greatest energy source, fossil fuels, alternate supplies must be developed and existing sources must be controlled with a worldwide usage plan. A key factor in the design of products must be minimum use of energy.

As demand increases and supplies become scarcer, the cost of obtaining the energy increases and places additional burdens on already financially strapped regions and individuals. Engineers with great vision are needed to develop alternative sources of energy from the sun, radioactive materials, wind, biomaterials, and ocean and to improve the efficiency of existing energy consumption devices (Fig. 3.8). Ethanol and biodiesel are two fuels that are produced in the United States from renewable resources that can assist in reducing America's dependence on foreign sources of energy. Waste-to-energy and biomass resources are also recognized by the U.S. Department of Energy as renewable energy source and are included in the department's tracking of progress toward achieving the federal government's renewable energy goal.

Along with the production and consumption of energy come the secondary problems of pollution and global warming. Such pollutants as smog, acid rain, heavy metals, nutrients, and carbon dioxide must receive attention in order to maintain the balance of nature. Also, increasing concentrations of greenhouse gases are likely to accelerate the rate of climate change, thus causing global warming. According to the National Academy of Sciences, the Earth's surface temperature has risen by about 1 degree Fahrenheit in the past century, with accelerated warming during the past two decades.

3.6.2 Environment

Our insatiable demand for energy, water, and other national resources creates imbalances in nature that only time and serious conservation efforts can

Figure 3.8

Windmill farms are an increasingly significant factor in the electrical infrastructure.

keep under control (Fig. 3.9). The concern for environmental quality is focused on four areas: cleanup, compliance, conservation, and pollution prevention. Partnerships among industry, government, and consumers are working to establish guidelines and regulations in the gathering of raw materials, the manufacturing of consumer products, and the disposal of material at the end of its designed use.

The American Plastics Council publishes a guide titled *Designing for the Environment*, which describes environmental issues and initiatives affecting product design. All engineers need to be aware of these initiatives and how they apply in their particular industries:

> *Design for the Environment (DFE): Incorporate environmental consider-ations into product designs to minimize impacts on the environment.*
>
> *Environmentally Conscious Manufacturing (ECM) or Green Manufacturing: Incorporating pollution prevention and toxics use reduction into product manufacturing.*
>
> *Extended Product or Producer Responsibility (Manufacturer's Responsibility or Responsible Entity): Product manufacturers are responsible for taking back their products at the product's end of life and managing them accord-ing to defined environmental criteria.*

Figure 3.9

Hydroelectric generating stations produce electricity important for industry and residence areas.

Life Cycle Assessment (LCA): Quantified assessment of the environmental impacts associated with all phases of a product's life, often from the extraction of base minerals through the product's end of life.

Pollution Prevention: Prevent pollution by reducing pollution sources (e.g., through design) as opposed to addressing pollution after it is generated.

Product Life Cycle Management (PLCM): Managing the environmental impacts associated with all phases of a product's life, from inception to disposal.

Product Takeback: The collection of products by manufacturer at the product's end of life.

Toxic Use Reduction: Reduce the amount, toxicity, and number of toxic chemicals used in manufacturing.

As you can see from these initiatives, all engineers regardless of discipline must be environmentally conscious in their work. In the next few decades we will face tough decisions regarding our environment. Engineers will play a major role in making the correct decisions for our small, delicate world.

The basic water cycle—from evaporation to cloud formation, then to rain, runoff, and evaporation again—is taken for granted by most people. (See Fig. 3.10.) However, if the rain or the runoff is polluted, then the cycle is interrupted

Figure 3.10

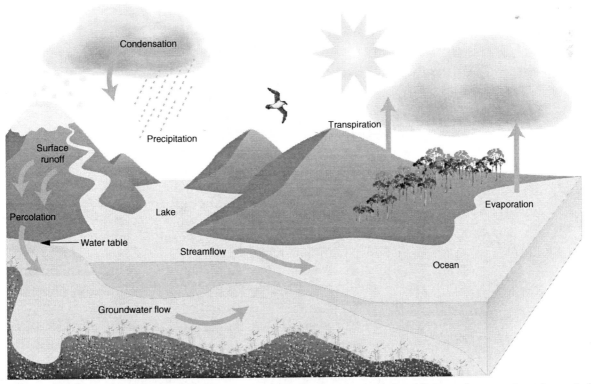

Understanding the water cycle (hydrologic cycle) is necessary in order to be able to engineer systems to control water pollution to our water resources.

and our water supply becomes a crucial problem. In addition, some highly populated areas have a limited water supply and must rely on water distribution systems from other areas of the country. Many formerly undeveloped agricultural regions are now productive because of irrigation systems. However, the irrigation systems deplete the underground streams of water that are needed downstream.

These problems must be solved in order for life to continue to exist as we know it. Because of the regional water distribution patterns, the federal government must be a part of the decision-making process for water distribution. One of the concerns that must be eased is the amount of time required to bring a water distribution plan into effect. Government agencies and the private sector are strapped by regulations that cause delays of several years in planning and construction. Greater cooperation and a better informed public are goals that public works engineers must strive to achieve. Developing nations around the world need additional water supplies because of increasing population growth. Many of these nations do not have the necessary freshwater and must rely on desalination, a costly process. The continued need for water is a concern for leaders of the world, and engineers will be asked to create additional sources of this life-sustaining resource.

3.6.3 Infrastructure

All societies depend on an infrastructure of transportation, waste disposal, and water distribution systems for the benefit of the population (Fig. 3.11). In the United States much of the infrastructure is in a state of deterioration without sound plans for upgrading. For example:

1. Commercial jet fleets include aircraft that are 35 to 40 years old. Major programs are now underway to extend safely the service life of these jets. In order to survive economically, airlines must balance new replacement jets with a program to keep older planes flying safely.
2. One-half of the sewage treatment plants cannot satisfactorily handle the demand.
3. The interstate highway system, over 50 years old in many areas, needs major repairs throughout. Over-the-road trucking has increased wear and tear on a system designed primarily for the automobile. Local paved roads are deteriorating because of a lack of infrastructure funds.
4. Many bridges are potentially dangerous to the traffic loads on them.
5. Railroads continue to struggle with maintenance of railbeds and rolling stock in the face of stiff commercial competition from the air freight and truck transportation industries.
6. Municipal water and wastewater systems require billions of dollars in repairs and upgrades to meet public demands and stricter water-quality requirements.

It is estimated that the total value of the public works facilities is over $2 trillion. To protect this investment, innovative thinking and creative funding must be fostered. Some of this is already occurring in road design and repair. For example, a new method of recycling asphalt pavement actually produces a stronger product. Engineering research is producing extended-life pavement

Figure 3.11

Development of new and improved infrastructure, such as this new rail system, are important to the economy of our nation.

with new additives and structural designs. New, relatively inexpensive methods of strengthening old bridges have been used successfully.

3.6.4 A Competitive Edge in the World Marketplace

We have all purchased or used products that were manufactured outside the country. Many of these products incorporate technology that was developed in the United States. In order to maintain our strong industrial base, we must develop practices and processes that enable us to compete not just with other U.S. industries but with international industries (Fig. 3.12). Engineers must also be able to design products that will be accepted by other cultures and work in their environments. It is therefore most important that engineers develop their global awareness and cultural adaptability competence.

The goal of any industry is to generate a profit. In today's marketplace this means creating the best product in the shortest time at a lower price than the competition. A modern design process incorporating sophisticated analysis procedures and supported by high-speed computers with graphical displays increases the capability for developing the "best" product. The concept of integrating the design and manufacturing functions shortens the design-to-market time for new products and for upgraded versions of existing products. The development of the automated factory is an exciting concept that is receiving a great deal of attention from manufacturing engineers today. Remaining

Figure 3.12

A global design team at work on an engineering design problem.

competitive by producing at a lesser price requires a national effort involving labor, government, and distribution factors. In any case engineers are going to have a significant role in the future of our industrial sector.

Problems

3.1   Complete the statement "I want to become an engineer to design . . ." in as much detail as you can.

3.2   Choose an engineering company that you would someday consider working for. From the information found on their Web site, write a one-page paper on the engineering problems that they are solving and how they are addressing their customer's needs.

3.3   Find three textbooks that introduce the engineering design process. Copy the steps in the process from each textbook. Compare with the six steps in Sec.

3.1. Note similarities and differences and write a paragraph describing your conclusions.

3.4 Interview an engineer working in your chosen field of study, describe in a one-page paper what steps of the design process he/she is engaged with in their job.

3.5 Select a specific discipline of engineering and list at least 20 different companies and/or government agencies that utilize engineers from this field.

3.6 Choose a product that was most likely designed by an engineer in your chosen field of study. Identify what problem this product solved, what constraints were applied to its design, and what criteria were most likely used to evaluate this design.

3.7 Choose one of the National Academy of Engineering's Greatest Challenges found in Sec. 3.6 and write a one-page paper on how you as an engineer could be involved in helping to solve this challenge.

3.8 Choose one of the products from the list below and note key features and functions for the product as produced today. Then, go back one generation (18–25 years) to family, relatives, or friends and ask them to describe the key features and functions of the same product as produced at that time. Note changes and improvements and prepare a brief report.

(a) toaster

(b) electric coffeemaker

(c) color television

(d) landline telephone

(e) cookware (pots, pans, skillets)

(f) vacuum cleaner

(g) microwave oven

3.9 Choose a product that you use every day and evaluate how effective the company that designed it was in meeting your customer needs and the needs of others. What suggestions would you make to help the designers improve the project? How could this product be used for another application?

3.10 Choose a device or product that you believe can be improved upon. Answer the following questions: 1) what do you already know about this device/product; 2) what do you think you know about this device/product; and (3) what do you need to know about this device/product? Based on your responses to these questions conduct research to confirm or reveal what you know and don't know. Write a short report to summarize your findings. Use proper citation methods to list your research sources.

3.11 Choose one of the following topics (or one suggested by your instructor) and write a paper that discusses technological changes that have occurred in this area in the past 15 years. Include commentary on the social and environmental impact of the changes and on new problems that may have arisen because of the changes.

(a) passenger automobiles

(b) electric power-generating plants

(c) computer graphics

(d) heart surgery

(e) heating systems (furnaces)

(f) microprocessors

(g) water treatment

(h) road paving (both concrete and asphalt)

(i) composite materials

(j) robotics

(k) air-conditioning

3.12 Investigate current designs for one or more of the items listed below. If you do not have the items in your possession, purchase them or borrow from friends. Conduct the following "reverse engineering" procedures on each of the items:

(*a*) Write down the need that the design satisfies.

(*b*) Disassemble the item and list all the parts by name.

(*c*) Write down the function of each of the parts in the item.

(*d*) Reassemble the item.

(*e*) Write down answers to the following questions:

- Does the item satisfactorily solve the need you stated in part (*a*)?
- What are the strengths of the design?
- What are the weaknesses of the design?
- Can this design be easily modified to solve other needs? If so, what needs and what modifications should be made?
- What other designs can solve the stated need?

The items for your study are the following:

- Mechanical pencil
- Safety razors from three vendors; include one disposable razor
- Flashlight
- Battery-powered slide viewer
- Battery-powered fabric shaver

3.13 The following list of potential design projects can be addressed by following the six-step design process discussed in the chapter. A team approach to a proposed solution, with three or four members on each team, is recommended. Develop a report and oral presentation as directed by your instructor.

- A device to prevent the theft of helmets left on motorcycles
- An improved rack for carrying packages or books on a motorcycle or bicycle
- A child's seat for a motorcycle or bicycle
- A device to permit easier draining of the oil pan by weekend mechanics
- A heated steering wheel for cold weather
- A sun shield for an automobile
- An SOS sign for cars stalled on freeways
- A storage system for a cell phone in a car (including charger)
- An improved wall outlet
- A beverage holder for a card table
- A better rural mailbox
- An improved automobile traffic pattern on campus
- An alert for drowsy or sleeping drivers
- Improved bicycle brakes
- A campus transit system
- Improved pedestrian crossings at busy intersections
- Improved parking facilities in and around campus
- A device to attach to a paint can for pouring
- An improved soap dispenser
- A better method of locking weights to a barbell shaft
- A shoestring fastener to replace the knot
- A better jar opener
- A system or device to improve efficiency of limited closet space

- A shoe transporter and storer
- A pen and pencil holder for college students
- A rack for mounting electric fans in dormitory windows
- A device to pit fruit without damage
- An automatic device for selectively admitting and releasing pets through an auxiliary door
- A device to permit a person loaded with packages to open a door
- A more efficient toothpaste tube
- A fingernail catcher for fingernail clippings
- A more effective alarm clock for reluctant students
- A clock with a display showing that the alarm has been set to go off
- A device to help a parent monitor small children's presence and activity in and around the house
- A simple pocket alarm that is difficult to shut off, used for discouraging muggers
- An improved storage system for luggage, books, and so on in dormitories
- A lampshade designed to permit one roommate to study while the other is asleep
- A device that would permit blind people to vote in an otherwise conventional voting booth
- A one-cup coffeemaker
- A silent wake-up alarm
- Home aids for the blind (or deaf)
- A safer, more efficient, and quieter air mover for room use
- A can crusher
- A rain-sensitive house window that would close automatically when it rains
- A better grass catcher for a riding lawn mower
- A built-in auto refrigerator
- A better camp cooler
- A dormitory cooler
- An impact-hammer adapter for electric drills
- An improved method of detecting and controlling the level position of the bucket on a bucket loader
- An automatic tractor-trailer-hitch aligning device
- A jack designed expressly for motorcycle use (special problems involved)
- Improved road signs for speed limits, curves, deer crossings, and so on
- Automatic light switches for rooms
- A device for dealing with oil slicks
- An egg container (light, strong, compact) for camping and canoeing
- Ramps or other facilities for handicapped students

CHAPTER 4

Engineering Solutions

a25 - 3745

Chapter Objectives

When you complete your study of this chapter, you will be able to:

- Recognize the importance of engineering problem analysis
- Recall and explain the engineering method
- Apply general guidelines for problem-solving presentation and solution documentation
- Develop an ability to solve and present simple or complex problems in an orderly, logical, and systematic way

4.1 Introduction

The practice of engineering involves the application of accumulated knowledge and experience to a wide variety of technical situations. Two areas, in particular, that are fundamental to all of engineering are design and problem solving. The professional engineer is expected to approach, analyze, and solve a range of technical problems intelligently and efficiently. These problems can vary from single-solution, reasonably simple problems to extremely complex, open-ended problems that require a multidisciplinary team of engineers.

Problem solving is a combination of experience, knowledge, process, and art. Most engineers through either training or experience solve many problems by a process. The design process, for example, is a series of logical steps that when followed produce an optimal solution given time and resources as two constraints. The total quality (TQ) method is another example of a process. This concept suggests a series of steps leading to desired results while exceeding customer expectations.

This chapter provides a basic guide to problem analysis, organization, and presentation. Early in your education, you must develop an ability to solve and present simple or complex problems in an orderly, logical, and systematic way.

4.2 Problem Analysis

A distinguishing characteristic of a qualified engineer is the ability to solve technical problems. Mastery of problem solving involves a combination of art and science. By *science* we mean the knowledge of the principles of mathematics, chemistry, physics, mechanics, and other technical subjects that must be learned so that they can be applied correctly. By *art* we mean the proper judgment, experience, common sense, and know-how that must be used to reduce a real-life problem to such a form that science can be applied to its solution. To know when and how rigorously science should be applied and whether the resulting answer reasonably satisfies the original problem is an art.

Much of the science of successful problem solving comes from formal education in school or from continuing education after graduation. But most of the art of problem solving cannot be learned in a formal course; rather, it is a result of experience and common sense. Its application can be more effective, however, if problem solving is approached in a logical and organized method—that is, if it follows a process.

To clarify the distinction, let us suppose that a manufacturing engineer and a logistics specialist working for a large electronics company are given the task of recommending whether the introduction of a new computer that will focus on the computer-aided-design (CAD) market can be profitably produced. At the time this task is assigned, the competitive selling price has already been estimated by the marketing division. Also, the design group has developed working models of the computer with specifications of all components, which means that the approximate cost of these components is known. The question of profit thus rests on the costs of assembly and distribution. The theory of engineering economy (the science portion of problem solving) is well known and applicable to the cost factors and time frame involved. Once the production and distribution methods have been established, these costs can be computed using standard techniques. Selection of production and distribution methods (the art portion of problem solving) depends largely on the experience of the engineer and logistics specialist. Knowing what will or will not work in each part of these processes is a must in the cost estimate; however, these data cannot be found in handbooks, but, rather, they are found in the minds of the logistics specialist and the engineer. It is an art originating from experience, common sense, and good judgment.

Before the solution to any problem is undertaken, whether by a student or a practicing professional engineer, a number of important ideas must be considered. Think about the following questions: How important is the answer to a given problem? Would a rough, preliminary estimate be satisfactory, or is a high degree of accuracy demanded? How much time do you have and what resources are at your disposal? In an actual situation, your answers may depend on the amount of data available or the amount that must be collected, the sophistication of equipment that must be used, the accuracy of the data, the number of people available to assist, and many other factors. Most complex problems require some level of computer support such as a spreadsheet or a math analysis program. What about the theory you intend to use? Is it state of the art? Is it valid for this particular application? Do you currently understand the theory, or must time be allocated for review and learning? Can you make assumptions that simplify without sacrificing needed accuracy? Are other assumptions valid and applicable?

The art of problem solving is a skill developed with practice. It is the ability to arrive at a proper balance between the time and resources expended on a problem and the accuracy and validity obtained in the solution. When you can optimize time and resources versus reliability, problem-solving skills will serve you well.

The *engineering method* is an example of process. It consists of six basic steps:

1. *Recognize and understand the problem.*   Perhaps the most difficult part of problem solving is developing the ability to recognize and define the problem precisely. This is true at the beginning of the design process and when applying the engineering method to a subpart of the overall problem. Many academic problems that you will be asked to solve have this step completed by the instructor. For example, if your instructor asks you to solve a quadratic–algebraic equation and provides all the coefficients, the problem has been completely defined before it is given to you, and little doubt remains about what the problem is.

    If the problem is not well defined, considerable effort must be expended at the beginning in studying the problem, eliminating the things that are unimportant, and focusing on the root problem. Effort at this step pays great dividends by eliminating or reducing false trials, thereby shortening the time taken to complete later steps.

2. *Accumulate data and verify accuracy.*   All pertinent physical facts, such as sizes, temperatures, voltages, currents, costs, concentrations, weights, times, and so on, must be ascertained. Some problems require that steps 1 and 2 be done simultaneously. In others, step 1 might automatically produce some of the physical facts. Do not mix or confuse these details with data that are suspect or only assumed to be accurate. Deal only with items that can be verified. Sometimes it will pay to verify data that you believe are factual but actually may be in error.

3. *Select the appropriate theory or principle.*   Select appropriate theories or scientific principles that apply to the solution of the problem; understand and identify limitations or constraints that apply to the selected theory.

4. *Make necessary assumptions.*   Perfect solutions to real problems do not exist. Simplifications need to be made if real problems are to be solved. Certain assumptions can be made that do not significantly affect the accuracy of the solution, yet other assumptions may result in a large reduction in accuracy.

    Although the selection of a theory or principle is stated in the engineering method as preceding the introduction of simplifying assumptions, there are cases when the order of these two steps should be reversed. For example, if you are solving a material balance problem, you often need to assume that the process is steady, uniform, and without chemical reactions so that the applicable theory can be simplified. Note that many of the engineering equations used in practice only apply when specific assumptions are made.

5. *Solve the problem.*   If steps 3 and 4 have resulted in a mathematical equation (model), it is normally solved by an application of mathematical theory, although a trial-and-error solution that employs the use of a computer or perhaps some form of graphical solution also may be applicable. The results normally will be in numerical form with appropriate units. Make sure to show the resulting answer with appropriate significant digits.

6. *Verify and check results.* In engineering practice, the work is not finished merely because a solution has been obtained. It must be checked to ensure that it is mathematically correct and that units have been properly specified. Correctness can be verified by reworking the problem by using a different technique or by performing the calculations in a different order to be certain that the numbers agree in both trials. The units need to be examined to ensure that all equations are dimensionally correct. And finally, the answer must be examined to see if it makes sense. An experienced engineer will generally have a good idea of the order of magnitude to expect.

If the answer doesn't seem reasonable, there is probably an error in the mathematics, in the assumptions, or perhaps in the theory used. Judgment is critical. For example, suppose that you are asked to compute the monthly payment required to repay a car loan of $5000 over a 3-year period at an annual interest rate of 12%. Upon solving this problem, you arrived at an answer of $11 000 per month. Even if you are inexperienced in engineering economy, you know that this answer is not reasonable, so you should reexamine your theory and computations. Examination and evaluation of an answer's reasonableness are habits you should strive to acquire. Your instructor and employer alike will not accept results that you have indicated are correct if the results are obviously incorrect by a significant percentage.

4.4 Problem Presentation

The engineering method of problem solving as presented in the previous section is an adaptation of the well-known *scientific problem-solving method*. It is a time-tested approach to problem solving that should become an everyday part of the engineer's thought process. Engineers should follow this logical approach to the solution of any problem while at the same time learn to translate the information accumulated into a well-documented problem solution.

The following steps parallel the engineering method and provide reasonable documentation of the solution. If these steps are properly executed during the solution of problems in this text and all other courses, it is our belief that you will gradually develop an ability to solve and properly document a wide range of complex problems.

1. *Problem statement.* State, as concisely as possible, the problem to be solved. The statement should be a summary of the given information, but it must contain all essential material. Clearly state what is to be determined. For example, find the temperature (K) and pressure (Pa) at the nozzle exit.

2. *Diagram.* Prepare a diagram (sketch or computer output) with all pertinent dimensions, flow rates, currents, voltages, weights, and so on. A diagram is a very efficient method of showing given and needed information. It also is an appropriate way of illustrating the physical setup, which may be difficult to describe adequately in words. Most often a two-dimensional representation is adequate (e.g., a free-body diagram of a beam with associated loads and moments). Data that cannot be placed in a diagram should be listed separately.

3. *Theory.* The theory used should be presented. In some cases, a properly referenced equation with completely defined variables is sufficient. At other times, an extensive theoretical derivation may be necessary because the appropriate theory has to be derived, developed, or modified.

4. *Assumptions.* Explicitly list, in complete detail, any and all pertinent assumptions that have been made to realize your solution to the problem. This step is vitally important for the reader's understanding of the solution and its limitations. Steps 3 and 4 might be reversed or integrated in some problems.

5. *Solution steps.* Show completely all steps taken in obtaining the solution. This is particularly important in an academic situation because your reader, the instructor, must have the means of judging your understanding of the solution technique. Steps completed, but not shown, make it difficult for evaluation of your work and therefore difficult to provide constructive guidance.

6. *Identify results and verify accuracy.* Clearly identify (double underline) the final answer. *Assign proper units.* An answer without units (when it should have units) is meaningless. Remember, this final step of the engineering method requires an examination of the answer to determine if it is realistic, so check solution accuracy and, if possible, verify the results.

7. *Discussion/Conclusion* It is important to write a concise summary of your results. What do the results mean? Do you have any observations? This step should include whether the results are reasonable and what would happen if one or more of the dependent variable were changed (e.g., what if the temperature increased by five degrees?).

4.5   Standards of Problem Presentation

Once the problem has been solved and checked, it is necessary to present the solution according to some standard. The standard will vary from school to school and industry to industry.

On most occasions, your solution will be presented to other individuals who are technically trained, but you should remember that many times these individuals do not have an intimate knowledge of the problem. However, on other occasions, you will be presenting technical information to persons with nontechnical backgrounds. This may require methods that are different from those used to communicate with other engineers; thus, it is always important to understand who will be reviewing the material so that the information can be clearly presented.

One characteristic of engineers is their ability to present information with great clarity in a neat, careful manner. In short, the information must be communicated accurately to the reader. (Discussion of drawings or simple sketches will not be included in this chapter, although they are important in many presentations.)

Employers insist on carefully prepared presentations that completely document all work involved in solving the problems. Thorough documentation may be important in the event of legal considerations for which the details of the work might be introduced into court proceedings as evidence. Lack of such documentation may result in the loss of a case that might otherwise have been won. Moreover, internal company use of the work is easier and more efficient if all aspects of the work have been carefully documented and substantiated by data and theory.

Each industrial company, consulting firm, government agency, and university has established standards for presenting technical information. These standards vary slightly, but all fall into a basic pattern, which we will discuss. Each organization expects its employees to follow its standards. Details can be easily modified in a particular situation once you are familiar with the general pattern that exists in all of these standards.

It is not possible to specify a single problem layout or format that will accommodate all types of engineering solutions. Such a wide variety of solutions exists that the technique used must be adapted to fit the information to be communicated. In all cases, however, one must lay out a given problem in such a fashion that it can be easily grasped by the reader. No matter which technique is used, it must be logical and understandable.

We have listed guidelines for problem presentation. Acceptable layouts for problems in engineering also are illustrated. The guidelines are not intended as a precise format that must be followed but, rather, as a suggestion that should be considered and incorporated whenever applicable.

Two methods of problem presentation are typical in academic and industrial environments. Presentation formats can be either freehand or computer generated. As hardware technology and software developments continue to provide better tools, the use of the computer as a method of problem presentation will continue to increase. If you were working on a team, you may need to utilize shared document software in order to collaborate more effectively on a problem presentation (e.g., Google Docs).

If a formal report, proposal, or presentation is the choice of communication, a computer-generated presentation is the correct approach. The example solutions that are illustrated in Figures 4.1 through 4.4 include both freehand work and computer output. Check with your instructor to determine which method is appropriate for your assignments. Figure 4.1 illustrates the placement of information.

The following nine general guidelines should be helpful as you develop the freehand skills needed to provide clear and complete problem documentation. The first two examples, Figsures 4.1 and 4.2, are freehand illustrations. The third example, Figure 4.3, is computer generated with a word processor, and Figure 4.4 uses a spreadsheet for the computations and graphing.

These guidelines are most applicable to freehand solutions, but many of the ideas and principles apply to computer generation as well.

1. One common type of paper frequently used is called engineering problems paper. It is ruled horizontally and vertically on the *reverse* side, with only heading and margin rulings on the front. The rulings on the reverse side, which are faintly visible through the paper, help one maintain horizontal lines of lettering and provide guides for sketching and simple graph construction. Moreover, the lines on the back of the paper will not be lost as a result of erasures.

Figure 4.1

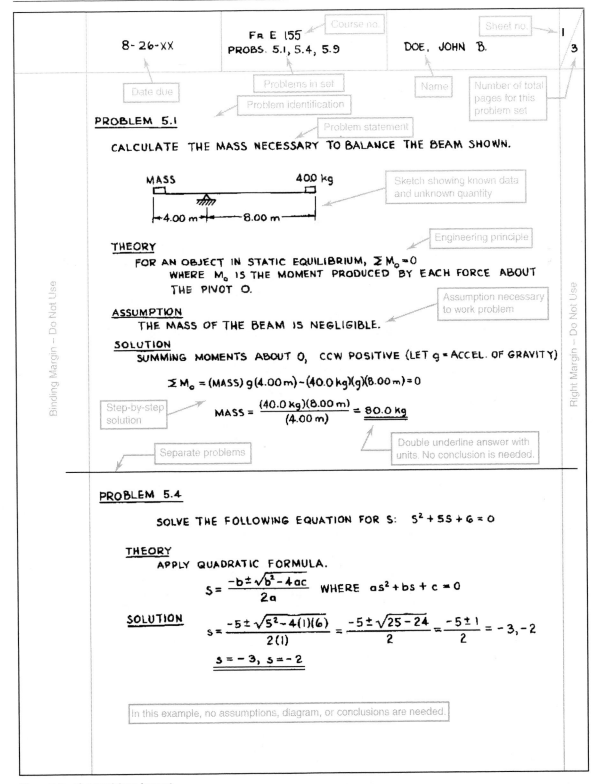

Elements of a problem layout.

Figure 4.2a

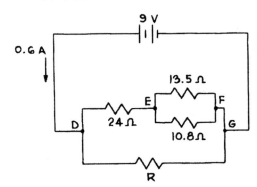

FR E 160

8-22-XX   PROBLEM 13.1   DOE, JANE A.

1

2

PROBLEM 13.1   SOLVE FOR THE VALUE OF RESISTANCE R
IN THE CIRCUIT SHOWN BELOW.

THEORY
- FOR RESISTANCES IN PARALLEL: $\frac{1}{R_{TOTAL}} = \frac{1}{R_1} + \frac{1}{R_2} + \frac{1}{R_3} + \cdots$

    THUS FOR 2 RESISTANCES IN PARALLEL
    $$R_{TOTAL} = \frac{R_1 R_2}{R_1 + R_2}$$

- FOR RESISTANCES IN SERIES: $R_{TOTAL} = R_1 + R_2 + R_3 + \cdots$

- OHM'S LAW: E = RI   WHERE E = ELECT. POTENTIAL IN VOLTS
                                    I = CURRENT IN AMPERES
                                    R = RESISTANCE IN OHMS

SOLUTION
- CALCULATE EQUIVALENT RESISTANCE BETWEEN POINTS E AND F.
  RESISTORS ARE IN PARALLEL.

    $$\therefore R_{EF} = \frac{R_1 R_2}{R_1 + R_2} = \frac{(13.5)(10.8)}{13.5 + 10.8} = \frac{145.8}{24.3} = 6.00 \ \Omega$$

- CALCULATE EQUIVALENT RESISTANCE OF UPPER LEG
  BETWEEN D AND G.

    SERIES CIRCUIT

    $$\therefore R'_{DG} = R_{24} + R_6 = 24 + 6 = 30 \ \Omega$$

In this example, no assumptions were necessary.

Sample problem presentation done freehand.

Figure 4.2b

| 8-22-XX | FR E 160 | | 2 |
| | PROBLEM 13.1 | DOE, JANE A. | 2 |

- CALCULATE EQUIVALENT RESISTANCE BETWEEN D AND G.

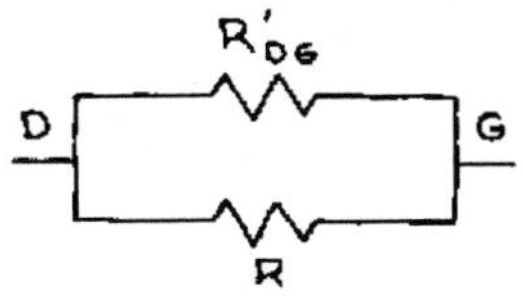

PARALLEL RESISTORS, SO

$$R_{DG} = \frac{(R'_{DG})(R)}{R'_{DG} + R}$$

- CALCULATE TOTAL RESISTANCE OF CIRCUIT USING OHM'S LAW.

$$R_{DG} = \frac{E}{I} = \frac{9V}{0.6A} = 15\,\Omega$$

- CALCULATE VALUE OF R
  FROM PREVIOUS EQUATIONS.

$$R_{DG} = 15\,\Omega = \frac{(R'_{DG})(R)}{R'_{DG} + R} = \frac{(30)(R)}{30 + R}$$

SOLVING FOR R:

$$(30 + R)(15) = 30R$$

$$30 + R = 2R$$

$$\underline{R = 30\,\Omega}$$

Figure 4.3a

Date   *Engineering*   *Name:*_____

Problem

A tank is to be constructed that will hold 5.00×10^5 L when filled. The shape is to be cylindrical, with a hemispherical top. Costs to construct the cylindrical portion will be \$300/m^2, while costs for the hemispherical portion are slightly higher at \$400/m^2.

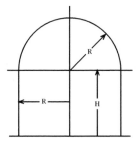

Find

Calculate the tank dimensions that will result in the lowest dollar cost.

Theory

Volume of cylinder is... $V_c = \pi R^2 H$

Volume of hemisphere is... $V_H = \dfrac{2\pi R^3}{3}$

Surface area of cylinder is... $SA_c = 2\pi R H$

Surface area of hemisphere is... $SA_H = 2\pi R^2$

Assumptions

Tank contains no dead air space
Construction costs are independent of size
Concrete slab with hermetic seal is provided for the base
Cost of the base does not change appreciably with tank dimensions

Solution

1. Express total volume in meters as a function of height and radius.

$$
\begin{aligned}
V_{Tank} &= f(H, R) \\
&= V_C + V_H \\
500 &= \pi R^2 H + \frac{2\pi R^3}{3}
\end{aligned}
$$

Note: $1\,\mathrm{m}^3 = 1000\ \mathrm{L}$

Sample problem presentation done with a word processor.

Figure 4.3b

2. Express cost in dollars as a function of height and radius

$$C = C(H, R)$$

$$= 300\,(SA_C) + 400\,(SA_H)$$

$$= 300\,(2\pi RH) + 400\,(2\pi R^2)$$

Note: Cost figures are exact numbers

3. From part 1 solve for $H = H(R)$

$$H = \frac{500}{\pi R^2} - \frac{2R}{3}$$

4. Solve cost equation, substituting $H = H(R)$

$$C = 300\left[2\pi R\left(\frac{500}{\pi R^2} - \frac{2R}{3}\right)\right] + 400\,(2\pi R^2)$$

$$C = \frac{300000}{R} + 400\pi R^2$$

5. Develop a table of cost versus radius and plot graph.

6. From graph select minimum cost.

$$R = \underline{\underline{5.00 \text{ m}}}$$
$$C = \underline{\underline{\$91\,000}}$$

7. Calculate H from part 3 above

$$H = \underline{\underline{3.033 \text{ m}}}$$

8. Verification/check of results from the calculus:

$$\frac{dC}{dR} = \frac{d}{dR}\left[\frac{300\,000}{R} + 400\pi R^2\right]$$

$$= \frac{-300\,000}{R^2} + 800\pi R = 0$$

$$R^3 = \frac{300\,000}{800\pi}$$

$$R = \underline{\underline{4.92\text{m}}}$$

9. Discussion/Conclusion: The minimum cost for the tank is found when the radius is 5.0 m and the height is 3.0 m. The height cost is found between a radius of 1.0 m and 2.0 m.

Cost versus Radius

Radius, R, m	Cost, C, $
1.0	301 257
2.0	155 027
3.0	111 310
4.0	95 106
5.0	91 416
6.0	95 239
7.0	104 432
8.0	117 925
9.0	135 121
10.0	155 664

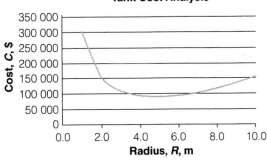

Tank Cost Analysis

Figure 4.4

Date: 10-14-xx   ENGR 160   John Q. Public

Problem 3-5

Analyze the buckling load for steel columns ranging from 50 to 100 ft long in increments of 5 ft.
The cross-sectional area is 7.33 in², the least radius of gyration is 3.19 in and modulus of elasticity is 30×10^6 lb/in².
Plot the buckling load as a function of column length for hinged ends and fixed ends.

Theory

Euler's equation gives the buckling load for a slender column.

$$F_B = \frac{n\pi^2 \, EA}{(L/r)^2}$$

where

F_B = buckling load, lb
E = modulus of elasticity, lb/in²   3.00E+07
A = cross-sectional area, in²   7.33
L = length of column, in
r = least radius of gyration, in   3.19
The factor n depends on the end conditions: If both ends are hinged, $n = 1$;
if both ends are fixed, $n = 4$; if one end is fixed and the other is hinged, $n = 2$

Assumption: The columns being analyzed meet the slenderness criterion for Euler's equation

Solution

Length, ft	Buckling load (fixed), lb	Buckling load (hinged), lb
50	245394	61348
55	202805	50701
60	170412	42603
65	145204	36301
70	125201	31300
75	109064	27266
80	95857	23964
85	84911	21228
90	75739	18935
95	67976	16994
100	61348	15337

Discussion: The buckling load decreases with length for end conditions. The buckling load for the fixed ends condition is always higher, but becomes closer to the hinged condition with increased length.

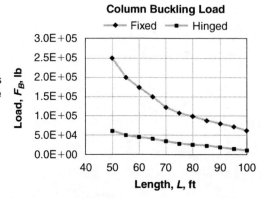

Sample problem presentation done with a spreadsheet.

2. The completed top heading of the problems paper should include such information as name, date, course number, and sheet number. The upper right-hand block should normally contain a notation such as a/b, where a is the page number of the sheet and b is the total number of sheets in the set.

3. Work should ordinarily be done in pencil using an appropriate lead hardness (HB, F, or H) so that the line work is crisp and not smudged. Erasures should always be complete, with all eraser particles removed. Letters and numbers must be dark enough to ensure legibility when photocopies are needed.

4. Either vertical or slant letters may be selected as long as they are not mixed. Care should be taken to produce good, legible lettering but without such care that little work is accomplished.

5. Spelling should be checked for correctness. There is no reasonable excuse for incorrect spelling in a properly done problem solution.

6. Work must be easy to follow and not crowded. This practice contributes greatly to readability and ease of interpretation.

7. If several problems are included in a set, they must be distinctly separated, usually by a horizontal line drawn completely across the page between problems. Never begin a second problem on the same page if it cannot be completed there. Beginning each problem on a fresh sheet is usually better, except in cases when two or more problems can be completed on one sheet. It is not necessary to use a horizontal separation line if the next problem in a series begins at the top of a new page.

8. Diagrams that are an essential part of a problem presentation should be clear and understandable. You should strive for neatness, which is a mark of a professional. Often a good sketch is adequate, but using a straight edge can greatly improve the appearance and accuracy of a diagram. A little effort in preparing a sketch to approximate scale can pay great dividends when it is necessary to judge the reasonableness of an answer, particularly if the answer is a physical dimension that can be seen on the sketch.

9. The proper use of symbols is always important, particularly when the International System (SI) of Units is used. It involves a strict set of rules that must be followed so that absolutely no confusion of meaning can result. There also are symbols in common and accepted use for engineering quantities that can be found in most engineering handbooks. These symbols should be used whenever possible. It is important that symbols be consistent throughout a solution and that they are all defined for the benefit of the reader and for your own reference.

The physical layout of a problem solution logically follows steps that are similar to those of the engineering method. You should attempt to present the process by which the problem was solved, in addition to the solution, so that any reader can readily understand all the aspects of the solution. Figure 4.1 illustrates the placement of the information.

Figures 4.2, 4.3, and 4.4 are examples of typical engineering problem solutions. You may find these examples to be helpful guides as you prepare your problem presentations.

Problems

4.1 The Cartesian components of a vector $\overline{B}$ are shown in Fig. 4.5. If B_x = 8.6 m and Δ = 35°, find α B_y, and $\overline{B}$.

4.2 Refer to Fig. 4.5. If α = 58° and B_y = 3.4 km, what are the values of Δ, B_x, and $\overline{B}$?

4.3 In Fig. 4.6, side YZ is 2.4 × 10⁴ m. Determine the length of side XZ.

4.4 Calculate the length of side AB in Fig. 4.7 if side AC = 2.75 × 10² m.

Figure 4.5

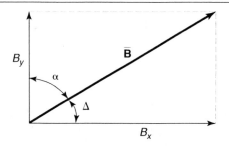

Figure 4.6

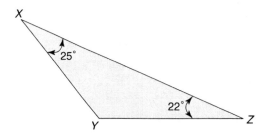

Figure 4.7

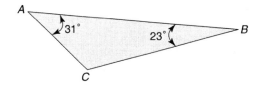

4.5 The vector $\overline{C}$ in Fig. 4.8 is the sum of vectors $\overline{A}$ and $\overline{B}$. Assume that vector $\overline{B}$ is horizontal. Given that α = 29°, β = 25°, and the magnitude of B = 29 m, find the magnitudes and directions of vectors $\overline{A}$ and $\overline{C}$.

4.6 Vector $\overline{R}$ in Fig. 4.9 is the difference between vectors $\overline{T}$ and $\overline{S}$. If $\overline{S}$ is inclined at 28° from the vertical and the angle between $\overline{S}$ and $\overline{T}$ is 32°, calculate the magnitude and direction of vector $\overline{R}$. The magnitudes of $\overline{S}$ and $\overline{T}$ are 19 cm and 36 cm, respectively.

4.7 An aircraft has a glide ratio of 12 to 1. (Glide ratio means that the plane drops 1 m in each 12 m it travels horizontally.) A building 45 m high lies directly in the glide path to the runway. If the aircraft clears the building by 12 m, how far from the building does the aircraft touch down on the runway?

Figure 4.8

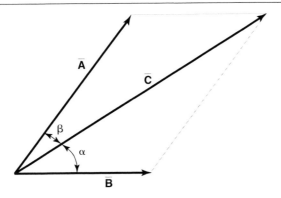

Figure 4.9

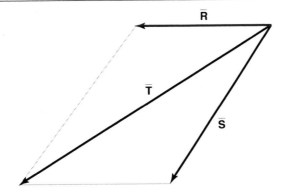

4.8 A pilot of an aircraft knows that the vehicle in landing configuration will glide 2.0×10^1 km from a height of 2.00×10^3 m. A TV transmitting tower is located in a direct line with the local runway. If the pilot glides over the tower with 3.0×10^1 m to spare and touches down on the runway at a point 6.5 km from the base of the tower, how high is the tower?

4.9 A simple roof truss design is shown in Fig. 4.10. The lower section, $VWXY$, is made from three equal length segments. UW and XZ are perpendicular to VT and TY, respectively. If $VWXY$ is 2.0×10^1 m and the height of the truss is 2.5 m, determine the lengths of XT and XZ.

4.10 An engineer is required to survey a nonrectangular plot of land but is unable to measure side UT directly due to a water obstruction (see Fig. 4.11). The following data are taken: RU = 121.0 m, RS = 116.0 m, ST = 83.5 m, angle RST = 113°, and angle RUT = 82°. Calculate the length of side UT and the area of the plot.

4.11 A park is being considered in a space between a small river and a highway as a rest stop for travelers (see Fig. 4.12). Boundary BC is perpendicular to the highway and boundary AD makes an angle of 75° with the highway. BC is measured to be 160.0 m, AD is 270.0 m, and the boundary along the highway is 190.0 m long. What are the length of side AB and the magnitude of angle ABC?

Figure 4.10

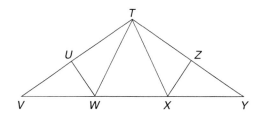

Figure 4.11

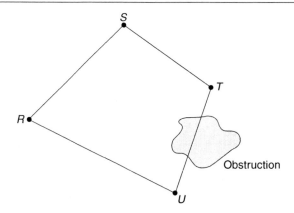

Figure 4.12

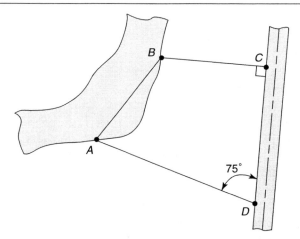

4.12 D, E, F, and G in Fig. 4.13 are surveyed points in a land development on level terrain so that each point is visible from each other. Leg DG is physically measured as 500.0 m. The angles at three of the points are found to be: angle GDE = 55°, angle DEF = 92°, angle FGD = 134°. Also, angle DGE is measured at 87°. Compute the lengths of DE, EF, FG, and EG.

4.13 The height of an inaccessible mountain peak, C, in Fig. 4.14 must be estimated. Fortunately, two smaller mountains, A and B, which can be easily scaled, are located near the higher peak. To make matters even simpler, the three peaks lie on a single straight line. From the top of mountain A, altitude 2.000×10^3 m, the elevation angle to C is 12.32°. The elevation of C from mountain B is 22.73°. Mountain B is 1.00×10^2 m higher than A. The straight line (slant) distance between peaks A and B is 3.000×10^3 m. Determine the unknown height of mountain C.

4.14 A narrow belt is used to drive a 20.00-cm-diameter pulley from a 35.00-cm-diameter pulley. The centers of the two pulleys are 2.000 m apart. How long must the belt be if the pulleys rotate in the same direction? In opposite directions?

Figure 4.13

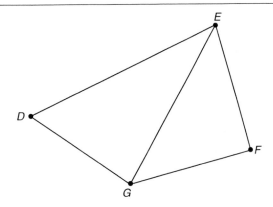

Figure 4.14

4.15 A motorcycle sprocket on the rear wheel has a diameter of 24 cm, and the driver sprocket has a diameter of 4.0 cm. The driver sprocket shaft and rear axle are 60 cm apart. What is the minimum chain length for this application?

4.16 A block of metal has a 90° notch cut from its lower surface. The notched part rests on a circular cylinder of diameter 2.0 cm, as shown in Fig. 4.15. If the lower surface of the part is 1.3 cm above the base plane, how deep is the notch?

4.17 A 1.00-cm-diameter circular gauge block is used to measure the depth of a 60° notch in a piece of tool steel. The gauge block extends a distance of 4.7 mm above the surface. How deep is the notch? See Fig. 4.16.

4.18 An aircraft moves through the air with a relative velocity of 3.00×10^2 km/h at a heading of N30°E. In a 35 km/h wind from the west,

(*a*) Calculate the *true* ground speed and heading of the aircraft.

(*b*) What heading should the pilot fly so that the *true* heading is N30°E?

4.19 To cross a river that is 1 km wide, with a current of 6 km/h, a novice boat skipper holds the bow of the boat perpendicular to the far riverbank, intending to cross to a point directly across the river from the launch point. At what position will the boat actually contact the far bank? What direction should the boat have been headed to actually reach a point directly across from the launch dock? The boat is capable of making 10 km/h.

4.20 What heading must a pilot fly to compensate for a 125 km/h west wind to have a ground track that is due south? The aircraft cruise speed is 6.00×10^2 km/h. What is the actual ground speed?

Figure 4.15

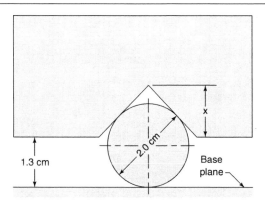

Figure 4.16

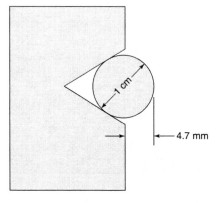

4.21 A tooling designer is designing a jig that will insert pins into the flip-up handles of a coffeemaker. The bin to hold the pins should hold enough pins for 3 h of work before reloading. The engineering estimate for the rate of inserting the pins is 300/h. The pin diameter is 0.125 in. Because of space constraints, the bin must be designed as shown in Fig. 4.17. The bin can be only the width of one pin. What is the minimum height that the bin should be if there is 0.250 in. at the top when it has been filled with the required number of pins?

4.22 Two friends are planning to go on RAGBRAI (Register's Annual Great Bike Ride Across Iowa) next year. One is planning to ride a mountain bicycle with 26-in. tires, and the other has a touring bicycle with 27-in. tires. A typical RAGBRAI is about 480 mi long.

    (*a*) How many more revolutions will the mountain bike tires make in that distance than the touring bike?

Figure 4.17

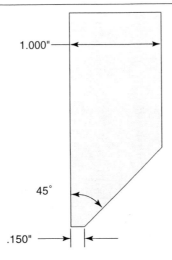

1.000"

45°

.150"

Figure 4.18

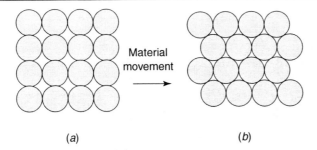

Material
movement

(a)   (b)

(b) Typical gearing for most bicycles ranges from 30 to 50 teeth on the chain wheel (front gears) and 12 to 30 teeth on the rear cog. Find how many more revolutions of the pedals the mountain biker will make during the trip, using an average pedaling time of 85% of the trip and a 42-tooth chain wheel and a 21-tooth rear cog for your calculations.

(c) If both cyclists have 170-mm cranks on their bikes, what will be the mechanical advantage (considering only the movement of the feet with a constant force for walking and riding), in percent, that each rider will have achieved over walking the same distance? (This can be found by dividing the distance walked by the distance the feet move in riding.)

4.23 An engineer has been given the assignment of finding how much money can be saved over a year's time by redesigning the press plates from the pattern shown in Fig. 4.18a to the pattern shown in Fig. 4.18b for stamping out 2.400-in.-diameter disks. The stamping material is 14-gauge sheet metal and can be purchased in 100-ft rolls in varying widths in 0.5-in. increments. One square foot of metal weighs 3.20 lb. The metal is sold for $0.20/lb. Do not consider the ends of the rolls. The company expects to produce 38 000 parts this year. How much can be saved?

4.24 Sally is making a sine bar, which is used to machine angles on parts (see Fig. 4.19). She has a 1.250-in. thick bar that needs 90° grooves machined into it for precision ground 1.0000-in. diameter cylinders. A sine bar is used by placing different thicknesses under one of the cylinders so that the proper angle is attained. Sally wants the distance between the centers of the cylinders to be 5.000 in.

(a) How deep should she mill the 90° grooves so that the top of the sine block is 2 in. tall?

(b) Once her sine block is finished, she wants to mill a 22.5° angle on a brass block. What thickness of gage blocks will produce this angle for this sine plate?

Figure 4.19

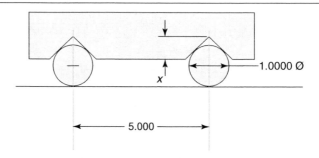

4.25 Standing at the edge of the roof of a tall building, you throw a ball upward with a velocity of 15 m/s (meters per second). The ball goes straight up and begins its downward descent just missing the edge of the building. The building is 40 m tall.

(a) What is the velocity of the ball at its uppermost position?

(b) How high above the building does the ball go before beginning its descent?

(c) What is the velocity of the ball as it passes the roof of the building?

(d) What is the speed of the ball just before it hits the ground?

(e) How long does it take for the ball to hit the ground after leaving your hand?

4.26 A stuntwoman is going to attempt a jump across a canyon 74 m wide. The ramp on the far side of the canyon is 25 m lower than the ramp from which she will leave. The takeoff ramp is built with a 15° angle from horizontal.

(a) If the stuntwoman leaves the ramp with a velocity of 28 m/s, will she make the jump?

(b) How many seconds will she be in the air?

4.27 An engineering student has been given the assignment of designing a hydraulic holding system for a hay-baling system. The system has four cylinders with 120-mm diameter pistons with a stroke of 0.320 m. The lines connecting the system are 1 cm id (inside diameter). There are 15.5 m of lines in the system. For proper design, the reserve tank should hold a minimum of 50% more than the amount of hydraulic fluid in the system. If the diameter of the reserve tank is 30.48 cm, what is the shortest height it should be?

4.28 The plant engineer for a large foundry has been asked to calculate the thermal efficiency of the generating plant used by the company to produce electricity for the aluminum melting furnaces. The plant generates 545.6 GJ of electrical energy daily. The plant burns 50 t (tons) of coal a day. The heat of combustion of coal is about 6.2×10^6 J/kg (joules/kilogram). What was the answer? (Efficiency = W/J_{heat})

4.29 Using these three formulas

$$V = IR \qquad R = (\rho L)/A \qquad A = \pi(0.5d)^2$$

find the difference in current (I) that a copper wire ($\rho = 1.72 \times 10^{-8}\ \Omega \cdot m$) can carry over an aluminum wire ($\rho = 2.75 \times 10^{-8}\ \Omega \cdot m$) with equal diameters ($d$) of 0.5 cm and a length (L) of 10 000 m carrying 110 V (volts).

4.30 The light striking a pane of glass is refracted as shown in Fig. 4.20. The law of refraction states that $n_a \sin \theta_a = n_b \sin \theta_b$, where n_a and n_b are the refractive indexes of the materials through which the light is passing and the angles are from a line that is normal to the surface. The refractive index of air is 1.00. What is the refractive index of the glass?

Figure 4.20

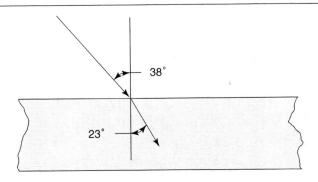

38°

23°

CHAPTER **7**

Dimensions, Units, and Conversions*

Chapter Objectives

When you complete your study of this chapter, you will be able to:

- Identify physical quantities in terms of dimensions and units
- Differentiate between fundamental and derived dimensions
- Understand the use of non-SI dimensional systems (gravitational and absolute)
- Recognize base, supplementary, and derived SI units
- Apply the appropriate SI symbols and prefixes
- Describe the relationship between U.S. Customary, Engineering System, and SI
- Systematically convert units from one system to another
- Use knowledge of dimensions and units, along with conversion rules, in the solution of engineering problems

7.1 Introduction

Years ago when countries were more isolated from one another, individual governments tended to develop and use their own set of measures. Today, primarily through the development of technology, global communication has brought countries closer together. As countries from one corner of the world to the other interact with each other, the need for a universal system of measurement has become abundantly clear. A standard set of dimensions, units, and measurements is vital if today's wealth of information and knowledge is to be shared and benefit all. The move toward a universal system first requires a thorough understanding of existing systems of measurement. This chapter begins with an explanation of the importance of physical quantities in engineering and explains the difference between dimensions and units. This is followed by the development of procedures for orderly conversion from one system of units to another, ultimately enabling measurements to be expressed in one system—that is, a metric international standard.

---

*Users will find Appendix A useful reference material for this chapter.

7.2 Progress in the United States toward Metrification

The United States Congress considered adoption of the metric system in the 1850s. In fact, the metric system was made legal in the United States in 1866, but its use was not made compulsory. In spite of many attempts in the intervening 150 years, full conversion to the metric system has not yet been realized.

In 1875, the United States together with 16 other nations signed an agreement called the Treaty of the Meter. These signatory nations established a governing body and gave that agency authority and overall responsibility for the metric system. The governing body is called the General Conference of Weights and Measures. That body approved an updated version of the metric system in 1960 called the international metric system, or Système International d'Unités, abbreviated SI. These units are a modification and refinement of earlier versions of the metric system (MKS) that designated the meter, kilogram, and second as fundamental units.

That 1960 standard is currently accepted in all industrial nations but still optional in the United States. In fact, the United States is the only industrialized nation on the globe that does not use the metric system as its predominant system of measurement. Current estimates suggest that the United States is at best 50% metric, so engineers must be well versed in the use of a variety of units as well as fluent in SI.

Some corporations within the U.S. economy have become almost 100% metric, others are somewhere in the middle, and many have far to go. That is not necessarily the fault of a given company or agency. For example, how many metric highway road signs have you seen lately driving across the United States? Figure 7.1 is an illustration of highway signs in Canada. Canada has a large population of French Canadians; as it happens, France was the first country, in 1840, to legislate adoption of the metric system and mandate its use. It takes a generation or two under a given system for a country's population to find it second nature. How many drivers in this country would actually know what 100 km/h really means?

To continue that train of thought, do you as a student give your weight in kilograms and buy gasoline by the liter? If someone tells you it is 30 degrees outside, do you immediately think in Celsius or Fahrenheit? How many of you knew that 30°C is 86°F? It is a difficult two-way street: Manufacturers, wholesalers, and distributors are not going to flood the market with products the consumer does not understand and therefore will not buy. As time marches on, a gradual increase in the use of SI will evolve, but in the meantime, be prepared to handle whatever system of units you encounter.

As a reminder of how important it is to understand the information presented in this chapter, let us review the NASA mission to send the Mars Climate Orbiter to the planet Mars. The $125 million spacecraft had almost completed a ten-month fight plan before it was lost on September 23, 1999, just as the spacecraft reached the planet's atmosphere. NASA convened three panels of experts to investigate what led to the loss of the orbiter. The reason for the loss was simple. One engineering team on a key navigational maneuver of the orbiter used metric units while a different team working on the same project used English units. The result was a major error in the entry trajectory resulting in the destruction of the vehicle.

Figure 7.1

Look for the **km/h** tab below the maximum speed limit sign, indicating that this is the new speed in metric.

100km/h This speed limit will likely be the most common on freeways. On most rural two-lane roadways, **80 km/h** will be typical.

50km/h A **50 km/h** speed limit will apply in most cities.

Actual speed limits will be established in accordance with local regulations.

Metric Commission Canada   Commission du système métrique Canada

Highway signs in Canada. (Metric Commission of Canada.)

7.3 Physical Quantities

Engineers are constantly concerned with the measurement of fundamental physical quantities such as length, time, temperature, force, and so on. In order to specify a physical quantity fully, it is not sufficient to indicate merely a numerical value. The magnitude of physical quantities can be understood only when they are compared with predetermined reference amounts, called *units*. Any measurement is, in effect, a comparison of how many (a number) units are contained within a physical quantity. Given length (L) as the physical quantity and 20.0 as the numerical value, with meters (m) as the designated unit, then a general relation can be represented by the expression

Length (L) = 20.0 m

For this relationship to be valid, the exact reproduction of a unit must be theoretically possible at any time. Therefore standards must be established and maintained. These standards are a set of fundamental unit quantities kept under normalized conditions in order to preserve their values as accurately as possible. We shall speak more about standards and their importance later.

7.4 Dimensions

Dimensions are used to describe physical quantities; however, the most important concept to remember is that dimensions are independent of units. As mentioned in Section 7.3, the physical quantity "length" can be represented by the dimension L, for which there are a large number of possibilities available when selecting a unit. For example, in ancient Egypt, the cubit was a unit related to the length of the arm from the tip of the middle finger to the elbow. At that time in history measurements were a function of physical stature, with variation from one individual to another. Much later, in Britain, the inch was specified as the distance covered by three barley corns, round and dry, laid end to end.

Today we require considerable more precision. For example, the meter is defined in terms of the distance traveled by light in a vacuum during a specified amount of time. We can draw two important points from this discussion: (1) Physical quantities must be accurately measured and be reproducible, and (2) these units (cubit, inch, and meter), although distinctly different, have in common the quality of being a length and not an area or a volume.

A technique used to distinguish between units and dimensions is to call all physical quantities of length a specific dimension (for example, L). In this way, each new physical quantity gives rise to a new dimension, such as T for time, F for force, M for mass, and so on. (Note that there is a dimension for each kind of physical quantity.)

However, to simplify the process, dimensions are divided into two areas—fundamental and derived. A fundamental dimension is a dimension that can be conveniently and usefully manipulated when expressing all physical quantities of a particular field of science or engineering. Derived dimensions are a combination of two or more fundamental dimensions. Velocity, for example, could be defined as a fundamental dimension V, but it is more customary as well as more convenient to consider velocity as a combination of fundamental dimensions, so that it becomes a derived dimension, $V = (L)(T)^{-1}$. L and T are fundamental dimensions, and V is a derived dimension because it is made up of two fundamental dimensions (L,T).

For simplicity it is advantageous to use as few fundamental dimensions as possible, but the selection of what is to be fundamental and what is to be derived is not fixed. In actuality, any dimension can be selected as a fundamental dimension in a particular field of engineering or science; for reasons of convenience, it may be a derived dimension in another field.

Once a set of primary dimensions has been adopted, a base unit for each primary dimension must then be specified. So let's look at how this works.

A *dimensional system* can be defined as the smallest number of fundamental dimensions that will form a consistent and complete set for a field of science. For example, three fundamental dimensions are necessary to form a complete mechanical dimensional system. Depending on the discipline, these dimensions may be specified as either length (L), time (T), and mass (M) or length (L),

Table 7.1 Two Basic Dimensional Systems

Quantity	Absolute	Gravitational
Length	L	L
Time	T	T
Mass	M	$FL^{-1}T^2$
Force	MLT^{-2}	F
Velocity	LT^{-1}	LT^{-1}
Pressure	$ML^{-1}T^{-2}$	FL^{-2}
Momentum	MLT^{-1}	FT
Energy	ML^2T^{-2}	FL
Power	ML^2T^{-3}	FLT^{-1}
Torque	ML^2T^{-2}	FL

time (T), and force (F). If temperature is important to the application, a fourth fundamental dimension may be added.

The *absolute system* (so called because the dimensions used are not affected by gravity) has as its fundamental dimensions L, T, and M. An advantage of this system is that comparisons of masses at various locations can be made with an ordinary balance, because the local acceleration of gravity has no influence upon the results.

The *gravitational system* has as its fundamental dimensions L, T, and F. It is widely used in many engineering branches because it simplifies computations when weight is a fundamental quantity in the computations. Table 7.1 lists the dimensions used in the absolute and gravitational systems; a number of other dimensional systems are commonly used depending on the specific discipline.

7.5 Units

After a consistent dimensional system has been identified, the next step is to select a specific unit for each fundamental dimension. The problem one encounters when working with units is that there can be a large number of unit systems to choose from for any given dimensional system. It is obviously desirable to limit the number of systems and combinations of systems. The Système International d'Unités (SI) is intended to serve as an international standard that will provide worldwide consistency.

There are three fundamental systems of units commonly used today. The metric system, used in almost every industrial country of the world, is a decimal-absolute system based on the meter, kilogram, and second (MKS) as the units of length, mass, and time, respectively.

In the United States, however, there are two other system of units commonly used. The first, called the U.S. Customary System (formerly known as the British gravitational system), has the fundamental units of foot (ft) for length, pound (lb) for force, and second (s) for time. The second system of units, called the Engineering System, is based on the foot (ft) for length, pound-force (lbf) for force, and second (s) for time. More information regarding the Customary and Engineering Systems will be presented in Section 7.8.

Numerous international conferences on weights and measures over the past 40 years have gradually modified the MKS system to the point that all countries previously using various forms of the metric system are beginning to standardize. SI is now considered the international system of units. Although the United States has officially adopted this system, as indicated earlier, full implementation will be preceded by a long and expensive period of change. During this transition period, engineers will have to be familiar with not only SI but also other systems and the necessary conversion process between or among systems. This chapter will focus on the international standard (SI units and symbols); however, examples and explanations of the Engineering System and the U.S. Customary System will be included.

7.6   SI Units and Symbols

SI, developed and maintained by the General Conference on Weights and Measures (Conférence Générale des Poids et Mesures, CGPM), is intended as a basis for worldwide standardization of measurements. The name and abbreviation were set forth in 1960.

This new international system is divided into three classes of units:

1. Base units
2. Supplementary units
3. Derived units

There are seven base units in the SI. The units (except the kilogram) are defined in such a way that they can be reproduced anywhere in the world.

Table 7.2 lists each base unit along with its name and proper symbol.

In the following list, each of the base units were defined and adopted at various meetings of the General Conference on Weights and Measures held between 1889 and 1983:

1. *Length.* The meter (m) is a length equal to the distance traveled by light in a vacuum during $1/299\,792\,458$ s.
2. *Time.* The second (s) is the duration of $9\,192\,631\,770$ periods of radiation corresponding to the transition between the two hyperfine levels of the ground state of the cesium-133 atom.
3. *Mass.* The standard for the unit of mass, the kilogram (kg), is a cylinder of platinum-iridium alloy kept by the International Bureau of Weights and Measures in France. A duplicate copy is maintained in the United States. It is the only base unit that is nonreproducible in a properly equipped lab.
4. *Electric current.* The ampere (A) is a constant current that, if maintained in two straight parallel conductors of infinite length and of negligible circular cross-sections and placed one meter apart in volume, would produce between these conductors a force equal to 2×10^{-7} newton per meter of length.
5. *Temperature.* The kelvin (K), a unit of thermodynamic temperature, is the fraction $1/273.16$ of the thermodynamic temperature of the triple point of water.

Table 7.2 Basic Units

Quantity	Name	Symbol
Length	meter	m
Mass	kilogram	kg
Time	second	s
Electric current	ampere	A
Thermodynamic temp.	kelvin	K
Amount of substance	mole	mol
Luminous intensity	candela	cd

6. *Amount of substance.* The mole (mol) is the amount of substance of a system that contains as many elementary entities as there are atoms in 0.012 kg of carbon-12.
7. *Luminous intensity.* The base unit candela (cd) is the luminous intensity in a given direction of a source that emits monochromatic radiation of frequency 540×10^{12} hertz and has a radiant intensity in that direction of 1/683 watts per steradian.

The units listed in Table 7.3 are called *supplementary units* and may be regarded either as base units or as derived units.

The unit for a plane angle is the radian (rad), a unit that is used frequently in engineering. The steradian is not as commonly used. These units can be defined in the following way:

1. Plane angle: The radian is the plane angle between two radii of a circle that cut off on the circumference of an arc equal in length to the radius.
2. Solid angle: The steradian (sr) is the solid angle which, having its vertex in the center of a sphere, cuts off an area of the sphere equal to that of a square with sides of length equal to the radius of the sphere.

As indicated earlier, derived units are formed by combining base, supplementary, or other derived units. Symbols for them are carefully selected to avoid confusion. Those that have special names and symbols, as interpreted for the United States by the National Bureau of Standards, are listed in Table 7.4 together with their definitions in terms of base units.

Additional derived units, such as those listed in Table 7.5, have no special SI unit names or symbols but are nevertheless combinations of base units and units with special names.

Table 7.3 Supplementary Units

Quantity	Name	Symbol
Plane angle	radian	rad
Solid angle	steradian	sr

Table 7.4 Derived Units

Quantity	SI Unit Symbol	Name	Base Units
Frequency	Hz	hertz	s^{-1}
Force	N	newton	$kg \cdot m \cdot s^{-2}$
Pressure or stress	Pa	pascal	$kg \cdot m^{-1} \cdot s^{-2}$
Energy or work	J	joule	$kg \cdot m^2 \cdot s^{-2}$
Quantity of heat	J	joule	$kg \cdot m^2 \cdot s^{-2}$
Power radiant flux	W	watt	$kg \cdot m^2 \cdot s^{-3}$
Electric charge	C	coulomb	$A \cdot s$
Electric potential	V	volt	$kg \cdot m^2 \cdot s^{-3} \cdot A^{-1}$
Potential difference	V	volt	$kg \cdot m^2 \cdot s^{-3} \cdot A^{-1}$
Electromotive force	V	volt	$kg \cdot m^2 \cdot s^{-3} \cdot A^{-1}$
Capacitance	F	farad	$A^2 \cdot s^4 \cdot kg^{-1} \cdot m^{-2}$
Electric resistance	Ω	ohm	$kg \cdot m^2 \cdot s^{-3} \cdot A^{-2}$
Conductance	S	siemens	$kg^{-1} \cdot m^{-2} \cdot s^3 \cdot A^2$
Magnetic flux	Wb	weber	$m^2 \cdot kg \cdot s^{-2} \cdot A^{-1}$
Magnetic flux density	T	tesla	$kg \cdot s^{-2} \cdot A^{-1}$
Inductance	H	henry	$kg \cdot m^2 \cdot s^{-2} \cdot A^{-2}$
Luminous flux	lm	lumen	cd
Illuminance	lx	lux	$cd \cdot m^{-2}$
Celsius temperature*	°C	degree Celsius	K
Activity (radionuclides)	Bq	becqueret	s^{-1}
Absorbed dose	Gy	gray	$m^2 \cdot s^{-2}$
Dose equivalent	S_v	sievert	$m^2 \cdot s^{-2}$

*The thermodynamic temperature (T_K) expressed in kelvins is related to Celsius temperature (t_c) expressed in degrees Celsius by the equation $t_c = T_K - 273.15$.

Table 7.5 Additional Derived Units

Quantity	Units	Quantity	Units
Acceleration	$m \cdot s^{-2}$	Molar entropy	$J \cdot mol^{-1} \cdot K^{-1}$
Angular acceleration	$rad \cdot s^{-2}$	Molar heat capacity	$J \cdot mol^{-1} \cdot K^{-1}$
Angular velocity	$rad \cdot s^{-1}$	Moment of force	$N \cdot m$
Area	m^2	Permeability	$H \cdot m^{-1}$
Concentration	$mol \cdot m^{-3}$	Permittivity	$F \cdot m^{-1}$
Current density	$A \cdot m^{-2}$	Radiance	$W \cdot m^{-2} \cdot sr^{-1}$
Density, mass	$kg \cdot m^{-3}$	Radiant intensity	$W \cdot sr^{-1}$
Electric charge density	$C \cdot m^{-3}$	Specific heat capacity	$J \cdot kg^{-1} \cdot K^{-1}$
Electric field strength	$V \cdot m^{-1}$	Specific energy	$J \cdot kg^{-1}$
Electric flux density	$C \cdot m^{-2}$	Specific entropy	$J \cdot kg^{-1} \cdot K^{-1}$
Energy density	$J \cdot m^{-3}$	Specific volume	$m^3 \cdot kg^{-1}$
Entropy	$J \cdot K^{-1}$	Surface tension	$N \cdot m^{-1}$
Heat capacity	$J \cdot K^{-1}$	Thermal conductivity	$W \cdot m^{-1} \cdot K^{-1}$
Heat flux density	$W \cdot m^{-2}$	Velocity	$m \cdot s^{-1}$
Irradiance	$W \cdot m^{-2}$	Viscosity, dynamic	$Pa \cdot s$
Luminance	$cd \cdot m^{-2}$	Viscosity, kinematic	$m^2 \cdot s^{-1}$
Magnetic field strength	$A \cdot m^{-1}$	Volume	m^3
Molar energy	$J \cdot mol^{-1}$	Wavelength	m

Being a decimal system, the SI is convenient to use because by simply affixing a prefix to the base, a quantity can be increased or decreased by factors of 10 and the numerical quantity can be kept within manageable limits. The proper selection of prefixes will also help eliminate nonsignificant zeros and leading zeros in decimal fractions. One rule to follow is that the numerical value of any measurement should be recorded as a number between 0.1 and 1 000. This rule is suggested because it is easier to make realistic judgments when working with numbers between 0.1 and 1 000. For example, suppose that you are asked the distance to a nearby town. It would be more understandable to respond in kilometers than meters. That is, it is easier to visualize 10 km than 10 000 m.

The use of prefixes representing powers of 1 000, such as kilo, mega, milli, etc., are preferred over multipliers such as deci, deka, etc. However, the three exceptions listed below are still in common used because of convention.

1. When expressing area and volume, the prefixes hecto-, deka-, deci-, and centi- may be used; for example, cubic centimeter.
2. When discussing different values of the same quantity or expressing them in a table, calculations are simpler to perform when you use the same unit multiple throughout.
3. Sometimes a particular multiple is recommended as a consistent unit even though its use violates the 0.1 to 1 000 rule. For example, many companies use the millimeter for linear dimensions even when the values lie far outside this suggested range. The cubic decimeter (commonly called liter) is also used in this manner.

Recalling the importance of significant figures, we see that SI prefix notations can be used to a definite advantage. Consider the previous example of 10 km versus 10 000 m. In an estimate of distance to the nearest town, a round number certainly implies an approximation. Suppose that we were talking about a 10 000 m Olympic track and field event. The accuracy of such a distance must certainly be greater than something between 5 000 and 15 000 m, which would be the implied accuracy with one significant figure. If, however we use prefix multipliers, such as 10.000 km, then all five numbers are in fact significant, and the race length is accurate to within 1 m (9 999.5 to 10 000.5). If only four numbers are significant (10.00 km), then the race length is accurate to within 10 m (9 995 to 10 005).

There are two logical and acceptable methods available for eliminating confusion concerning zeros or the correct number of significant figures:

1. Use proper prefixes to denote intended significance.

Distance	Precision	Number of significant figures
10.000 km	9 999.5 to 10 000.5 m	5
10.00 km	9 995 to 10 005 m	4
10.0 km	9 950 to 10 050 m	3
10 km	5 000 to 15 000 m	1

How would you express a degree of significance between 10.0 km and 10 km? One viable solution is to use scientific notation.

2. Use scientific notation to indicate significance.

Distance	Precision	Number of significant figures
$1.000\ 0 \times 10^4$ m	9 999.5 to 10 000.5 m	5
$1.000\ 0 \times 10^4$ m	9 995 to 10 005 m	4
1.00×10^4 m	9 950 to 10 050 m	3
1.0×10^4 m	9 500 to 10 500 m	2
1×10^4 m	5 000 to 15 000 m	1

Selection of a proper prefix is customarily the logical way to handle problems of significant figures; however, there are conventions that do not lend themselves to the prefix notation. An example would be temperature in degrees Celsius; that is, $4.00(10^3)$°C is the conventional way to handle it, not 4.00 k°C.

7.7   Rules for Using SI Units

Along with the adoption of SI comes the responsibility to thoroughly understand and properly apply the new system. Obsolete practices involving both English and metric units are widespread. This section provides rules that should be followed when working with SI units.

7.7.1   Unit Symbols and Names

1. Periods are never used after SI symbols unless the symbol is at the end of a sentence (that is, SI unit symbols are not abbreviations).
2. Unit symbols are written in lowercase letters unless the symbol derives from a proper name, for example, Ampere (A) or Kelvin (K), in which case the first letter is capitalized.

Lowercase	Uppercase
m, kg, s, mol, cd	A, K, Hz, Pa, C

3. Symbols rather than self-styled abbreviations should always be used to represent units.

Correct	Not correct
A	amp
s	sec

4. An s is never added to the symbol to denote plural.
5. A space is always left between the numerical value and the unit symbol.

Correct	Not correct
43.7 km	43.7km
0.25 Pa	0.25Pa

Exception: No space should be left between numerical values and the symbols for degree, minute, and second of angles and for degree Celsius.

6. There should be no space between the prefix and the unit symbols.

Correct	Not correct
mm, MΩ	k m, μ F

7. A unit name is written in lowercase (except at the beginning of a sentence), even if the unit is derived from a proper name.
8. Plurals are used as required when writing unit names. For example, henries is plural for henry. The following exceptions are noted:

Singular	Plural
lux	lux
hertz	hertz
siemens	siemens

With these exceptions, unit names form their plurals in the usual manner.

9. No hyphen or space should be left between a prefix and the unit name. In three cases the final vowel in the prefix is omitted: megohm, kilohm, and hectare.
10. The symbol should be used following a number in preference to the unit name because unit symbols are standardized. An exception to this is made when a number is written in words preceding the unit; for example, we would write *nine meters,* not *nine m.* The same is true the other way, for example, 9 m, not 9 meters.

7.7.2 Multiplication and Division

1. When writing unit names as a product, always use a space (preferred) or a hyphen.

Correct usage

newton meter or newton-meter

2. When expressing a quotient using unit names, always use the word *per* and not a solidus (/). The solidus, or slash mark, is reserved for use with symbols.

Correct usage	Not correct
meter per second	meter/second

3. When writing a unit name that requires a power, use a modifier, such as squared or cubed, after the unit name. For area or volume, the modifier can be placed before the unit name.

Correct usage

millimeter squared or square millimeter

4. When expressing products using unit symbols, the center dot is preferred.

Correct usage

N · m for newton meter

5. When denoting a quotient by unit symbols, any of the following are accepted form:

    Correct usage

    $$m/s \quad \text{or} \quad m \cdot s^{-1} \quad \text{or} \quad \frac{m}{s}$$

    In more complicated cases, consider using negative powers or parentheses. For acceleration use m/s^2 or $m \cdot s^{-2}$ but not $m/s/s$. For electrical potential use $kg \cdot m^2/(s^3 \cdot A)$ or $kg \cdot s^{-3} \cdot A^{-1}$ but not $kg \cdot m^1/s^3/A$.

7.7.3 Numbers

1. To denote a decimal point, use a period on the line. When expressing numbers less than 1, a zero should be written before the decimal marker.

    Example

    15.6
    0.93

2. Since a comma is used in many countries to denote a decimal point, its use is to be avoided in grouping data. To avoid confusion, separate the digits into groups of three, counting from the decimal to the left or right, and use a small space to separate the groups.

    Correct and recommended procedure

    6.513 824   76 851   7 434   0.187 62

7.7.4 Calculating with SI Units

Before we look at some suggested procedures that will simplify calculations in SI, let us review the following positive characteristics of the system.

Only one unit is used to represent each physical quantity, such as the meter for length, the second for time, and so on. The SI metric units are *coherent*; that is, each new derived unit is a product or quotient of the fundamental and supplementary units without any numerical factors. Since coherency is a strength of the SI system, it would be worthwhile to demonstrate this characteristic by the following two examples. The relationship among force, mass and time can be illustrated by Newton's second law, $F \propto ma$. To satisfy coherency the newton (N) becomes a derived unit. Its magnitude is defined as the force required to impart an acceleration of one meter per second squared to a mass of one kilogram. It was not arbitrary determined independent of mass and time. Thus,

$$1.0\,N = (1.0\,kg)(1.0\,m/s^2)$$

Newton's second law can now be written in equation form as follows:

$$F = \frac{ma}{g_C}, \text{ where } g_C = \frac{ma}{F} \text{ or } g_C = \frac{1.0\,kg \cdot 1.0\,m}{N \cdot s^2}$$

This constant of proportionality serves as a reminder that the units are in fact coherent and that the conversion factor is 1.0.

Consider next the joule, the SI equivalent of the British thermal unit, the calorie, foot-pound-force, the electron volt, and the horsepower-hour, intended to represent most forms of energy. The joule is defined as the amount of work done when an applied force of one newton acts through a distance of one meter in the direction of the force. Thus,

$$1.0\ J = (1.0\ N)(1.0\ m)$$

To maintain coherency of units, however, time must be expressed in seconds rather than minutes or hours, since the second is the base unit. Once coherency is violated, then a conversion factor must be included and the advantage of the system is diminished.

But there are certain units *outside* SI that are accepted for use in the United States, even though they diminish the system's coherence. These exceptions are listed in Table 7.6.

Calculations using SI can be simplified if you;

1. Remember that fundamental relationships are simple and easier to use because of coherence.
2. Recognize how to manipulate units and gain a proficiency in doing so. Since watt = J/s = N · m/s, you can algebraically rearrange the units to produce N · m/s = $(N/m^2)(m^3/s)$ = (pressure)(volume flow rate).
3. Understand the advantage of occasionally adjusting all variables to base units; for example, replacing N with kg · m/s^2 and Pa with kg · $m^{-1}s^{-2}$.
4. Develop a proficiency with exponential notation of numbers to be used in conjunction with unit prefixes.

$$1\ mm^3 = (10^{-3}\ m)^3 = 10^{-9}\ m^3$$

$$1\ ns^{-1} = (10^{-9}\ s)^{-1} = 10^9\ s^{-1}$$

When calculating with SI the term "weight" can be confusing. Frequently we hear statements such as "The person weighs 100 kg." A correct statement

Table 7.6 Non-SI Units Accepted for Use in the United States

Quantity	Name	Symbol	SI equivalent
Time	minute	min	60 s
	hour	h	3 600 s
	day	d	86 400 s
Plane angle	degree	°	$\pi/180$ rad
	minute	'	$\pi/10\ 800$ rad
	second	"	$\pi/648\ 000$ rad
Volume	liter	L*	$10^{-3}\ m^3$
Mass	metric ton	t	10^3 kg
	unified atomic mass unit	u	$1.660\ 57 \times 10^{-27}$ kg (approx)
Land area	hectare	ha	$10^4\ m^2$
Energy	electronvolt	eV	1.602×10^{-19} J (approx)

*Both "L" and "l" are acceptable international symbols for liter. The uppercase letter is recommended for use in the United States because the lowercase "l" can be confused with the numeral 1.

would be "The person has a mass of 100 kg." To clear up any confusion, let's look at some basic definitions.

First, the term *mass* should be used to indicate only a quantity of matter. Mass is measured in kilograms (kg) or pound-mass (lbm) and is always measured against a standard.

Force, as defined by the International Standard of Units, is measured in newtons. By definition the newton was established as the force required to accelerate a mass of one kilogram to one meter per second squared.

The acceleration of gravity varies at different points on the surface of the Earth as well as distance from the Earth's surface. The accepted standard value of gravitational acceleration is 9.806 650 m/s² at sea level and 45 degrees latitude.

Gravity is instrumental in measuring mass with a beam balance or scale. If you use a beam balance to compare an unknown quantity against a standard mass, the effect of gravity on the two masses cancels out. If you use a spring scale, mass is measured indirectly, since the instrument responds to the local force of gravity. Such a scale can be calibrated in mass units and be reasonably accurate when used where the variation in the acceleration of gravity is not significant.

The following example problem clarifies the confusion that exists in the use of the term *weight* to mean either force or mass. In everyday use, the term *weight* nearly always means mass; thus, when a person's weight is discussed, the quantity referred to is mass.

Example Problem 7.1   A "weight" of 100.0 kg (the unit itself indicates mass) is suspended by a cable from an I-beam. Calculate the force or tension in the cable in newtons to hold the mass stationary when the local gravitational acceleration is (a) 9.807 m/s² and (b) 1.63 m/s² (approximate value for the surface of the Moon).

Theory   Tension in the cable or force required to hold the object when the mass is at rest or moving at constant velocity is

$$F = \frac{mg_{\mathrm{L}}}{g_{\mathrm{c}}}$$

where g_{L} is the local acceleration of gravity and replaces acceleration in Newton's equation $F = ma$, g_{c} is the proportionality constant, and m is the mass of object. Remember that due to coherence

$$g_{\mathrm{c}} = 1.0 \left[\frac{\mathrm{kg} \cdot \mathrm{m}}{\mathrm{N} \cdot \mathrm{s}^2} \right]$$

Assumption   Neglect the mass of the cable.

Solution

(a) For $g_L = 9.807 \text{ m/s}^2$

$$F = \frac{mg_L}{g_c}$$

$$F = \frac{(100.0\,\text{kg})(9.807\,\text{m})}{\text{s}^2} \times \frac{\text{N} \cdot \text{s}^2}{1.0\,\text{kg} \cdot \text{m}} = 980.7 \text{ N}$$

$$= 0.980\,7 \text{ kN}$$

(b) For $g_L = 1.63 \text{ m/s}^2$

$$F = \frac{(100.0\,\text{kg})(1.63\,\text{m})}{\text{s}^2} \times \frac{\text{N} \cdot \text{s}^2}{1.0\,\text{kg} \cdot \text{m}} = 0.163\,0 \text{ kN}$$

7.8   U.S. Customary and Engineering Systems

Before you study the material in this section, ask yourself why it is necessary to consider any system of dimensions and units other than SI. Next, think about a few common products that you might purchase for a home remodeling project: threaded fasteners, lumber, nails, paint, and so on. How many of these are available in metric units?

Although SI is ultimately intended to be adopted worldwide, at the present time many segments of the U.S. industrial complex regularly use other systems. For many years to come, engineers in the United States will have to be comfortable and proficient with a variety of unit systems.

As noted earlier in this chapter, there are two systems of units other than SI commonly used in the United States.

7.8.1   U.S. Customary System

The first, the U.S. Customary System has the fundamental units of foot (ft) for length, pound (lb) for force, and second (s) for time (see Table 7.7). However, in this system mass (m) is not a fundamental unit; it is a new derived unit called the slug. Since it is a new derived unit, its magnitude can be established. A slug is defined as a specific amount of mass. In fact, it is the amount of mass that would be accelerated to one foot per second squared given a force of one pound. This system works perfectly well as long as mass is derived totally independent of force. In fact, since we define the derived unit mass as the slug and establish its mass as a quantity of matter that will be accelerated to 1.0 ft/s² when a force of 1.0 lb is applied, we have a coherent system of units. We can once again write Newton's second law as an equality,

$$F = \frac{ma}{g_c}, \text{ where } g_c = \frac{ma}{F} \text{ or } g_c = \frac{(1.0)\,\text{slug} \cdot 1.0\,\text{ft}}{\text{lbf} \cdot \text{s}^2}$$

Note that the constant of proportionality, g_c, is included to clarify units, but the conversion factor is (1.0).

Table 7.7   The U.S. Customary System

Quality	Unit	Symbol
Mass	slug	slug
Length	foot	ft
Time	second	s
Force	pound	lb

7.8.2   The Engineering System

The Engineering System, uses length, time, mass, and force as the fundamental dimensions (see Table 7.8). In the Engineering System, the fundamental dimension force was established independently from the other primary dimensions. Recall that in the SI system of units force was determined with relation to Newton's second law. However, in this case, sometime during the fourteenth century, a quantity of matter was selected to be one pound-mass (lbm). At a later time it was decided that one pound-force (lbf) would be the force required to hold a one pound-mass in a gravitational field where the local acceleration of gravity was the standard value of 32.174 0 ft/ s². In fact one pound-force (lbf) is the amount of force that would be required to accelerated a mass of 32.174 0 (lbm) to one foot per second squared. Unfortunately, in the Engineering System of units the independent selection of four fundamental dimensions require that we insert a conversion factor in the constant of proportionality (g_c). It is for this reason that we included (g_c) in equations that relate pound-mass and pound-force. It provides us with a visual reminder that

$$g_C = 32.1740 \frac{\text{lbm} \cdot \text{ft}}{\text{lbf} \cdot \text{s}^2}$$

When calculating in the Engineering System, the constant of proportionality g_c and the local gravitational constant g_L can be particularly confusing when using the term "weight." If you were to hold a child in your arms, you might say that this child is heavy, and ask the question, how much does this child weigh? Does the question refer to the amount of force exerted to hold the child (lbf) or the child's mass (lbm)?

Normally the term "weight" refers to pound-mass. In other words the child's mass is 50.0 lbm. Holding the child requires a force of 50.0 lbf where the local acceleration of gravity is exactly 32.1740 ft/s².

$$F = \frac{mg_L}{g_C} = \frac{50.0 \text{ lbm}}{1.0} \times \frac{32.174 \text{ ft}}{s^2} \times \frac{\text{lbf} \cdot \text{s}^2}{32.1740 \text{ lbm} \cdot \text{ft}} = 50.0 \text{ lbf}$$

Table 7.8   The Engineering System

Quality	Unit	Symbol
Mass	pound-mass	lbm
Length	foot	ft
Time	second	s
Force	pound-force	lbf

If the local gravitational constant were any value other than 32.1740, then the force required to hold the child would either be greater than or less than the force required in the example. For instance, on planet x the local acceleration of gravity is 8.72 ft/s^2. In this case the force required to hold the 50.0 lbm child (mass never changes) would be determined as follows.

$$F = \frac{mg_L}{g_C} = \frac{50.0 \text{ lbm}}{1.0} \times \frac{8.72 \text{ ft}}{s^2} \times \frac{\text{lbf} \cdot s^2}{32.1740 \text{ lbm} \cdot \text{ft}} = 13.6 \text{ lbf}$$

So the next time someone asks how much you can bench press, say, "About 600 lbm,"—just don't mention on what planet.

Once again a word of caution when using the Engineering System in expressions such as Newton's second law (F α ma). This particular combination of units—lbf, lbm, ft, and s^2—do not constitute a coherent set. Recall a coherent set of non-SI units involving lbf, slug, and ft/s^2 was the U.S Customary system. So you have a choice. You can either include the conversion factor or always convert mass quantities from lbm to slugs (1.0 slug = 32.174 0 lbm). For example, in the problem above it would be necessary to first convert 50.0 lbm to slugs and then simply use the U.S. Customary system.

$$50.0 \text{ lbm} = \frac{50.0 \text{ lbm}}{1.0} \times \frac{\text{slugs}}{32.174 \text{ lbm}} = 1.554 \text{ slugs}$$

$$F = \frac{mg_L}{g_C} = \frac{1.554 \text{ slugs}}{1.0} \times \frac{32.174 \text{ ft}}{s^2} \times \frac{\text{lbf} \cdot s^2}{1.0 \text{ slugs} \cdot \text{ft}} = 50.0 \text{ lbf}$$

7.9 Conversion of Units

The two dimensional systems listed in Table 7.1 can be further divided into the four systems of mechanical units presently encountered in the United States. See Table 7.9. The table does not provide a complete list of all possible quantities; this list is presented to demonstrate the different units that are associated with each unique system. As an example, the physical quantity L (length) can be expressed in a variety of units. Fortunately, it is a simple matter to convert the units from any system to the one in which you are working. To do this, the basic conversion for the units involved must be known and a logical series of steps must be followed. This procedure is often referred to as dimensional analysis or the unit-factor method.

Mistakes can be minimized if you remember that a conversion factor simply relates the same physical quantity in two different unit systems. For example, 1.0 in. and 25.4 mm each describe the same length quantity. So let's say you wish to convert 65.7 in to mm. The five steps outlined below summarizes a method to follow during any conversion of units.

1. Write the following identity starting with the quantity you wish to convert

    $$65.7 \text{ in} = \frac{65.7 \text{ in}}{1.0}$$

2. Recall or lookup appropriate conversion factor

    $$1.0 \text{ in} = 25.4 \text{ mm}$$

Table 7.9 Mechanical Units

| Quality | Absolute System | | Gravitational System | |
	MKS	CGS	Type I	Type II
Length	m	cm	ft	ft
Mass	kg	g	slug	lbm
Time	s	s	s	s
Force	N	dyne	lbf	lbf
Velocity	$m \cdot s^{-1}$	$cm \cdot s^{-1}$	$ft \cdot s^{-1}$	$ft \cdot s^{-1}$
Acceleration	$m \cdot s^{-2}$	$cm \cdot s^{-2}$	$ft \cdot s^{-2}$	$ft \cdot s^{-2}$
Torque	$N \cdot m$	$dyne \cdot cm$	$lbf \cdot ft$	$lbf \cdot ft$
Moment of inertia	$kg \cdot m^2$	$g \cdot cm^2$	$slug \cdot ft^2$	$lbm \cdot ft^2$
Pressure	$N \cdot m^{-2}$	$dyne \cdot cm^{-2}$	$lbf \cdot ft^{-2}$	$lb \cdot ft^{-2}$
Energy	J	erg	$ft \cdot lbf$	$ft \cdot lbf$
Power	W	$erg \cdot s^{-1}$	$ft \cdot lbf \cdot s^{-1}$	$ft \cdot lbf \cdot s^{-1}$
Momentum	$kg \cdot m \cdot s^{-1}$	$g \cdot cm \cdot s^{-1}$	$slug \cdot ft \cdot s^{-1}$	$lbm \cdot ft \cdot s^{-1}$
Impulse	$N \cdot s$	$dyne \cdot s$	$lbf \cdot s$	$lbf \cdot s$

Type I—U.S. Customary
Type II—Engineering

Remember, you can divide both sides by 1.0 in or you can divide both sides by 25.4 mm.

3. Arrange this equality such that the desired unit conversion is in the numerator, i.e., mm.

$$\frac{1.0 \text{ in}}{1.0 \text{ in}} = \frac{25.4 \text{ mm}}{1.0 \text{ in}} = 1.0$$

4. Multiply the two identities to obtain desired answer

$$65.7 \text{ in} = \frac{65.7 \text{ in}}{1.0} \times \frac{25.4 \text{ mm}}{1.0 \text{ in}} = 1\,668.78 \text{ mm}$$

5. Consider significant figures

$$65.7 \text{ in} = 1\,670 \text{ mm}$$

Thus, when using the conversion factor 25.4 mm/in. to convert a quantity in inches to millimeters, you are multiplying a factor that is not numerically equal to 1 but is physically identical. This fact allows you to readily avoid the most common error, that of using the reciprocal of a conversion. Let's say you are to convert ft to m. From the conversion tables in the Appendix we obtain 1.0 ft = 0.3048 m or 0.3048 m/ft. Just imagine that the value in the numerator of the conversion must describe the same physical quantity as that in the denominator. When so doing, you will never use the incorrect factor 0.3048 ft/m, since 0.3048 ft is clearly not the same length as 1 m.

The following five example problems review the procedure outlined above and presents a systematic series of steps that can be used when performing a unit conversion. Often times the five steps outlined are condensed to some smaller number, i.e., individual steps are combined, nevertheless, the construction of a series of individual steps will aid the thought process and help ensure a correct unit analysis. Notice the units to be eliminated will cancel algebraically, leaving the desired results. The final answer should be checked to make sure it is reasonable.

Example Problem 7.2 Convert 375 lbm/s to slugs/hr

Step 1: Write the identity and list conversion factors

$$375 \text{ lbm/s} = \frac{375 \text{ lbm}}{1.0 \text{ s}}$$

$$1.0 \text{ slug} = 32.174 \text{ 0 lbm} \quad \text{and} \quad 1.0 \text{ hr} = 3\,600 \text{ s}$$

Step 2: Multiply this identity by the appropriate conversion factors

$$375 \text{ lbm/s} = \frac{375 \text{ lbm}}{1.0 \text{ s}} \times \frac{\text{slugs}}{32.174 \text{ lbm}} \times \frac{3\,600 \text{ s}}{\text{hr}} = 41\,959 \text{ slugs/hr}$$

Notice that by the correct positioning of conversion factors the desired answer can be realized, i.e., lbm and seconds cancel leaving slugs per hr.

Step 3: Check for reasonable answer and significant figures

$$375 \text{ lbm/s} = 4.20 \times (10)^4 \text{ slugs/hr}$$

Example Problem 7.3 Convert 85.0 lbm/ft³ to kilograms per cubic meter.

Solution

Step 1: Write the identity and list conversion factors

$$85.0 \text{ lbm/ft}^3 = \frac{85.0 \text{ lbm}}{1.0 \text{ ft}^3}$$

$$1.0 \text{ ft} = 0.304 \text{ 8 m} \qquad \text{and} \qquad 1.0 \text{ lbm} = 0.453 \text{ 6 kg}$$

Step 2: Multiply this identity by the appropriate conversion factors

$$85.0 \text{ lbm/ft}^3 = \frac{85.0 \text{ lbm}}{1.0 \text{ ft}^3} \times \frac{0.4536 \text{ kg}}{1.0 \text{ lbm}} \times \frac{(1.0 \text{ ft})^3}{(0.3048 \text{ m})^3} = 1.36 \times 10^3 \text{ kg/m}^3$$

Step 3: Check for reasonable answer and significant figures

Example Problem 7.4 Determine the gravitation force (in newtons) on an automobile with a mass of 3 645 lbm. The acceleration of gravity is known to be 32.2 ft/s².

Solution A Force, mass, and acceleration of gravity are related by

$$F = \frac{mg_L}{g_C}$$

Convert lbm to kilograms

$$m = \frac{3\,645 \text{ lbm}}{1.0} \times \frac{1 \text{ kg}}{2.204 \text{ 6 lbm}} = 1\,653.36 \text{ kg}$$

$$g_L = \frac{32.2 \text{ ft}}{s^2} \times \frac{0.304 \text{ 8 m}}{1.0 \text{ ft}} = 9.814 \text{ 6 m/s}^2$$

$$F = \frac{mg_L}{g_C} = (1\,653.36 \text{ kg})\left(\frac{9.814 \text{ 6 m}}{s^2}\right)\left(\frac{1.0 \text{ kg} \cdot \text{m}}{\text{N} \cdot s^2}\right)$$

$$= 16\,227 \text{ N} = 16.2 \text{ kN}$$

Note: Intermediate values were not rounded to final precision, and we have used either exact or conversion factors with at least one more significant figure than contained in the final answer.

Solution B (combine steps in Solution A into one step)

$$F = \frac{mg_L}{g_C} = \frac{3\,645\text{ lbm}}{1} \times \frac{32.2\text{ ft}}{1s^2} \times \frac{1\text{ kg}}{2.2046\text{ lbm}} \times \frac{0.304\,8\text{ m}}{1\text{ ft}} \times \frac{N \cdot s^2}{1.0\text{ kg} \cdot m}$$

$$= 16\,227\text{ N} = 16.2\text{ kN}$$

Note: It is often convenient to include conversions with the appropriate engineering relationship in a single calculation.

Example Problem 7.5   Convert a mass flow rate of 195 kg/s (typical of the airflow through a turbofan engine) to slugs per minute.

Solution: $195\text{ kg/s} = \dfrac{195\text{ kg}}{1\text{ s}} \times \dfrac{1\text{ slug}}{14.954\text{ kg}} \times \dfrac{60\text{ s}}{1\text{ min}} = 782\text{ slug/min}$

Example Problem 7.6   Compute the power output of a 225-hp engine in (a) British thermal units per minute and (b) kilowatts.

Solution

(a) $225\text{ hp} = \dfrac{225\text{ hp}}{1} \times \dfrac{2.5461 \times 10^3\text{Btu}}{1\text{ hp} \cdot \text{h}} \times \dfrac{1\text{ hr}}{60\text{ min}}$

$= 9.55 \times 10^3\text{ Btu/min}$

(b) $225\text{ hp} = \dfrac{225\text{ hp}}{1}\,\dfrac{0.745\,70\text{ kW}}{1\text{ hp}} = 168\text{ kW}$

7.10 Celsius, Fahrenheit, and Absolute Scales

Temperature scales also appear in two common forms, the Celsius scale (previously called centigrade) and the Fahrenheit scale. The Celsius scale has the same temperature increment as its absolute thermodynamic scale, the Kelvin scale. However, the zero point on the Celsius scale is 273.15 K above absolute zero.

$$t(°C) = T(K) - 273.15 \tag{7.1}$$

Scales more commonly used in the United States are the Fahrenheit scale and its corresponding absolute thermodynamic scale, the Rankine scale. A unit degree on the Fahrenheit scale is precisely the same as a unit degree on the Rankine scale. However, the zero point on the Fahrenheit scale is 459.67°R above absolute zero. (See Table 7.10.)

$$t(°F) = T(°R) - 459.67 \tag{7.2}$$

When these relationships are combined, a convenient equation can be developed for conversion between Celsius and Fahrenheit or vice versa.

$$t(°F) = 9/5t(°C) + 32°F \tag{7.3}$$

$$t(°C) = 5/9[t(°F) - 32°F] \tag{7.4}$$

Table 7.10 Temperature scales

	°R	K	°F	°C
Abs Zero	0	0	−459.67	−273.15
°F = °C	419.67	233.15	−40	−40
Zero on °F	459.67	255.37	0	−17.78
Zero on °C	491.67	273.15	32	0
Boiling	671.67	373.15	212	100

If you were to construct the above Rankine and Kelvin scales parallel to each other, they would begin at absolute zero and be graduated and calibrated to the boiling point of water. To simplify the comparison consider only the portion of the scales from freezing to boiling. On the Rankine scale there are 180 degrees (671.67 − 491.67) and on the Kelvin scale only 100 (373.15 − 273.15). When you divide these two quantities by 20 (180/20) and (100/20) it becomes apparent that 9 degrees on the Rankine scale is equivalent to 5 degrees on the Kelvin scale or 9°R = 5 K. So if you are converting from one scale to the other you must use the conversion factor 9°R = 5 K, the factor that makes the scales equivalent.

Example Problem 7.7   Convert 373.15 K to a Rankine temperature.

$$373.15 \text{ K} = \frac{373.15 \text{ K}}{1.0} \times \frac{9°R}{5 \text{ K}} = 671.67 °R$$

Example Problem 7.8   The Universal Gas Constant (UGC) in the different unit systems has been determined as follow:

UGC = 1545 ft · lbf/lbmol · °R = 1.986 Btu/lbmol · °R = 8.314 kJ/kmol · K

Show how you would convert from 1545 · lbf/lbmol · °R to 8.314 kJ/kmol · K

$$1545 \frac{\text{ft} \cdot \text{lbf}}{\text{lbmol} \cdot °R} = \frac{1545 \text{ ft} \cdot \text{lbf}}{\text{lbmol} \cdot °R} \times \frac{4.4482 \text{ N}}{\text{lbf}} \times \frac{\text{lbmol}}{0.45359 \text{ kmol}} \times \frac{\text{m}}{3.2808 \text{ ft}}$$

$$\times \frac{9°R}{5 \text{ K}} \times \frac{J}{N \cdot m} \times \frac{kJ}{1000 J} = 8.313 \text{ kJ/kmol} \cdot K$$

Example Problem 7.9   Convert 98.6°F to °C.

Solution A

$$t(°C) = [(t°F) − 32]5/9 = 333/9 = 37.0°C$$

Solution B

$$T(°R) = 98.6 + 459.67 = 558.27°R$$

$$558.27°R = \frac{558.27°R}{1.0} \times \frac{5 \text{ K}}{9°R} = 310.15 K$$

$$t(°C) = 310.15 − 273.15 = 37.0°C$$

The problem of unit conversion becomes more complex if an equation has a constant with hidden dimensions. It is necessary to work through the equation converting the constant K_1 to a new constant K_2 consistent with the equation units.

Consider the following example problem.

Example Problem 7.10 The velocity of sound in air (c) can be expressed as a function of temperature (T):

$$c = 49.02\sqrt{T}$$

where c is in feet per second and T is in degrees Rankine.

Find an equivalent relationship when c is in meters per second and T is in kelvins.

Procedure

1. First, the given equation must have consistent units; that is, it must have the same units on both sides. Squaring both sides we see that

$$c^2 \, (\text{ft}^2/\text{s}^2) = 49.02^2 \; T°R$$

From this equation it is apparent that the constant $(49.02)^2$ must have units in order to maintain unit consistency. (The constant must have the same units as c^2/T.)

Solving for the constant,

$$(49.02)^2 = c^2 \, \frac{\text{ft}^2}{\text{s}^2}\left[\frac{1}{T \cdot °R}\right] = \frac{c^2}{T}\left[\frac{\text{ft}^2}{\text{s}^2 °R}\right]$$

2. The next step is to convert the constant $49.02^2 \; \text{ft}^2/(\text{s}^2°R)$ to a new constant that will allow us to calculate c in meters per second given T in kelvins. We recognize that the new constant must have units of square meters per second squared per kelvin.

$$\frac{(49.02)^2 \text{ft}^2}{\text{s}^2°R} = \frac{(49.02)^2 \text{ft}^2}{1.0 \, \text{s}^2°R} \times \frac{(0.3048 \, \text{m})^2}{(1 \, \text{ft})^2} \times \frac{9°R}{5 \, K} = \frac{401.84 \, \text{m}^2}{1 \, \text{s}^2 K}$$

3. Substitute this new constant 401.84 back into the original equation

$$c^2 = 401.84T$$
$$c = 20.05\sqrt{T}$$

where c is in meters per second and T is in kelvins. If you wish to verify this new equation, take a temperature in Fahrenheit (80°F) and convert to Rankine (540°R). Take the original equation and compute the value of c (1 139 ft/s).

Next convert 80°F to kelvins (26.67 + 273.15), calculate c (347.17 m/s), and convert back to ft/s.

$$1 \, 139 \, \text{ft/s} = \frac{1 \, 139 \, \text{ft}}{1.0 \, \text{s}} \times \frac{0.3048 \, \text{m}}{1.0 \, \text{ft}} = 347.17 \, \text{m/s}$$

You will have verified the new constant.

Problems

7.1 Using the correct number of significant figures, convert the following physical quantities into the proper SI units.
- (a) 215 hp
- (b) 960 acres
- (c) 3.7×10^4 ft³
- (d) 212 ft/s
- (e) 65 mph
- (f) 72 slugs
- (g) 155 lbm
- (h) 2 140 ft
- (i) 4 325 gal
- (j) 1 535 miles

7.2 Convert the following to SI units, using the correct significant figures.
- (a) 615 slugs/min
- (b) 14.7 Btu/min
- (c) 115 °C
- (d) 61 oz
- (e) 7.91 atm
- (f) 217 bushels/acre
- (g) 185 hp·hr
- (h) 18.5 lbm/ft³
- (i) 3.77×10^4 ft³/hr
- (j) 4 695 lbf

7.3 Convert as indicated giving the answer using proper significant figures.
- (a) 9.72 ft to millimeters
- (b) 65.4 ft² to L
- (c) 255 K to degrees Rankin
- (d) 7 595 bushels to cubic meters
- (e) 105 250 Btu/h to kilowatts

7.4 Convert as indicated giving the answer using proper significant figures.
- (a) 7 980 ft·lbf to joules
- (b) 14.7 lbf/in² to pascals
- (c) 29 028 ft to m
- (d) 94.5 slugs/ft³ to grams per cubic centimeter
- (e) 212°F to Kelvin

7.5 Using the rules for expressing SI units, correct each of the following if given incorrectly.
- (a) 12 amps
- (b) 12.5 cm's
- (c) 250 degrees Kelvin
- (d) 125.0 m m
- (e) 152 KW/hours
- (f) 6.7 m/s/s
- (g) 86.3 j
- (h) 3500 K
- (i) 375 n
- (j) 4 225 pa

7.6 Using the rules for expressing SI units, correct each of the following if given incorrectly.
- (a) 5..50 N
- (b) 63.5 C
- (c) 108 farads
- (d) 65 nM
- (e) 17 m per s
- (f) 725 N/m/m
- (g) 72.0 Kg
- (h) 750 J/sec
- (i) 95 A's
- (j) 1.5 m · m

7.7 If a force of 1.15×10^3 N is required to lift an object with a uniform velocity and an acceleration of gravity shown as follows, determine the mass, in kg, of the object:
- (a) 32.5 ft/s²
- (b) 7.86 m/s²

7.8 If you were on another planet, say, Mars, which of the following, g_C or g_L, would change and which would stay constant? Explain the difference.

7.9 Determine the acceleration of gravity required (meters per second squared) to lift a 1 500 kg object at a uniform velocity when the force exerted is
- (a) 3.580×10^3 lbf
- (b) 8.90×10^3 N

7.10 The average density of Styrofoam is 1.00 kg/m^3. If a Styrofoam cooler is made with outside dimensions of $50.0 \times 35.0 \times 30.0$ cm and the uniform thickness of the Styrofoam is 3.00 cm (including the lid), what is the volume of the Styrofoam used in cubic inches? What is the mass in lbm? How many gallons of liquid could be stored in the cooler?

7.11 A small town purchased a 25 ft diameter cylindrical tank for potable water in the event of an emergency. The town consists of 3 600 family units. If each family were to collect 25 gallons of water, what would be the minimum height of the tank?

7.12 The *Eurostar* provides international high speed train service between Paris, London, and Brussels through the English Channel Tunnel. *Eurostar* trainsets can operate at maximum speeds of 3.00×10^3 km/h. Assume that the resistance between the train and the track is 115×10^3 newtons. If air resistance adds an additional 25.5×10^3 newtons, determine the horsepower needed to power the engine at maximum speed. [Note: Power = (force) × (velocity)]

7.13 *Eurostar's* nose is computer-optimized for running in the Channel Tunnel where pressure waves can affect passenger comfort. The tunnel itself is passed at a reduced speed of 1.6×10^2 km/h. Determine the length of time it takes to complete the 23 mile underwater portion of the trip from London to Paris.

7.14 Assume that your hometown is growing so rapidly that an additional water tower will be necessary to meet the needs of the community. Engineers predict that the water tower will need to hold 1.25×10^6 kilograms of water, with a density of 999 kilograms per cubic meter.
  (a) What will the volume of the tower have to be?
  (b) Determine the vertical force, in kN, acting on each of the four evenly spaced legs from the weight of the water alone.
  (c) If the tower is spherical, what would be the diameter of the tower?

7.15 The Hubert H. Humphrey Metrodome in Minneapolis, Minnesota opened in 1982 at a cost of $55 million. To prepare for the footings, etc. 300 000 cubic yards of dirt were removed. Its inflatable roof covers 10.0 acres and its interior volume is 60.0×10^6 cubic feet. During construction, 40.0×10^3 cubic yards of concrete, 11.9×10^3 tons of reinforcing steel and 5.00×10^2 tons of structural steel were utilized. The roof material includes an outer layer of Teflon-coated fiberglass and an inner layer of woven fiberglass. Given this information, answer the following:
  (a) If removed evenly over the 10 acres, how deep of a hole would be formed as a result of the excavation?
  (b) What is the total mass of concrete and steel in lbm?
  (c) If the two-layer fiberglass roofing material has a mass of 0.6667 lbm/ft^2, what is the total mass of the roof?
  (d) If 10.0 inches of wet snow collected on the roof (this happened in 1982), what is the added mass to the roof? (Assume 1 inch of water equals 10 inches of snow.)

7.16 The U.S. currently imports 15.0×10^6 barrels of oil each day. If a cylindrical storage tank were to be constructed with a base of 50.0 ft.
  (a) What would be the height of the container to store this daily consumption?
  (b) Recall that Mt. Everest is 29 028 ft. What would the diameter of the cylinder have to be to match the height of Mt. Everest?

7.17 Construction sand is piled in a right cone that has a height of 25.0 feet and a diameter of 110.0 feet. If this sand has a density of 97.0 lbm/ft^3,
  (a) determine the volume of the cone

   (b) determine the mass of the sand in the cone

   (c) during the winter months the sand will be spread on county roads. Using a spreadsheet, determine the volume and mass of the sand remaining if the height decreases from 25.0 to 5.00 ft in increments of 0.500 ft. Assume that the base remains constant.

7.18 A cylindrical underground storage tank with a diameter of 22.0 ft and a height of 30.0 ft is filled with gasoline. Given a density of 675 kg/m³, determine the mass of the gas in the tank in both lbm and kg. If the average automobile gas tank holds 25.0 gal, calculate the number of autos that may be filled from this underground facility.

7.19 A cylindrical tank is 25.0 ft long and 10.0 ft in diameter is oriented such that is longitudinal axis is horizontal. Develop a table that will

   (a) Show how many gallons of diesel fuel are in the tank if the fluid level is measured in 1.00 ft increments from the bottom of the tank

   (b) Show the corresponding mass at each increment, in kg, if the specific gravity is 0.73.

7.20 A southwest rancher constructs a spherical water tank that is 10 ft in diameter. Develop a table that will

   (a) Show how many gallons of water are contained in the tank if the volume is measured in 1.00 ft increments from the bottom to the top of the container.

   (b) Determine the mass of water at each increment in lbm.

7.21 The ideal gas law shows the relationship among some common properties of ideal gases.

$$pV = nRT$$

where

p = pressure

V = volume

n = number of moles of the ideal gas

R = universal gas constant = 8.314kJ/(kmol K)

T = absolute temperature

If you have 5 moles of an ideal gas at twenty-two degrees Celsius and it is stored in a container that is 0.650 meters on each side, calculate the pressure in Pa.

7.22 Approximately 50 000 years ago a meteorite hit the earth near Winslow, Arizona. The impact crater is 1 200 m in diameter and 170 m deep. Determine the volume of earth in ft³ removed assuming the crater to be a spherical segment. Verify that the radius of the sphere is approximately 1 150 m.

7.23 Conservation of energy suggests that potential energy is converted to kinetic energy when an object falls in a vacuum. $KE = \dfrac{mV^2}{2g_C}$ and $PE = \dfrac{mg_Lh}{g_C}$ Velocity at impact can be determined as follows:

$$V = \text{Constant } \sqrt{h}$$

   (a) Determine the constant so that the equation is valid for h in ft and V in feet per second (ft/s)

   (b) Determine the constant so that the equation is valid for h in ft but V in mph.

   (c) If you drop an object from 225 ft, what is the velocity on impact with the ground in mph and ft/s?

7.24 A small portable cylindrical pressure tank has inside dimensions of 14.0 inches (dia) and 36.0 inches end to end. The maximum recommended safety pressure at 70°F is 200 psi. The device has a safety release value set at 250 psi.
   (a) Determine the inside volume of the pressure tank in ft³.
   (b) Calculate the specific volume of the tank at 70°F and 200 psi. (See below)
   (c) Find the mass of air in the tank from part b.
   (d) If the homeowner inserts 3.5 lbm of air into the tank at 70°F, what would be the reading on the tank pressure gauge.
   (e) With the aid of a spreadsheet determine the temperature from part d at which the safety gauge would release starting at 70°F and increasing in 10 degree increments.

$$P_v = RT$$

Pressure, P, lbf/ft²

Sp. Vol., v − ft³/lbm

Gas constant for air, ($R_{air} = 53.33$ ft · lbf/lbm°R)

Temperature, T − °R

7.25 A weir is used to measure flow rates in open channels. For a rectangular weir the expression can be written $Q = 288.8\ LH^{1.5}$ (See Fig. 7.2.)

where   Q = discharge rate, in gal/h

L = length of weir opening parallel to liquid, in inches

H = height of fluid above crest, in inches

   (a) As the channel becomes larger, the weir opening can be expressed as follows: Q in cubic feet per second, with L and H in feet. Determine the new constant.
   (b) Prepare a spreadsheet resulting in a table of values of Q in both ft³/s and gal/h, with L and H in inches. Use values of L that range from 1 to 16 in 1 inch increments and let H range from 2 to 32 in 2 inch increments. For example when L = 6, H = 12.

Figure 7.2

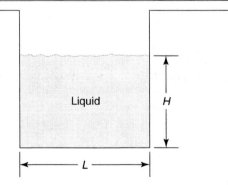

CHAPTER 14

Material Balance

Chapter Objectives

When you complete your study of this chapter, you will able to:

- Define the principle of the conservation of material (mass)
- Define systems to solve material (mass) balance problems
- Write the specific equations for overall and constituent balances
- Solve for unknowns using an independent set of mass balance equations

14.1 Introduction

In engineering analyses, it is extremely important to observe and account for all changes in physical quantities, such as mass, momentum, energy, charge, chemical composition, and other quantities. In this chapter the focus will be on accounting for material (mass) in engineering analyses of problems found in process industries.

We depend a great deal on industries that produce food, household cleaning products, energy for heating and cooling homes, fertilizers, and many other products and services. These process industries are continually involved with the distribution, routing, blending, mixing, sorting, and separation of materials. Figure 14.1 shows an oil refinery where crude oil is separated into many different petroleum products for use in various applications. The primary separation process is fractional distillation, in which hot crude oil is fed to the bottom of a distillation column. The weight and boiling point of the crude oil components (heavy and hot at the bottom and light and cool at the top of the column) allow bitumen, oils, diesel, kerosene, naptha, and gasoline to be withdrawn at appropriate points along the column.

Analysis of the process occurring in a typical oil refinery involves the application of *material balance*, a technique based on the *principle of conservation of mass*.

14.2 Conservation of Mass

The *principle of conservation of mass* states that in any process mass is neither created nor destroyed.

Antoine Lavoisier (1743–1794), regarded as the father of chemistry, conducted experiments demonstrating that matter, although undergoing

Figure 14.1

An oil refinery produces many petroleum products for consumers.

transformation from one form to another, was neither created nor destroyed during the experiments. The results were expressed as an empirical law called conservation of mass, material balance, or mass balance. Like many empirical laws, this one has an exception: nuclear reactions, in which mass is transformed into energy. To solve problems involving nuclear processes, both a material balance and an energy balance must be conducted jointly.

Before we apply the conservation-of-mass principle to a material balance problem, we will introduce additional concepts and terminology. Figure 14.2 illustrates a number of these terms.

Figure 14.2

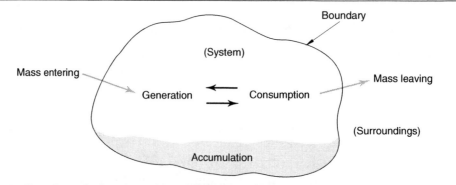

Illustration of a typical system with a defined boundary.

A *system* can be any designated portion of the universe with a definable boundary. Whenever mass crosses the boundary either into or out of the system, it must be accounted for. In certain situations, the amount of mass entering the system is greater than the amount leaving. In the absence of chemical reactions, this results in an increase of mass within the system called *accumulation*. If the mass leaving the system is greater than that entering, the accumulation is negative.

When chemical reactions occur within the system boundary, consumption of reactants through the formation or generation of reaction products is possible. A simple example would be the dehydrogeneration of ethane in a reactor: $C_2H_6 \rightarrow C_2H_4 + H_2$. One constituent is consumed and two others are generated. Thus, if chemical reactions occur, it is necessary to account for the consumption of some elements or compounds and the generation of others. It is important to understand that, even considering chemical reactions, mass is conserved. In the preceding example ($C_2H_6 \rightarrow C_2H_4 + H_2$), the number of atoms of carbon and hydrogen remains constant.

In summary, a system is an arbitrary specification that must conform to the following:

1. Once specified, the system cannot change during the analysis.
2. The system boundary can be fixed or flexible and must be a closed surface.

Consider the following examples to more clearly visualize the definition of a system. First, the simple distillation system is shown in Figure 14.3. This distillation process involves three items of equipment, a heater, column and condenser with associated piping and connections. The feed, which may include several components is introduced to the column where it is heated. The component(s) with the lower boiling temperature are vaporized, drawn from the top of the column into a condenser where they are cooled to liquid form. Some of the concentrated product (distillate) is drawn off and part of it (reflux) is sent back to the column to be reboiled. The portion of the feed that is not vaporized is drawn off at the bottom of the column as waste. The dashed outline represents the system boundary. Therefore we must account for the feed, product and bottoms in a material balance analysis. The vapor and reflux piping do not need to be accounted for since they remain within the system.

Second, consider the dewatering process in Figure 14.4. It consists of a centrifuge that removes some of the water and a dryer that removes more water down to a very small percentage of the solid material. Three systems are available for analysis: the overall system in Figure 14.4(a), the centrifuge in Figure 14.4(b), and the dryer in Figure 14.4(c). Note here that each system shows inputs and outputs but no generation, consumption, or accumulation.

When all considerations are included, the conservation-of-mass principle applied to a system or to system constituents can be expressed, from Figure 14.2, as

$$\text{input} + \text{generation} - \text{output} - \text{consumption}$$
$$= \text{accumulation} \tag{14.1}$$

Actually Eq. (14.1) is more general than just a material (mass) balance. It is a convenient way to express a general conservation principle to account for the physical quantities mentioned at the beginning of this chapter. For a specified

Figure 14.3

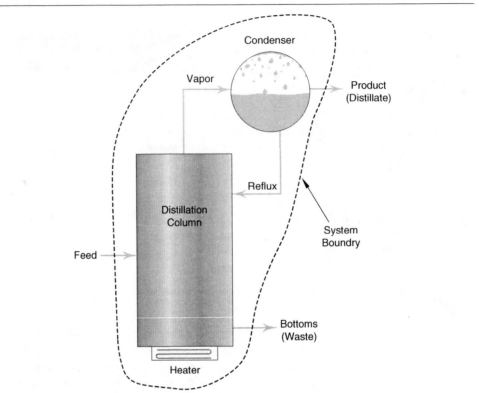

System designation for a distillation column.

Figure 14.4

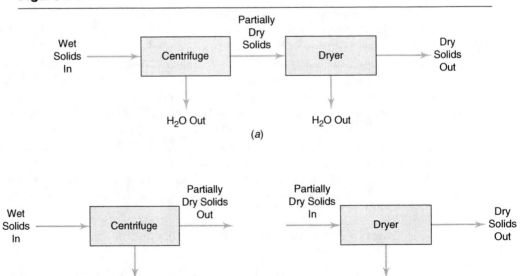

(a)

(b)   *(c)*

Possible systems for analyzing a centrifuge and dryer process.

system, such as a mass of air passing through a jet engine, an energy balance accounts for heat in and out and for work done on or by the system, heat and work being forms of energy. Heat input would come from burning of fuel, heat output would be the hot exhaust gases, work in would be compression of free stream air, and work out would be the thrust generated by the accelerated gases. Energy balances are studied in thermodynamics.

14.3 Processes

For our introductory look at material balance, we will now make an assumption that simplifies our investigations but will not reduce our understanding of the conservation of mass.

Many engineering problems involve chemical reactions, but if we assume no such reactions then there will be no generation and consumption of mass, and Eq. (14.1) can be reduced to

$$\text{input} - \text{output} = \text{accumulation} \qquad (14.2)$$

Two types of processes typically analyzed are the batch process and the rate process. In a *batch process*, materials are put or placed into the system before the process begins and are removed after the process is complete. Cooking is a familiar example. Generally, you follow a recipe that calls for specific ingredients to be placed into a system that produces a processed food. Figure 14.5 illustrates a batch process for a concrete mixer.

Figure 14.5

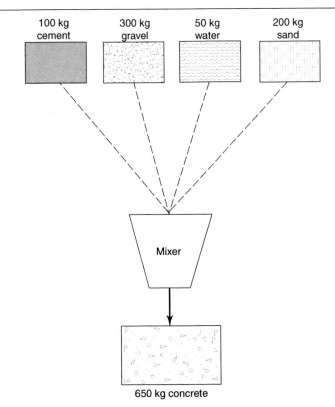

The constituents of a proper batch mix of concrete.

Figure 14.6

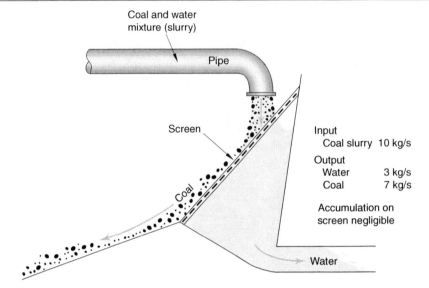

Coal and water
mixture (slurry)

Pipe

Screen

Coal

Input
  Coal slurry 10 kg/s

Output
  Water   3 kg/s
  Coal   7 kg/s

Accumulation on
screen negligible

Water

A coal-dewatering system shown as a rate process.

If we assume for a batch process that we take out at the end of the process all of the mass we placed into the system at the beginning, then the accumulation term is zero and Eq. (14.2) can be written as

$$\text{total input} = \text{total output} \qquad (14.3)$$

A *rate-flow process* involves the continuous time rate of flow of inputs and outputs. The process is performed continuously as mass flows through the system. See Figure 14.6.

Rate processes may be classified as either *uniform* or *nonuniform, steady* or *unsteady*. A process is uniform if the flow rate is the same throughout the process, which means the input rate must equal the output rate. It is steady if rates do not vary with time. Solution of material balance problems involving nonuniform and/or unsteady flows may require the use of differential equations and will not be considered here.

A class of nonuniform, steady processes involves the filling or draining of tanks. For this situation we have a fixed rate of input and a different fixed rate of output, thus producing an accumulation. Equation (14.2) for such processes becomes

$$\text{rate of input} - \text{rate of output} = \text{rate of accumulation} \qquad (14.4)$$

For continuous flow, if we assume a uniform, steady rate process, the accumulation term is also zero, so Eq. (14.2) written on a rate basis reduces to

$$\text{rate of input} = \text{rate of output} \qquad (14.5)$$

Figure 14.6 is an example of a uniform, steady rate process.

Although Eqs. (14.3), (14.4), and (14.5) seem so overly simple as to be of little practical use, application to a given problem may be complicated by the need to account for several inputs and outputs as well as for many constituents in each input or output. The simplicity of the equations is in fact the advantage of a material balance approach, because order is brought to seemingly disordered data.

14.4 A Systematic Approach

Material balance computations require the manipulation of a substantial amount of information. Therefore, it is essential that a systematic procedure be developed and followed. If a systematic approach is used, material balance equations can be written and solved correctly in a straightforward manner. The following procedure is recommended:

1. Identify the system(s) involved.
2. Determine whether the process is a batch or rate process and whether a chemical reaction is involved. If no reaction occurs, all compounds will maintain their chemical makeup during the process. If a reaction is to occur, elements must be involved and must be balanced. In a process involving chemical reactions, additional equations based on chemical composition may be required in order to solve for the unknown quantities.
3. Construct a schematic diagram showing the feeds (inputs) and products (outputs).
4. Label known material quantities or rates of flow.
5. Identify each unknown input and output with a symbol.
6. Apply Eq. (14.3), (14.4), or (14.5) for each constituent as well as for the overall process. Note that not all equations written will be algebraically independent. This will become apparent in the example problems.
7. Solve the equations (selecting an independent set) for the desired unknowns and express the result in an understandable form.

Example Problem 14.1 Anna's Purification Co. produces drinking water from saltwater by partially freezing the saltwater to create salt-free ice and a brine solution. If saltwater is 3.50% salt by mass and the brine solution is found to be an 8.00% concentrate by mass, determine how many kilograms of saltwater must be processed to form 2.00 kg of ice.

Figure 14.7

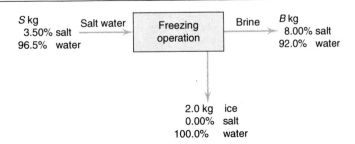

Schematic diagram of the saltwater freezing operation.

Solution

1. The system in this example problem involves a freezing process.
2. The freezing process is a batch process because a fixed amount of product (ice) is required. There are no chemical reactions.
3. A diagram of the process is shown in Figure 14.7.
4. Saltwater is the input to the system, with brine and ice taken out at the end.
5. Appropriate symbols are used to identify unknown quantities.
6. The material balance equation for each constituent as well as for the overall process is written. It is important to understand that the material balance equation (Eq. 14.3) is applicable for each constituent as well as for the overall process. In this example, three equations are written, but only two are independent. That is, the overall balance equation is the sum of the salt and water balance equations. Thus we have a good method of checking the accuracy of the equations we have written.

Equation	Input = Output
Overall balance	$S = B + 2.00$
Salt balance	$0.035S = 0.08B$
Water balance	$0.965S = 0.920B + 2.00$

7. The equations are solved by substitution for S from the overall balance equation into the salt balance equation.

$$0.035(B + 2.00) = 0.08B$$

$$0.045B = 0.070$$

$$B = 1.56 \text{ kg}$$

Since $\qquad\qquad S = B + 2.00$, then

$$S = 3.56 \text{ kg}$$

The water balance equation was not used to solve for B and S but can serve as a check of the results (that is, it should balance). Substituting the computed values for B and S into the water balance equation:

$$(0.965)(3.56) = [(0.920)(1.56)] + 2.00$$

$$3.435\ 4 = 3.435\ 2$$

which does balance within the round-off error.

Example Problem 14.2   A process to remove water from solid material consists of a centrifuge and a dryer. If 35.0 t/h of a mixture containing 35.0% solids is centrifuged to form a sludge consisting of 65.0% solids and then the sludge is dried to 5.00% moisture in a dryer, how much total water is removed in 24-hour period? *Note:* This problem is a specific application of the system definition shown in Figure 14.4.

Solution   There are three possible systems involved in this problem: the centrifuge, the dryer, and the combination (see Fig. 14.8). The operation in this

Figure 14.8

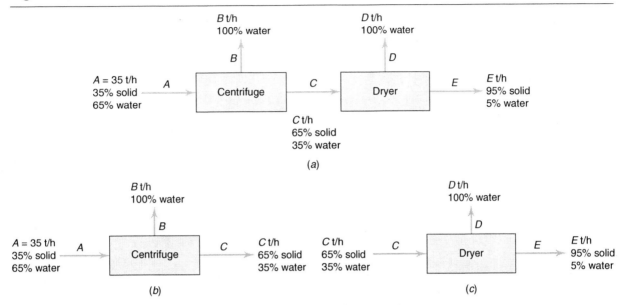

(a)

(b)   (c)

Systems defining the flow process inputs and outputs for centrifuge and dryer.

system is a continuous flow process. There are no chemical reactions and the process is steady and uniform, thus Eq. (14.5) applies.

rate of input = rate of output

The following equations are written for the process illustrated in Figure 14.8. The overall process is illustrated in Figure 14.8a, with subsystem diagrams for the centrifuge and the dryer shown in Figure 14.8b and Figure 14.8c, respectively. The overall balance equation for a selected system is the sum of the constituent balance equations for that system. This means that the set of equations written for a selected system are not all independent when the overall balance equation and the constituent balance equations are included.

For the entire system (Fig. 14.8a):

1. Solid balance $0.35\,(35) = 0.95E$
2. Water balance $0.65\,(35) = B + D + 0.05E$
3. Overall balance $35 = B + D + E$

For the centrifuge (Fig. 14.8b):

4. Solid balance $0.35\,(35) = 0.65C$
5. Water balance $0.65\,(35) = B + 0.35C$
6. Overall balance $35 = B + C$

For the dryer (Fig. 14.8c):

7. Solid balance $0.65C = 0.95E$
8. Water balance $0.35C = D + 0.05E$
9. Overall balance $C = D + E$

Solve for rate of mass out of centrifuge (C) from Eq. (4)

$$C = \frac{0.35(35)}{0.65}$$
$$= 18.85 \text{ t/h}$$

Solve for rate of water out of centrifuge (B) from Eq. (6):

$$B = 35 - C$$
$$= 35 - 18.85$$
$$= 16.15 \text{ t/h}$$

Solve for rate of mass out of dryer (E) from Eq. (7):

$$E = \frac{0.65C}{.095}$$
$$= \frac{0.65(18.85)}{0.95}$$
$$= 12.90 \text{ t/h}$$

Solve for rate of water out of dryer (D) from Eq. (9):

$$D = C - E$$
$$= 18.85 - 12.90$$
$$= 5.95 \text{ t/h}$$

Check the results obtained in the three balance equations for the entire system, Eqs. (1), (2), and (3).

Eq. (1) $(0.35)(35) = (0.95)(12.90)$
          $12.25 = 12.25$ (checks)

Eq. (2) $(0.65)(35) = 16.15 + 5.95 + (0.05)(12.90)$
          $22.75 = 22.75$ (checks)

Eq. (3) $35 = 16.15 + 5.95 + 12.90$
          $35 = 35$ (checks)

All the results check, so then calculate total water removed in 24 h:

$$\text{Total water} = (B + D)\ 24$$
$$= (16.15 + 5.95)\ 24$$
$$= (22.10)\ 24$$
$$= 5.30 \times 10^2 \text{ t}$$

A general problem that would involve typical material balance consideration is a standard evaporation, crystallization, recycle process. Normally this type of system involves continuous flow of some solution through an evaporator. Water is removed, leaving the output stream more concentrated. This stream is fed into a crystallizer where it is cooled, causing crystals to form. These crystals are then filtered out, with the remaining solution recycled to join the feed stream back into the evaporator. This system is illustrated in the following example problem.

Example Problem 14.3 A solution of potassium chromate (K_2CrO_4) is to be used to produce K_2CrO_4 crystals. The feed to an evaporator is 2.50×10^3 kilograms per hour of 40.0% solution by mass. The stream leaving the evaporator is 50.0% K_2CrO_4. This stream is then fed into a crystallizer and is passed through a filter. The resulting filter cake is entirely crystals. The remaining solution is 45.0% K_2CrO_4, and is recycled. Calculate the total input to the evaporator, the feed rate to the crystallizer, the water removed from the evaporator, and the amount of pure K_2CrO_4 produced each hour.

Solution See Figure 14.9. There are different ways the system boundaries can be selected for this problem—that is, around the entire system, around the evaporator, around the crystallizer-filter, and so on. There are no chemical reactions that occur in the process, and the process is steady and uniform, thus

Rate of input = rate of output

Figure 14.9

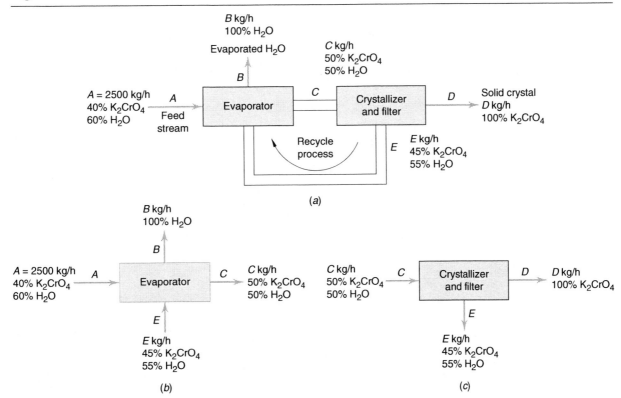

(a) Diagram of the overall system; (b) and (c) are diagrams where boundaries are selected around individual process components.

The following balance equations can be written, not all of which are independent.

For the entire system (Fig. 14.9a):

1. K_2CrO_4 balance $0.40 (2\,500) = D$
2. H_2O balance $0.60 (2\,500) = B$
3. Overall balance $2\,500 = B + D$

For the evaporator (Fig. 14.9b):

4. K_2CrO_4 balance $(0.40)(2\,500) + 0.45E = 0.50C$
5. H_2O balance $(0.60)(2\,500) + 0.55E = B + 0.50C$
6. Overall balance $2\,500 + E = B + C$

For the crystallizer-filter (Fig. 14.9c):

7. K_2CrO_4 balance $0.50C = D + 0.45E$
8. H_2O balance $0.50C = 0.55E$
9. Overall balance $C = D + E$

We will first develop the solution by selecting appropriate equations from the preceding set and solving them by hand. Then we will place a set of four equations with four unknowns in a math solver (Mathcad) to obtain (and verify in this case) the solution we have found by hand.

Solve for K_2CrO_4 out of crystallizer-filter from Eq. (1):

$$D = 0.4 (2\,500)$$
$$= 1.00 \times 10^3 \text{ kg/h}$$

Solve for H_2O out of evaporator from Eq. (2):

$$B = 0.6 (2\,500)$$
$$= 1.50 \times 10^3 \text{ kg/h}$$

Solve for recycle rate from crystallizer-filter from Eqs. (9) and (7):

(9) $$C = D + E$$
$$= 1\,000 + E$$

(7) $$0.50C = D + 0.45E$$
$$0.50(1\,000 + E) = 1\,000 + 0.45E$$
$$E = 10\,000 \text{ kg/h}$$

Calculate total input for evaporator:

$$\text{Total input} = E + A$$
$$= 10\,000 + 2\,500$$
$$= 1.25 \times 10^4 \text{ kg/h}$$

Calculate feed rate for crystallizer-filter from Eq. (6):

$$C = 2\,500 + E - B$$
$$= 2\,500 + 10\,000 - 1\,500$$
$$= 1.10 \times 10^4 \text{ kg/h}$$

Alternative solution method: math solver   To use the math solver, we will select four independent equations from the nine that were written to solve for the four unknowns B, C, D, and E. The math solver requires an initial guess. Each of the four unknowns were somewhat arbitrarily given the same initial guess. The equations selected were (other combinations could also have been selected): (4), (5), (7), and (8). The results are shown below in Example Problem 14.3 (continued).

From these values for B, C, D, and E, the total input for the evaporator and the feed rate for the crystallizer-filter can be found as before.

Example Problem 14.3 (continued)   Mathcad solution of simultaneous equations in Example Prob. 14.3.

Four equations containing four unknowns are entered into a math solver, in this case Mathcad. The Find function is used to determine the solution to the simultaneous equations once an initial guess for unknown is given.

Initial guesses for the unknowns:

$$B = 1\,200$$
$$C = 1\,200$$
$$D = 1\,200$$
$$E = 1\,200$$

The given section defines the simultaneous equations:

Given

$$1\,000 + 0.45E = 0.5C$$
$$0.5C = D + 0.45E$$
$$0.5C = 0.55E$$
$$1\,500 + 0.55E = B + 0.5C$$

The find section provides the solutions

Find

$$(B, C, D, E) = \begin{bmatrix} 1.5 \times 10^3 \\ 1.1 \times 10^4 \\ 1 \times 10^3 \\ 1 \times 10^4 \end{bmatrix}$$

To solve for N unknowns from a system of linear equations, N independent equations are needed. From an engineering point of view, this means that each equation of the set must bring new information to the set. In preparing the system of equations, if you choose an equation that can be obtained from the ones already present [for example, Eq. (3) is the sum of Eqs. (1) and (2)], so this new equation does not provide any new information. Likewise, if the new equation is simply one of the current ones multiplied by a constant, no new information is provided.

The consequence of not having a linearly independent set of N equations to solve for N unknowns is that you will not be able to obtain a unique solution.

There will be many sets of the N unknowns that will satisfy the set of equations rather than the single set you are seeking.

To show one way to check for linear independence, consider the four equations in unknowns $B, C, D,$ and E just solved in the math solver. Organize them as follows:

$$0B + 0.5C + 0D - 0.45 = 1\ 000$$

$$1B + 0.5C + 0D - 0.55 = 1\ 500$$

$$0B + 0.5C - 1D - 0.45 = 0$$

$$0B + 0.5C + 0D - 0.55 = 0$$

or in matrix form:

$$\begin{bmatrix} 0 & 0.5 & 0 - 0.45 \\ 1 & 0.5 & 0 - 0.55 \\ 0 & 0.5 - 1 - 0.45 \\ 0 & 0.5 & 0 - 0.55 \end{bmatrix} \begin{bmatrix} B \\ C \\ D \\ E \end{bmatrix} = \begin{bmatrix} 1000 \\ 1500 \\ 0 \\ 0 \end{bmatrix}$$

For the set of equations to be linearly independent, the determinant of the coefficient matrix must be nonzero. Here

$$\begin{bmatrix} 0 & 0.5 & 0 - 0.45 \\ 1 & 0.5 & 0 - 0.55 \\ 0 & 0.5 - 1 - 0.45 \\ 0 & 0.5 & 0 - 0.55 \end{bmatrix} = -0.05$$

Since the determinant is nonzero, the equations are independent and a unique solution can be expected.

Note that with the equations in this form, many math solvers, spreadsheets, or modern calculators can be used to solve the set using matrix procedures.

Example Problem 14.4   A water storage facility has a volume of 85 m³. It has one inlet pipe that provides a flow rate of 15 kg/s and two outlets, one providing a flow rate of 3 kg/s and the other 2 kg/s. The tank is initially empty.
  (a) How long will it take to fill the empty tank if both outlets are shut off?
  (b) How long will it take to fill the tank if both outlets are open?
  (c) If the inlet and both outlets are open for 1.5 h and then a pump malfunction stops the input, how long will the tank be able to supply water?

Solution: Part (a)   For a full tank the mass of water is

Mass = (1 000 kg/m³)(85 m³) = 85 000 kg

This is an accumulation process, thus Eq. (14.4) applies.

$$\text{Rate of input} - \text{Rate of output} = \text{Rate of accumulation}$$

$$15 \text{ kg/s} - 0 = \text{Rate of accumulation} = 15 \text{ kg/s}$$

$$\text{Time to fill} = 85\,000 \text{ kg/15 kg/s} = 5\,667 \text{ s}$$

$$(5\,667 \text{ s})/(3\,600 \text{ s/h}) = 1.6 \text{ h}$$

Solution: Part (b)

$$15 \text{ kg/s} - 3 \text{ kg/s} - 2 \text{ kg/s} = \text{Rate of accumulation} = 10 \text{ kg/s}$$

$$\text{Time to fill} = 85\,000 \text{ kg/10 kg/s} = 8\,500 \text{ s}$$

$$(8\,500 \text{ s})/(3\,600 \text{ s/h}) = 2.4 \text{ h}$$

Solution: Part (c)   This is a two-step solution because the system definition changes after 1.5 h.

Step 1: $15 \text{ kg/s} - 5 \text{ kg/s} = \text{Rate of accumulation} = 10 \text{ kg/s}$

$\quad\quad (10 \text{ kg/s})(3\,600 \text{ s/h})(1.5 \text{ h}) = 54\,000 \text{ kg} = \text{Accumulation}$

Step 2: $0 - 5 \text{ kg/s} = \text{Rate of accumulation} = 5 \text{ kg/s drainage}$

$\quad\quad \text{Time to drain} = 54\,000 \text{ kg/5 kg/s} = 10\,800 \text{ s}$

$\quad\quad (10\,800 \text{ s})/(3\,600 \text{ s/h}) = 3.0 \text{ h}$

Problems

For each problem, follow the steps of Sec. 14.4—that is, (1) identify the system, (2) determine whether the process is batch or rate, and so on.

14.1   Two liquids, A and B, are mixed together. A is 5.00% solids, the rest water. B is 11.0% solids, the rest water. To the mixture is added 18.5 kg of bone-dry solids resulting in a mixture of 2 150 kg containing 8.25% solids. What were the original amounts of the liquids A and B?

14.2   At the Grace Foods facility, a cereal product containing 53% water is produced at a rate of 750 pounds per hour. A dried product containing 75% cereal is desired. How much water must be removed in an eight-hour period and how much dried product is produced?

14.3   An order is placed with a plant to deliver 2500 kg of a 9.5% solution of cellulose nitrate. The only product on hand is a 5.5% solution. How much dry cellulose nitrate must be added to the solution to meet the requirement?

14.4   A slurry (mix of water and insoluble material) of crushed mine coal is fed to a cyclone separator at a rate of 8.0 t/h. The mine coal averages 78% pure coal and 22% pyrite. Pure coal is recovered at the top of the separator. The waste from the bottom of the separator contains 3.0% pure coal and 35% pyrite; the rest is water. How much pure coal can be obtained in a 12 h time period?

14.5 Casein, a dairy product used in making cheese, contains 25% moisture when wet. A dairy sells this product for $40/100 kg. If requested they will dry the casein to 12% moisture. The drying costs are $5/100 kg of water removed. What should the dairy sell the dried product for in order realize the same margin of profit?

14.6 A vat holds $2.25(10^3)$ kg of a 22.0% solution of ethylene glycol and water. How much must be drained from the tank and replaced with an 85.0% ethylene glycol solution to obtain a 33.0% concentrate? Assume percentage values are based on mass.

14.7 Three brine solutions, B1, B2, B3, are mixed. B1 is one-half of the total mixture. Brine B1 is 2.5% salt, B2 is 4.5% salt, and B3 is 5.5% salt. To this mixture is added 35 lbm of dry salt while 280 lbm of water is evaporated leaving 3 200 lbm of 5.1% brine. Determine the initial amounts of B1, B2, and B3.

14.8 Pure ethyl alcohol is produced by feeding a distillation column a 40% alcohol solution (the remainder water) mixed with benzene. The benzene serves as a promoter of the process. The distillate from the top of the column consists of 75% benzene, 24% water, and 1% pure ethyl alcohol. The product is pure ethyl alcohol recovered at the bottom. The process must produce 550 kg/hr of pure alcohol. Find the required feeds of the 40% solution and benzene and the amount of pure alcohol lost at the top of the column. This material balance analysis is needed to size the column and associated piping and connections.

14.9 In a distillation process 550 lbm/h of a benzene, toluene, and water mixture is fed to the distiller. This feed contains $2.0(10^1)$% toluene. The distilled product is 93% benzene and 7.0% water. The waste contains 35% water and $1.0(10^1)$% benzene. Determine the rate of production of the distilled product and the percentages of benzene and water in the feed.

14.10 An ethanol plant distills alcohol from corn. The distiller processes 2.0 t/h of feed containing 15% alcohol and 82% water; the rest is inert material. The bottoms (waste) produced is 85% of the feed and contains 94% water, 3.5% alcohol, and 2.5% inert material. The vapor (product) from the top of the distiller is passed through a condenser and cooled to produce the final product. Determine the rate of production of the final product and its composition.

14.11 A freezing process takes in 1.5 t/h of saltwater (4.0% salt) and produces salt-free ice and a brine solution (8.5% salt). How much ice is produced in an 8-hour day?

14.12 A centrifuge and dryer are used to remove water from solid material. A mixture of 38% solids is centrifuged to 65% solids and then dried to 4.0% moisture in the dryer. If 35 kg/h of the final dried material is needed, how much of the 38% solid mixture must be fed to the centrifuge per hour, and how much water is removed per hour?

14.13 A solution of potassium chromate (K_2CrO_4) is to be used to produce K_2CrO_4 crystals using an evaporator and crystallizer/filter. A 38% solution is fed to the evaporator. The stream leaving the evaporator is 48% K_2CrO_4 and is fed to the crystallizer/filter. Pure K_2CrO_4 crystals are produced and the remaining solution is 44% K_2CrO_4. This solution is cycled back to the evaporator. If 1.2 t/h of pure crystals are needed, calculate the total input to the evaporator, the feed rate to the crystallizer/filter, and the water removed from the evaporator.

14.14 A stream of fluid feeds $1.05(10^3)$ kg/h of a mixture containing 39.8% ethane, 31.2% propane, and 29% butane into a distiller. Three streams are drawn off: Stream A is 94.0% ethane, 4.20% propane, the rest butane; Stream B is 91.8% propane, 1.20% ethane, the rest butane; and Stream C is 94.2% butane and 5.8% propane. What is the rate of production of each of the streams?

14.15 The Lena Chemical Co. concentrates leftover acids from various chemical processes. Leftover acid from a nitrating process contains 24.0% nitric acid (HNO_3),

55.0% sulfuric acid (H_2SO_4), and 21.0% water (H_2O). This acid is to be concentrated (strengthened in acid content) by adding sulfuric acid with 92.0% H_2SO_4 and nitric acid containing 89.0% HNO_3. The final product is to contain 31.0% HNO_3 and 58.0% H_2SO_4. Compute the mass of the initial acid solution and the mass of the concentrated acids that must be combined to produce $2.00(10^3)$ lbm of the desired mixture.

14.16 An industry is required to clean up 4.0 t of a by-product containing both toxic and inert material. The toxic content is 15%; the rest is inert. The by-product is treated with 45 t of solvent resulting in an amount of dirty solvent containing 0.35% toxic material and a discard containing 1.2% toxic material, some solvent, and all the inert materials. Determine the amount of dirty solvent produced, the percentage of solvent in the discard, and the percentage of toxic substance removed in the discard.

14.17 The drain valve on a 25 m^3 water tank allows 0.60 kg/s to drain. The fill valve allows 1.2 kg/s to flow into the tank. If the tank is initially one-half full, how long will it take to fill the tank if both valves are open? If the tank is full and the fill valve is shut off, how long will it take the tank to empty?

14.18 A distillation column (see Fig. 14.3) is used to distill ethanol (chemical formula C_2H_5OH). If the feed to the column is 15 000 lb of 11% ethanol (the rest water) and the distillate amount is one-tenth of the feed and contains 62% ethanol, determine the amount of ethanol that is in the bottoms.

14.19 A batch of 250 lb of sulfuric acid (90% concentrate) is needed. Unlimited supplies of 98% and 40% concentrates of sulfuric acid are available. How much of each is needed to produce the required 90% concentrate?

14.20 Dilute sulfuric acid (19% acid, the rest water) is required for activating car batteries. A tank of weak acid (12.5% concentrate, the rest water) is available. If 450 lb of 78% concentrate acid is added to the tank to get the required 19% acid, how much of the 19% acid is now available?

14.21 A special mud formed by mixing dry clay and water is used to assist drilling through rock. The optimum amount of clay in the mud is determined from a chart that relates the percentage of clay to the hardness of the rock. If a supply of mud containing 42% clay and 58% water is available, how much of this mud and how much dry clay need to be mixed to produce one ton of a mix containing 48% clay?

14.22 A company has a large vat of brine containing 5.0% salt (95% water) and wishes to prepare 45 kg batches of brine having salt content varying from 6.0% to $3.0(10^1)$%. Prepare a graph showing the required amount of original brine and dry pure salt that must be mixed to obtain a brine with a specified salt content in the range. Consider the desired salt content of the 45 kg batch as the independent variable.

14.23 Andrew Foods, Inc., produces a sweet syrup made from corn syrup and beet syrup mixed with pure sugar. For each batch, 680 lbm of beet syrup (13% sugar, the remainder water) and 650 lbm of corn syrup (8.0% sugar, the remainder water) are mixed with pure sugar and 350 lbm of water is boiled off. Determine the amount of pure sugar that needs to be added to produce an 18% sugar content in the final product.

14.24 The feed to a distillation column contains 37% benzene, the remainder toluene. The overhead (product) contains 55% benzene and the bottoms (waste) contains 5.0% benzene. Calculate the percentage of the total feed that leaves as product.

14.25 In a mechanical coal-washing process, a portion of the inorganic sulfur and ash material in the mined coal can be removed. A feed stream to the process consists of 73% coal, 11% ash, 11% sulfur, and 5.0% water (to suppress dust). The clean coal side of the process consists of 88% coal, 6.0% sulfur, 3.0% ash, and 3.0%

water. The refuse side consists of 32% sulfur, with the remainder being ash, coal, and water. If $8.0(10^1)$ metric tons per hour of clean coal is required, determine the feed rate required for the mined coal and the composition of the refuse material.

14.26 Because of environmental concerns, your plant must install an acetone recovery system. Your task is to calculate the size of the various components of the system, which includes an absorption tank into which is fed $1.25(10^3)$ kg of water per hour and $7.00(10^3)$ kg of air containing 1.63% acetone. The water absorbs the acetone and the purified air is expelled. The water and acetone solution go to a distillation process where the solution is vaporized and then fed to a condenser. The resulting product is 98.9% acetone and 1.10% water. The bottoms (waste) of the distillation process contain 4.23% acetone and 95.77% water. To assist in the determination of the volume of a holding tank, calculate how much product is generated in kilograms per hour.

14.27 A process requires two distillation columns. The first column is fed a solution containing 21% component A, 31% component B, the rest component C. The product amount is one-fourth of the feed amount and contains 61% A, 5% B, the rest C. The bottoms amount is fed to a second column which then produces a product of 15% A,79% B, the rest C. The waste from the second column contains 0.50% A, the rest B and C. If 2200 lb of solution is fed to the first column, determine the unknown compositions and amounts of the feed to and the product and waste from the second column.

14.28 Ether is used in the process of extracting cod-liver oil from livers. Livers enter the extractor at a rate of 1 500 lbm/h and consist of 32% oil and 68% inert material. The solvent is introduced to the extractor at a rate of 3 100 lbm/h and consists of 2.80% oil and 97.2% ether. The cod-liver oil extract leaves the process at a rate of 2 600 lbm/h and consists of 21% oil and 79% ether. Calculate the flow rate and composition of the leaving processed livers.

14.29 Two liquids, A and B, are mixed together. A is 3.0% solids, the remainder water. B is 8.0% solids, the remainder water. An amount S of pure, dry solids is mixed with A and B to form $2.0(10^2)$ kg of a mixture with 5.0% solids. Develop a table of combinations of amounts of A, B, and S that will satisfy the final mixture requirements. What is the maximum amount of B that can be used to meet the requirements without having to remove pure, dry solids from the mixture? Hint: Write a short computer program or use a spreadsheet and start with B = 0 and increase in increments of 2 kg.

14.30 A 2 200 lbm, finely ground mixture of salt and sand is to be separated by adding 1 500 lbm of water to dissolve the salt and then filtering the salt solution from the insoluble sand. The resulting salt solution is then separated by the distillation of 1 350 lbm of water, leaving a final solution that is 92% salt and 8.0% water. Determine the percentages of salt and sand in the original mixture.

CHAPTER **5**

Representation of Technical Information*

Chapter Objectives

When you complete your study of this chapter, you will be able to:

- Recognize the importance of collecting, recording, plotting, and interpreting technical data for engineering analysis and design
- Put into practice methods for graphical presentation of scientific data and graphical analysis of plotted data
- Develop the ability to graph data using uniform and nonuniform scales
- Apply methods of selected points and least squares for determining the equation that gives the best-fit line to the given data
- Determine the most appropriate family of curves (linear, power, or exponential) that gives the best fit to the given data

5.1   Introduction

This chapter begins with an example of an actual freshman engineering student team project. This team consisted of aerospace, electrical, and mechanical engineering students who were assigned to find how temperature and pressure varied with altitude in the atmosphere. The team was not given specific instructions as to how this might be accomplished, but once the information had been collected, they were expected to record, plot, and analyze the data.

After a bit of research, the team decided to request a university-owned plane that was equipped with the latest Rockwell Collins avionics gear, and since it was a class assignment, they asked if the university's Air Flight Service would consider helping them conduct this experiment free of charge. Because the pilots do periodic maintenance flights, they agreed to allow the students to ride along.

Using the plane's sophisticated data-acquisition equipment, the students were able to collect and record the data needed for the assignment (see Table 5.1) along the flight path as the plane ascended to 12 000 feet. They decided that one would record, one would make temperature readings, and the third would make pressure readings.

---

*Users will find Appendices A, F, and the inside covers useful reference material for this chapter.

Table 5.1

Height, H, ft	Temperature, T, °F	Pressure, P, lbf/in²
0	59	14.7
1000	55	14.2
2000	52	13.7
3000	48	13.2
4000	44	12.7
5000	41	12.2
6000	37	11.8
7000	34	11.3
8000	30	10.9
9000	27	10.5
10000	23	10.0
11000	19	9.7
12000	16	9.3

When the students returned to the hangar, they made a freehand plot (with straightedge) of the collected information (see Fig. 5.1).

Since the plot demonstrated linear results, the students returned to campus to prepare the required report, including an analysis of the data collected.

They decided the written report should include a computer-generated table, a computer-generated plot of the data, and a computer-generated least-squares curve fit to determine the mathematical relationship between the variables.

Table 5.2 shows the computer-generated table prepared after the students returned to campus. This could have been done with word processing, spreadsheet, or other commercially available software packages.

Figures 5.2 and 5.3 show how spreadsheet applications can be powerful and convenient for plotting once the fundamentals of good graph construction are understood. Figure 5.2 is an example of a Microsoft Excel spreadsheet using a scatter plot with each data point connected with a straight line. Figure 5.3 is an example of a scatter plot with only the data points plotted. A *trendline*

Table 5.2

Height, *H*, ft	Temperature, *T*, °F	Pressure, *P*, lbf/in²
0	59	14.7
1 000	55	14.2
2 000	52	13.7
3 000	48	13.2
4 000	44	12.7
5 000	41	12.2
6 000	37	11.8
7 000	34	11.3
8 000	30	10.9
9 000	27	10.5
10 000	23	10.0
11 000	19	9.7
12 000	16	9.3

Figure 5.1

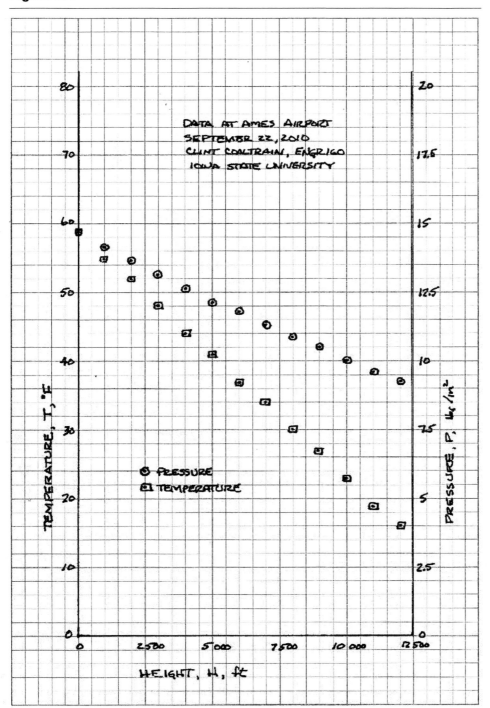

Freehand plot of how temperature and pressure vary with altitude.

Figure 5.2

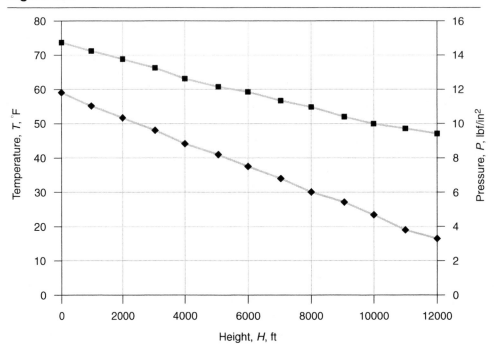

Excel spreadsheet hard copy of data displayed in Fig. 5.1.

Figure 5.3

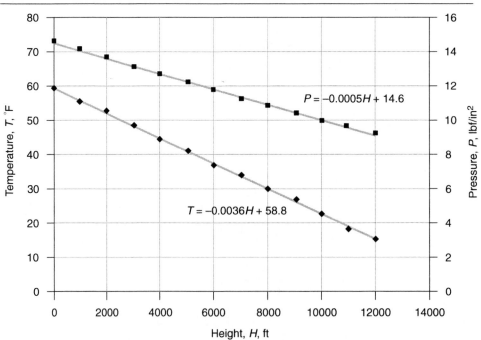

Excel spreadsheet hard copy of data displayed in Fig. 5.1 with trendline.

is then applied using the method of least squares with the equation of the line included. Further discussion of the use of the trendline/method of least squares will occur later in this chapter, with more details given in the chapter on statistics.

This chapter contains examples and guidelines as well as helpful information that will be needed when collecting, recording, plotting, and interpreting technical data. Two processes are: (1) graphical presentation of scientific data and (2) graphical analysis of plotted data.

Humans find it difficult to observe relationships among data shown in a table. We are much better at understanding relationships when the data are put into a graphical or pictorial format. We can immediately recognize the form of the relationship between two data sets (for example) when they are plotted on a graph. We can see whether the relationship is linear (straight line) or curved in some fashion. Perhaps we can even determine that the relationship appears to be in the form of a sine wave or a parabolic curve. Sometimes, just the impression of how the data relate is enough. More often, though, we need to obtain an equation that relates one variable to the other.

We have at our disposal computers and software that can make the production of a graph easy to accomplish and can help us to determine the relationship between variables in equation form. Much of this chapter is devoted to learning about engineering standards for graph production and methods for producing equations between variables that have been presented on a graph.

5.1.1 Software for Recording and Plotting Data

Data are recorded in the field as shown in Table 5.1. A quick freehand plot of the data is produced to provide a visual impression of the results while still in the field (see Fig. 5.1). This allows you to obtain corrected or additional data if the quick plot suggests it. Alternatively, the data could be entered into a laptop computer and processed initially in the field.

Upon returning to the laboratory, however, spreadsheet software, such as Excel, provides enormous recording and plotting capability. The data are entered into the computer, and by manipulation of software options, both the data and a graph of the data can be configured, stored, and printed (Table 5.2 and Figs. 5.2 and 5.3).

Programs such as Mathematica, MATLAB, and Mathcad provide a range of powerful tools designed to help analyze numerical and symbolic operations as well as to present a visual image of the results.

Software is also widely available to provide methods of curve fitting once the data have been collected and recorded.

Even though it is important for the engineer to interpret, analyze, and communicate different types of data, it is not practical to include in this chapter all forms of graphs and charts that may be encountered. For that reason, popular-appeal or advertising charts such as bar charts, pie diagrams, and distribution charts, although useful to the engineer, are not discussed here.

Even though commercial software is very helpful during the presentation and analysis process, the results are only as good as the original software design and its use by the operator. Some software provides a wide range of tools but only allows limited data applications and minimal flexibility to modify default outputs. Other software provides a high degree of in-depth analysis for a particular subject area with considerable latitude to adjust and modify parameters.

Inevitably, the computer together with its array of software will continue to provide an invaluable analysis tool. However, it is absolutely essential that you be knowledgeable of the software and demonstrate considerable care when manipulating the data. You need to understand the software's limitations and accuracies, but above all you must know what plotted results are needed and what the engineering standards are for producing them.

For this reason, the sections that follow are a combination of manual collection, recording, plotting, and analysis and computer-assisted collection, recording, plotting, and analysis.

5.2 Collecting and Recording Data

5.2.1 Manual Entry

Modern science was founded on scientific measurement. Meticulously designed experiments, carefully analyzed, have produced volumes of scientific data that have been collected, recorded, and documented. For such data to be meaningful, however, certain procedures must be followed. Field books, such as those shown in Figure 5.4, or data sheets should be used to record all observations. Information about equipment, such as the instruments and experimental apparatus used, should be recorded. Sketches illustrating the physical arrangement of equipment can be very helpful. Under no circumstances should observations be recorded elsewhere or data points erased. The data sheet or field book is the "notebook of original entry." If there is reason for doubting the value of any entry, it may be canceled (i.e., not considered) by drawing a line through it. The cancellation should be done in such a manner that the original entry is not obscured in case you want to consider it later.

As a general rule it is advantageous to make all measurements as carefully as time and the economics of the situation allow. Errors do enter into all experimental work regardless of the amount of care exercised.

It can be seen from what we have just discussed that the analysis of experimental data involves not only measurements and collection of data but also careful documentation and interpretation of results.

Experimental data once collected are normally organized into some tabular form, which is the next step in the process of analysis. Data, such as that shown in Table 5.1, should be carefully labeled and neatly lettered so that the data are not misunderstood. This particular collection of data represents atmospheric pressure and temperature measurements recorded at various altitudes by students during a flight in a light aircraft.

Although the manual tabulation of data is frequently a necessary step, you will sometimes find it difficult to visualize a relationship between variables when simply viewing a column of numbers. Therefore, a most important step in the sequence from collection to analysis is the construction of appropriate graphs or charts.

Figure 5.4

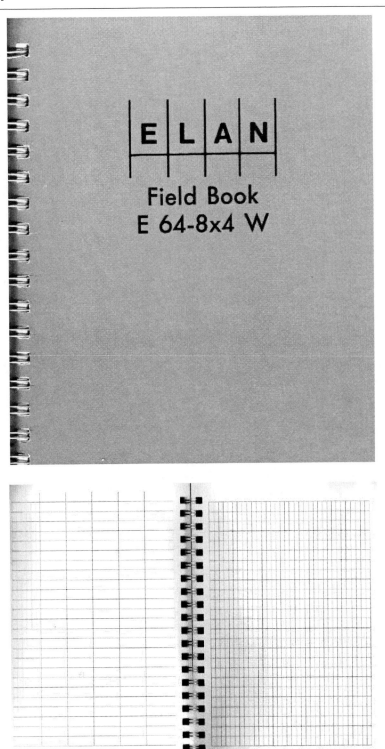

Field book typically used by civil engineers.

5.2.2 Computer-Assisted Techniques

A variety of equipment has been developed that will automatically sample experimental data for analysis. We expect to see expansion of these techniques along with visual displays that will allow us to interactively control the experiments. As an example, the flight data collected onboard the aircraft could be entered directly into a laptop computer through digital interfaces with the flight instruments and then printed as in Table 5.2.

5.3 General Graphing Procedures

Many examples appear throughout this chapter to illustrate methods of graphical presentation because their effectiveness depends to a large extent on the details of construction.

The proper manual construction of a graph from tabulated data can be described by a series of steps. Each of these steps will be discussed and illustrated in detail in the following sections. Once you understand the manual process of graph construction, the step to computer-generated graphs will be simple.

1. Select the type of graph paper (rectangular [also known as rectilinear], semilog, log-log) and grid spacing for best representation of the given data.
2. Choose the proper location of the horizontal and vertical axes.
3. Determine the scale units (range) for each axis to display the data appropriately.
4. Graduate and calibrate the axes using the 1, 2, 5 rule.
5. Identify each axis completely.
6. Plot points and use permissible symbols.
7. Check any point that deviates from the slope or curvature of the line.
8. Draw the curve or curves.
9. Identify each curve, add title, and include other necessary notes.
10. Darken lines for good reproduction.

5.3.1 Graph Paper

Printed coordinate graph paper is commercially available in various sizes with a variety of grid spacing. Rectangular ruling can be purchased in a range of lines per inch or lines per centimeter, with an overall paper size of 8.5 x 11 in. most typical.

Closely spaced coordinate ruling is generally avoided for results that are to be printed or photoreduced. However, for accurate engineering analyses requiring some amount of interpolation, data are normally plotted on closely spaced, printed coordinate paper. Graph paper is available in a variety of colors, weights, and grades. Translucent paper can be used when the reproduction system requires a material that is not opaque.

If the data require the use of log-log or semilog paper, such paper can also be purchased in different formats, styles, weights, and grades. Both log-log and semilog grids are available from 1 to 5 cycles per axis. (A later section will

Figure 5.5

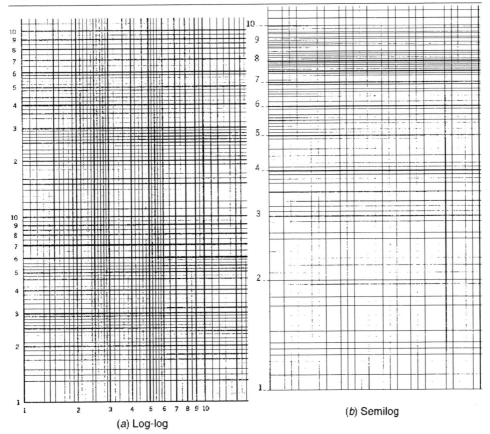

(a) Log-log

(b) Semilog

Commercial graph paper.

discuss different applications of log-log and semilog paper.). Examples of commercially available log and semilog paper are given in Figures 5.5a and 5.5b.

5.3.2 Axes Location and Breaks

The axes of a graph consist of two intersecting straight lines. The horizontal axis, normally called the *x-axis*, is the *abscissa*. The vertical axis, denoted by the *y-axis*, is the *ordinate*. Common practice is to place the independent variable values along the abscissa and the dependent variable values along the ordinate, as illustrated in Figure 5.6.

It is not always clear which variable is the independent variable and which is the dependent variable. You can think in terms of an experiment where one variable is set (independent variable) and another is determined (dependent variable). For example, in a test of an electrical circuit, if the voltage is set it is the independent variable and if the current is read from an instrument as a result of this voltage setting it is the dependent variable. You can also think in terms of reading from a graph. Normally you would find the value of the variable you set along the horizontal axis (independent variable) and read the value of the other (dependent variable) from the curve using the vertical axis.

Figure 5.6

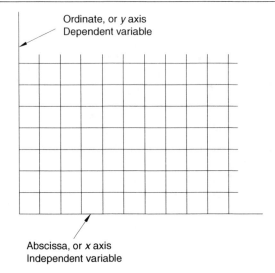

Abscissa (X) and ordinate (Y) axes.

Sometimes mathematical graphs contain both positive and negative values of the variables. This necessitates the division of the coordinate field into four quadrants, as shown in Figure 5.7. Positive values increase toward the right and upward from the origin.

On any graph, a full range of values is desirable, normally beginning at zero and extending slightly beyond the largest value. To avoid crowding, one should use the entire coordinate area as completely as possible. However, certain circumstances require special consideration to avoid wasted space. For

Figure 5.7

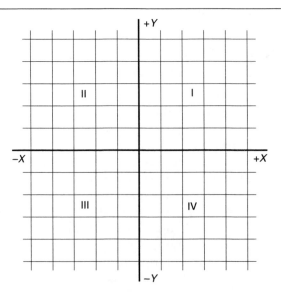

Coordinate axes.

Figure 5.8

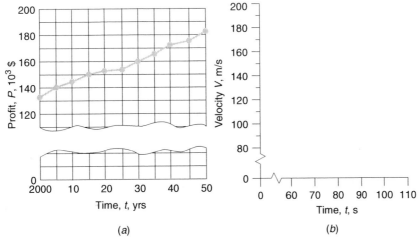

(a)   (b)

Typical axis breaks.

example, if values plotted along the axis do not range near zero, a "break" in the grid or the axis may be used, as shown in Figures 5.8a and 5.8b.

When judgments concerning relative amounts of change in a variable are required, the axis or grid should not be broken or the zero line omitted, with the exception of time in years, such as 2009, 2010, and so on, because that designation normally has little relation to zero.

Since most commercially prepared grids do not include sufficient border space for proper labeling, the axes should preferably be placed 20 to 25 mm (approximately 1 in.) inside the edge of the printed grid to allow ample room for graduations, calibrations, axes labels, reproduction, and binding. The edge of the grid may need to be used on log scales because it is not always feasible to move the axis inside the grid. However, with careful planning, the vertical and horizontal axes can usually be repositioned.

5.3.3 Scale Graduations, Calibrations, and Designations

The scale is a series of marks, called *graduations*, laid down at predetermined distances along the axis. Numerical values assigned to significant graduations are called *calibrations.*

A scale can be *uniform* or *linear*, with equal spacing along the axis, as found on the metric or engineer's scales. If the scale represents a variable whose exponent is not equal to 1 or a variable that contains trigonometric or logarithmic functions, the scale is called a *nonuniform*, or *functional, scale.* Examples of both these scales together with graduations and calibrations are shown in Figure 5.9. When you plot data, one of the most important considerations is the proper selection of scale graduations. A basic guide to follow is the *1, 2, 5 rule*, which only applies to uniform axes and can be stated as follows:

> Scale graduations are selected so that the smallest division of the axis is a positive or negative integer power of 10 times 1, 2, or 5.

Figure 5.9

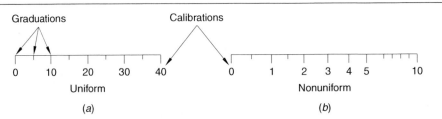

(*a*)   (*b*)

Scale graduations and calibrations.

Figure 5.10

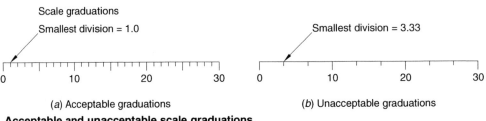

(*a*) Acceptable graduations   (*b*) Unacceptable graduations

Acceptable and unacceptable scale graduations.

The justification and logic for this rule are clear. Graduation of an axis by this procedure allows better (more accurate) interpolation of data between graduations when plotting or reading a graph. Figure 5.10 illustrates both acceptable and unacceptable examples of scale graduations.

Violations of the 1, 2, 5 rule that are acceptable even for uniform axes involve certain units of time as a variable. Days, months, and years can be graduated and calibrated as illustrated in Figure 5.11.

Figure 5.11

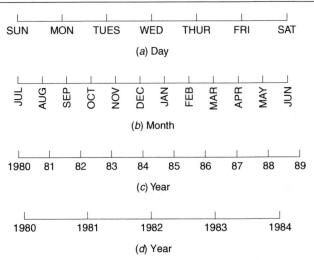

Time as a variable.

Figure 5.12

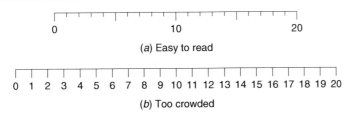

(a) Easy to read

(b) Too crowded

Acceptable and unacceptable scale calibrations.

Scale graduations follow a definite rule, but the number of calibrations included is a matter of good judgment. Each application requires consideration based on the scale length and range as well as the eventual use. Figure 5.12 demonstrates how calibrations can differ on a scale with the same range. Both examples obey the 1, 2, 5 rule, but as you can see, too many closely spaced calibrations make the axis difficult to read.

The selection of a scale deserves attention from another point of view. If the rate of change is to be depicted accurately, the slope of the curve should represent a true picture of the data. By compressing or expanding one of the axes, you could communicate an incorrect impression of the data. Such a procedure should be avoided. Figure 5.13 demonstrates how the equation $Y = X$ can be misleading if not properly plotted. Occasionally, distortion is desirable, but it should always be carefully labeled and explained to avoid misleading conclusions.

Figure 5.13

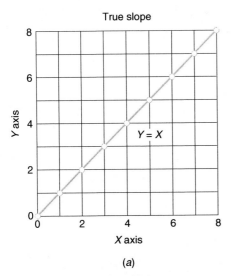

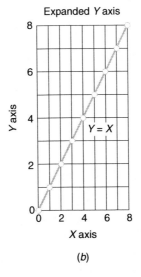

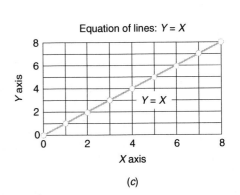

(a)

(b)

(c)

Proper representation of data.

Figure 5.14

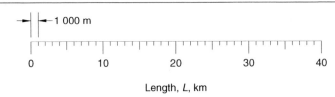

Length, *L*, km

Reading the scale.

If plotted data consist of very large or small numbers, the SI prefix names (milli-, kilo-, mega-, etc.) may be used to simplify calibrations. As a guide, if the numbers to be plotted and calibrated consist of more than three digits, it is customary to use the appropriate prefix; an example appears in Figure 5.14.

The length scale calibrations in Figure 5.14 contain only two digits, but the scale can be read by understanding that the distance between the first and second graduation (0 to 1) is a kilometer; therefore, the calibration at 10 represents 10 km.

Certain quantities, such as temperature in degrees Celsius and altitude in meters, have traditionally been tabulated without the use of prefix multipliers. Figure 5.15 depicts a procedure by which these quantities can be conveniently calibrated. Note in particular that the distance between 0 and 1 on the scale represents 1000°C.

The calibration of logarithmic scales is illustrated in Figure 5.16. Since log-cycle designations start and end with powers of 10 (i.e., 10^{-1}, 10^0, 10^1, 10^2, etc.) and since commercially purchased paper is normally available with each cycle printed 1 through 10, do not use the printed values as your calibrations. Instead, provide your own calibrations and use the printed numbers as a reference to be sure you understand what each line of the grid represents. Since the axes are nonuniform, it is sometimes difficult to determine what each grid line represents without those printed numbers. Figures 5.16a and 5.16b demonstrate two preferred methods of calibration.

Figure 5.15

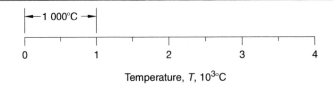

Temperature, *T*, 10^3°C

Reading the scale.

Figure 5.16

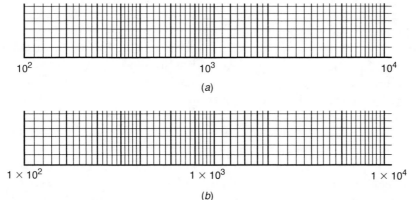

10^2 10^3 10^4

(a)

1×10^2 1×10^3 1×10^4

(b)

Calibration of log scales.

Figure 5.17

0   10   20   30

Time, t, s

Axis identification.

5.3.4 Axis Labeling

Each axis should be clearly identified. At a minimum, the axis label should contain the name of the variable, its symbol, and its units. Since time is frequently the independent variable and is plotted on the x-axis, it has been selected as an illustration in Figure 5.17. Scale designations should preferably be placed outside the axes, where they can be shown clearly. Labels should be lettered parallel to the axis and positioned so that they can be read from the bottom or right side of the page, as illustrated in Figure 5.22.

5.3.5 Point-Plotting Procedure

Data can be described in one of three ways: as observed, empirical, or theoretical. Observed and empirical data points are usually located by various symbols, such as a small circle or square around each data point, whereas graphs of theoretical relations (equations) are normally constructed smooth, without the use of symbol designation. Figure 5.18 illustrates each type.

5.3.6 Curves and Symbols

On graphs prepared from observed data resulting from laboratory experiments, points are usually designated by various symbols (see Fig. 5.19). If more than one curve is plotted on the same grid, several of these symbols may be used (one type for each curve). To avoid confusion, however, it is good practice to label each curve. When several curves are plotted on the same grid, another way they can be distinguished from each other is by using different types of lines, as illustrated in Figure 5.20. Solid lines are normally reserved for single curves, and dashed lines are commonly used for extensions; however, a different line type can be used for each separate curve. The line weight of plotted curves should be heavier than the grid ruling.

A key, or legend, should be placed in an available portion of the grid, preferably enclosed in a border, to define point symbols or line types that are used for curves. Remember that the lines representing each curve *should never be drawn through the symbols,* so that the precise point is always identifiable. Figure 5.21 demonstrates the use of a key and the practice of breaking the line at each symbol.

Figure 5.18

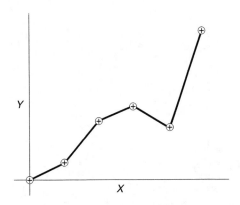

(*a*) Observed: Usually plotted with observed data points connected by straight, irregular line segments. Line does not penetrate the circles.

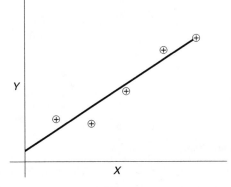

(*b*) Empirical: Reflects the author's interpretation of what occurs between known data points. Normally represented as a smooth curve or straight line fitted to data. Data points may or may not fall on curve.

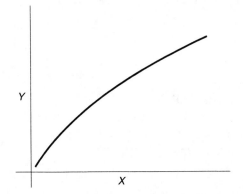

(*c*) Theoretical: Graph of an equation. Curves or lines are smooth and without symbols. Every point on the curve is a data point.

Plotting data points.

Figure 5.19

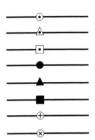

Symbols.

Figure 5.20

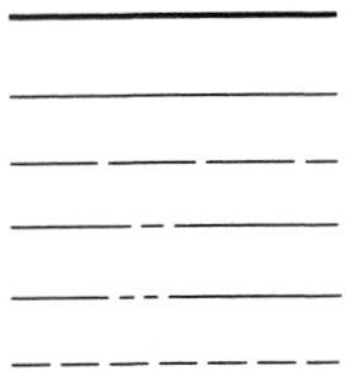

Line types.

Figure 5.21

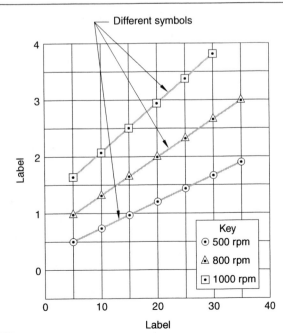

An example of a key.

5.3.7 Titles

Each graph must be identified with a complete title. The title should include a clear, concise statement of the data represented, along with items such as the name of the author, the date of the experiment, and any and all information concerning the plot, including the name of the institution or company. Titles may be enclosed in a border.

All lettering, the axes, and the curves should be sufficiently bold to stand out on the graph paper. Letters should be neat and of standard size. Figure 5.22 is an illustration of plotted experimental data incorporating many of the items discussed in the chapter.

5.3.8 Computer-Assisted Plotting

Several types of software are available to produce graphs (e.g., Mathcad, MATLAB, Minitab, Mathematica, Excel). The quality and accuracy of these computer-generated graphs vary depending on the sophistication of the

Figure 5.22

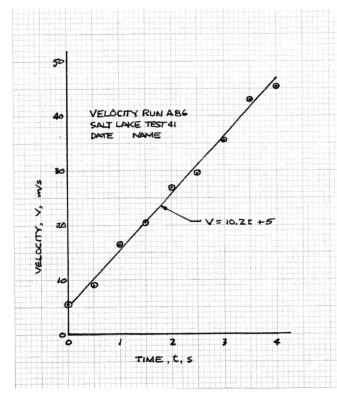

Necessary steps to follow when manually plotting a graph:

1. Select the type of graph paper (rectilinear, semilog, log-log) and grid spacing for best representation of the given data.

2. Choose the proper location of the horizontal and vertical axes.

3. Determine the scale units (range) for each axis to display the data appropriately.

4. Graduate and calibrate the axes using the 1, 2, 5 rule.

5. Identify each axis completely.

6. Plot points using permissible symbols.

7. Check any point that deviates from the slope or curvature of the line.

8. Draw the curve or curves.

9. Identify each curve, add title and necessary notes.

10. Darken lines for good reproduction.

Sample plot.

software as well as on the plotter or printer employed. Typically, the software will produce an axis scale graduated and calibrated to accommodate the range of data values that will fit the paper. This may or may not produce a readable or interpretable scale. Therefore, it is necessary to apply judgment depending on the results needed. For example, if the default plot does not meet needed scale readability, it may be necessary to specify the scale range to achieve an appropriate scale graduation, since this option allows greater control of the scale drawn.

Computer-produced graphs with uniform scales may not follow the 1, 2, 5 rule, particularly because the software plots the independent variable based on the data collected. If the software has the option of separately specifying the range—that is, plotting the data as an *X-Y* scatter plot—you will be able to achieve scale graduations and calibrations that do follow the 1, 2, 5 rule, making it easier to read values from the graph. The hand-plotted graph that was illustrated in Figure 5.22 is plotted using Excel with the results shown in Figure 5.23 using an *X-Y* scatter plot with a linear curve-fit and the equation of the line using the method of least squares (see section 5.6).

Figure 5.23

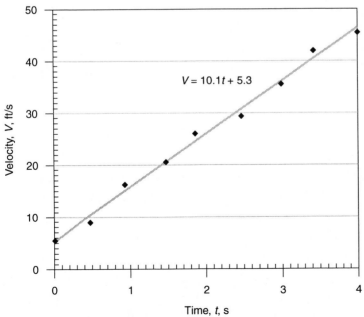

$V = 10.1t + 5.3$

Necessary steps to follow when using a computer-assisted alternative:
1. Input via keyboard or import data into spreadsheet.
2. Select independent (*x*-axis) and dependent variable(s).
3. Select appropriate graph (style or type) from menu.
4. Produce trial plot with default parameters.
5. Examine (modify as necessary) origin, range, graduation, and calibrations: Note, use the 1, 2, 5 rule.
6. Label each axis completely.
7. Select appropriate plotting-point symbols and legend.
8. Create complete title.
9. Examine plot and store the data.
10. Plot or print the data.

Excel spreadsheet hard copy of data displayed in Fig. 5.22.

5.4   Empirical Functions

Empirical functions are generally described as those based on values obtained by experimentation. Since they are arrived at experimentally, equations normally available from theoretical derivations are not always available. However, mathematical expressions can be modeled to fit experimental data, and it is possible to classify many empirical results into one of four general categories: (1) linear, (2) exponential, (3) power, or (4) periodic.

A linear function, as the name suggests, will plot as a straight line on uniform rectangular coordinate paper. Likewise, when a curve representing experimental data is a straight line or a close approximation to a straight line, the relationship of the variables can be expressed by a linear equation, such as $y = mx + b$.

Correspondingly, exponential functions, when plotted on semilog paper, will be linear. Why? Because the basic form of the equation is $y = be^{mx}$, all we do is take the log of both sides. If it is written in log (base 10) form, it becomes $\log y = mx \log e + \log b$. Alternatively, using natural logarithms, the equation becomes $\ln y = mx + \ln b$ because $\ln e = 1$. The independent variable x is plotted on the abscissa, and the dependent variable y is plotted on the functional ln (natural log) scale as $\ln y$.

The power equation has the form of $y = bx^m$. Written in log form, it becomes $\log y = m \log x + \log b$. This equation will plot as a straight line on log-log paper because the log of the independent variable x is plotted against the log of the dependent variable y.

The periodic type, often seen in alternating current, for example, is not covered in this text.

When the data represent experimental results and a series of points are plotted to represent the relationship between the variables, it is unlikely that a straight line can be constructed through every point because some error (instruments, readings, recordings) is inevitable. If all points do not lie on a straight line, an approximation technique or averaging method may be used to arrive at the best possible fit. This method of straight-line approximation is called curve fitting.

5.5   Curve Fitting

Different methods or techniques are available to arrive at the best "straight-line" fit. Two methods commonly employed for finding the best fit are

1. Method of selected points
2. Method of least squares

The most accurate method, least squares, is discussed in more detail in the chapter on statistics. However, several examples are presented in this chapter to demonstrate correct methods for plotting technical data using both the method of selected points and the method of least squares.

5.6 Method of Selected Points and Least Squares

The method of selected points is a valid method of determining the equation that best fits data that exhibit a linear relationship. Once the data have been plotted and you have decided that a linear equation would be a good fit, a line is positioned that appears to best fit the data. This is most often accomplished by visually selecting a line that goes through as many data points as possible and has approximately the same number of data points on either side of the line.

Once the line has been drawn, two points, such as A and B, are selected *on the line* and at a reasonable distance apart (the further apart the better). The coordinates of both points $A(X_1, Y_1)$ and $B(X_2, Y_2)$ must satisfy the equation of the line because both are points on the line.

The method of least squares is a more accurate approach that will be illustrated as computer-assisted examples in most problems that follow. The method of least squares is a most appropriate technique for determination of the best-fit line. You should understand that the method presented represents a technique called *linear regression* and is valid only for *linear* relationships. The technique of least squares can, however, be applied to power ($y = bx^m$) and exponential ($y = be^{mx}$) relationships as well as $y = mx + b$, if done correctly. The power function can be handled by noting that there is a linear relationship between log y and log x (log y = m log x + log b, which plots as a straight line on log-log paper). Thus, we can apply the method of least squares to the variables log y and log x to obtain parameters m and log b.

The exponential function written in natural logarithm form is ln y = mx + ln b. Therefore, a linear relationship exists between ln y and x (this plots as a straight line on semilog paper). The next examples will demonstrate the use of the selected point method for power and experimental curves.

5.7 Empirical Equations: Linear

When experimental data plot as a straight line on rectangular grid paper, the equation of the line belongs to a family of curves whose basic equation is given by

$$y = mx + b \tag{5.1}$$

where m is the slope of the line, a constant, and b is a constant referred to as the *y intercept* (the value of y when $x = 0$).

To demonstrate how the method of selected points works, consider the following example.

Example problem 5.1   The velocity V of an experimental automobile is measured at specified time t intervals. Determine the equation of a straight line constructed through the points recorded in Table 5.3. Once an equation has been determined, velocities at intermediate values can be computed.

Procedure

1. Plot the data on rectangular paper. If the results form a straight line (see Fig. 5.24), the function is linear and the general equation is of the form

    $$V = mt + b$$

    where m and b are constants.

2. Select two points on the line, $A(t_1, V_1)$ and $B(t_2, V_2)$, and record the value of these points. Points A and B should be widely separated to reduce the effect on m and b of errors in reading values from the graph. Points A and B are identified in Figure 5.24 for instructional reasons. They should not be shown on a completed graph that is to be displayed.

    $$A(10, 60)$$
    $$B(35, 165)$$

Table 5.3

Time t, s	0	5	10	15	20	25	30	35	40
Velocity V, m/s	24	33	62	77	105	123	151	170	188

3. Substitute the points A and B into $V = mt + b$.

    Eq(1) $60 = m(10) + b$
    Eq(2) $165 = m(35) + b$

Figure 5.24

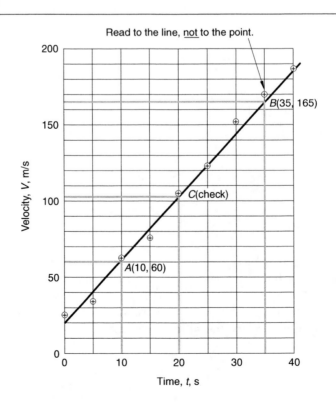

Data plot.

4. The equations are solved simultaneously for the two unknowns.

    $$m = 4.2$$
    $$b = 18$$

5. The equation of the line for this specific problem can be written as

    $$V = 4.2t + 18$$

6. Using another point $C(t_3, V_3)$, check for verification:

    $$C(20, 102)$$
    $$102 = 4.2(20) + 18$$
    $$102 = 84 + 18 = 102$$

7. A computer-assisted alternate:

    The data set can be entered into a spreadsheet, and the software will provide a more precise solution. Figure 5.23 illustrates a software solution for data provided in the previous sample plot (Fig. 5.22). The computer solution provides a plot of data on rectangular paper with the equation of the line determined by the method of least squares. Once you understand the fundamentals, it can be very time efficient to use computer technology and commercial software.

5.8 Empirical Equations: Power Curves

When experimentally collected data are plotted on rectangular coordinate graph paper and the points do not form a straight line, you must determine which family of curves the line most closely approximates. If you have no idea as to the nature of the data, plot the experimentally collected points on log-log paper and/or semilog paper to determine if the data approximate a straight line. Consider the following familiar example. Suppose a solid object is dropped from a tall building. To anyone who has studied fundamental physics, it is apparent that distance and time should correspond to the general equation for a free-falling body (neglecting air friction): $s = 1/2\, gt^2$.

However, let's assume for a moment that we do not know this relationship and that all we have is a table of values experimentally measured on a free-falling body.

Example problem 5.2   A solid object is dropped from a tall building, and the values time versus distance are as recorded in Table 5.4.

Procedure

1. Make a freehand plot to observe the data visually (see Fig. 5.25). From this quick plot, the data points are more easily recognized as belonging to a family of curves whose general equation can be written as

    $$y = bx^m \qquad\qquad (5.2)$$

Figure 5.25

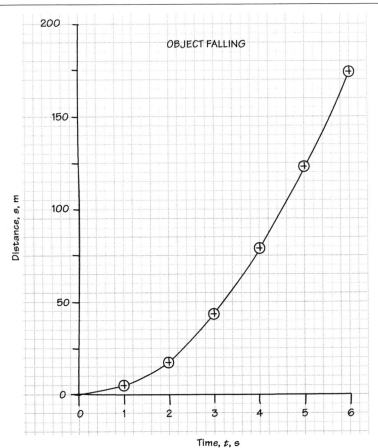

Rectangular graph paper (freehand).

Table 5.4

Time t, s	Distance s, m
0	0
1	4.9
2	19.6
3	44.1
4	78.4
5	122.5
6	176.4

Remember that before the method of selected points can be applied to determine the equation of the line, the plotted line must be straight because two points on a curved line do not uniquely identify the line. Mathematically, this general equation can be modified by taking the logarithm of both sides,

$$\log y = m \log x + \log b, \text{ or } \ln y = m \ln x + \ln b$$

This equation suggests that if the logs of all table values of y and x were computed and the results plotted on rectangular paper, the line would likely be straight.

Table 5.5

Time t, s	Distance s, m	Log t	Log s
0	0		
1	4.9	0.0000	0.6902
2	19.6	0.3010	1.2923
3	44.1	0.4771	1.6444
4	78.4	0.6021	1.8943
5	122.5	0.6990	2.0881
6	176.4	0.7782	2.2465

Realizing that the log of zero is undefined and plotting the remaining points that are recorded in Table 5.5 for log s versus log t, the results are shown in Figure 5.26.

Since the graph of log s versus log t does plot as a straight line, it is now possible to use the general form of the equation

$$\log s = m \log t + \log b$$

and apply the method of selected points.

When reading values for points A and B from the graph, we must remember that the logarithm of each variable has already been determined and the values plotted.

$$A(0.2, 1.09)$$
$$B(0.6, 1.89)$$

Points A and B can now be substituted into the general equation log $s = m$ log $t + \log b$ and solved simultaneously.

Figure 5.26

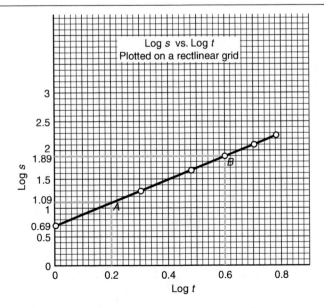

Log-log on rectangular grid paper.

$$1.89 = m(0.6) + \log b$$
$$1.09 = m(0.2) + \log b$$
$$m = 2.0$$
$$\log b = 0.69, \text{ or}$$
$$b = 4.9$$

As examination of Figure 5.26 shows, the value of log b (0.69) can be read from the graph where log $t = 0$. This, of course, is where $t = 1$ and is the y intercept for log-log plots.

The general equation can then be written as

$$s = 4.9t^{2.0}$$

or

$$s = 1/2gt^2,$$

where $g = 9.8 \ m/s^2$

Note: One obvious inconvenience is the necessity of finding logarithms of each variable and then plotting the logs of these variables. This step is not necessary since functional paper is commercially available with log x and log y scales already constructed. Log-log paper allows the variables themselves to be plotted directly without the need of computing the log of each value.

2.   An alternate method for the solution of this problem is as follows:

In the preceding part, once the general form of the equation is determined [Eq. (5.2)], the data can be plotted directly on log-log paper. Since the resulting curve is a straight line, the method of selected points can be used directly (see Fig. 5.27).

Figure 5.27

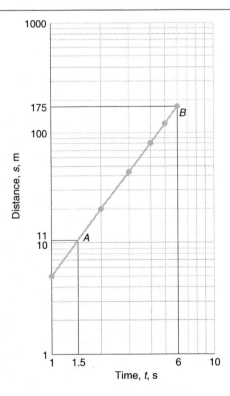

Log-log paper.

The log form of the equation is again used:

$$\log s = m \log t + \log b$$

Select points A and B on the line:

$$A(1.5, 11)$$
$$B(6, 175)$$

Substitute the values into the general equation $\log s = m \log t + \log b$, taking careful note that the numbers are the variables and *not* the logs of the variables.

$$\log 175 = m \log 6 + \log b$$
$$\log 11 = m \log 1.5 + \log b$$

Again, solving these two equations simultaneously results in the following approximate values for the constants b and m:

$$b = 4.8978 \cong 4.9$$
$$m = 1.9957 \cong 2.0$$

Identical conclusions can be reached:

$$s = 1/2gt^2$$

This time, however, one can use functional scales rather than calculate the log of each number.

3. A computer-assisted alternate:

The data set can be entered into a spreadsheet, and the software will provide an identical solution. Figure 5.28 illustrates software that provides a plot

Figure 5.28

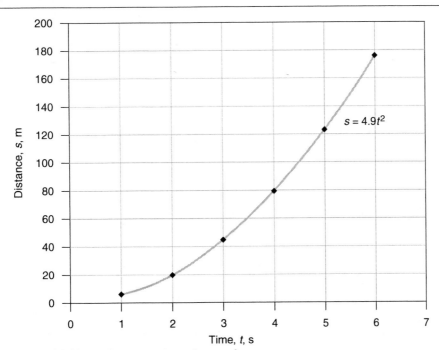

Graph of a free-falling object on rectangular graph paper.

Figure 5.29

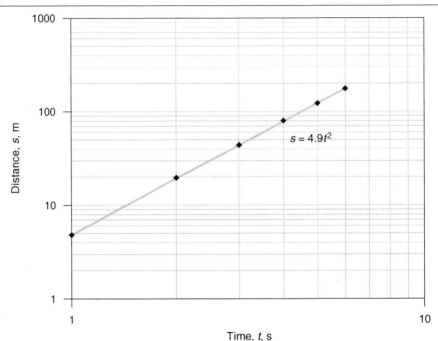

Graph of a free-falling object on log-log paper.

of data on rectangular paper, including the equation of the line. Figure 5.29 is an example of the data plotted on log-log paper with the software providing the equation.

5.9   Empirical Equations: Exponential Curves

Suppose your data do not plot as a straight line on rectangular coordinate paper or the line is not approximately straight on log-log paper. Without experience in analyzing experimental data, you may feel lost about how to proceed. Normally, when experiments are conducted, you have an idea as to how the parameters are related and you are merely trying to quantify that relationship. If you plot your data on semilog graph paper and it produces a reasonably straight line, then it has the general form

$$y = be^{mx} \tag{5.3}$$

Example problem 5.3   Vehicle fuel consumption is recorded as shown in Table 5.6. Determine the best-fit equation for the data by the method of selected points and by the method of least squares.

Procedure

1.   The data (Table 5.6) when plotted on semilog paper produce the graph shown as Fig. 5.30. To determine the constants in the equation $y = be^{mx}$, write it in linear form, either as

$$\log y = mx \log e + \log b$$

Table 5.6

Velocity *V*, m/s	Fuel Consumption (*FC*), mm³/s
10	25.2
20	44.6
30	71.7
40	115
50	202
60	367
70	608

or

$$\ln y = mx + \ln b$$

The method of selected points can now be employed for $\ln FC = mV + \ln b$ (choosing the natural log form). Points $A(15,33)$ and $B(65,470)$ are carefully selected on the line, so they must satisfy the equation. Substituting the values of V and FC at points A and B, we get

$$\ln 470 = 65\,m + \ln b$$

and

$$\ln 33 = 15\,m + \ln b$$

Solving simultaneously for m and b, we have

$$m = 0.0529$$

and

$$b = 14.8$$

Figure 5.30

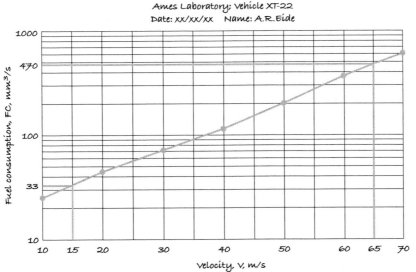

Ames Laboratory; Vehicle XT-22
Date: xx/xx/xx   Name: A.R. Eide

Semilog paper.

Figure 5.31

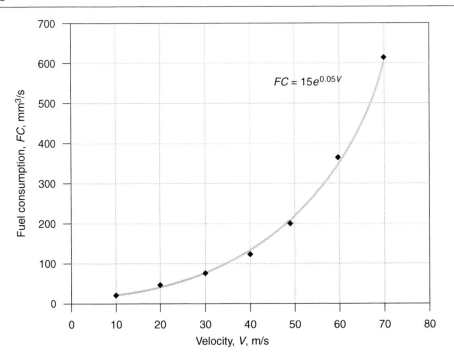

$$FC = 15e^{0.05V}$$

Graph of the fuel consumption of a rocket engine on rectangular graph paper.

The desired equation then is determined to be $FC = 15e^{(0.05V)}$. This determination can be checked by choosing a third point, substituting the value for V, and solving for FC.

2.   A computer-assisted alternate:

The data set can be entered into a spreadsheet, and the software will provide an identical solution. Figure 5.31 illustrates software that provides a plot of data on rectangular paper, including the equation of the line. Figure 5.32 is an example of the data plotted on semilog paper with the software providing the equation.

Problems

5.1   The table shows data from a trial run on the Utah salt flats made by an experimental turbine-powered vehicle.

Time, t, s	Velocity, V, m/s
10.0	15.1
20.0	32.2
30.0	63.4
40.0	84.5
50.0	118.0
60.0	139.0

Figure 5.32

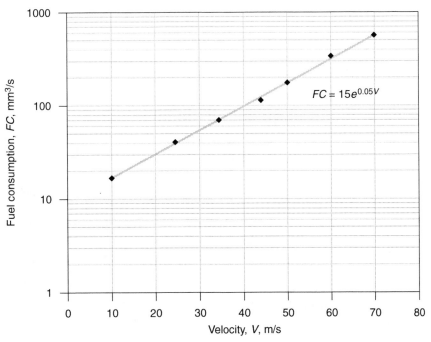

Graph of the fuel consumption of a rocket engine on semilog paper.

(*a*) Plot the data on rectangular graph paper.

(*b*) Determine the equation of the line using the method of selected points.

(*c*) Determine the equation of the line using computer-assisted methods.

(*d*) Interpret the slope of the line.

5.2   The table lists the values of velocity recorded on a ski jump in Colorado this past winter.

Time, *t*, s	Velocity, *V*, m/s
1.0	5.3
4.0	18.1
7.0	26.9
10.0	37.0
14.0	55.2

(*a*) Plot the data on rectangular graph paper.

(*b*) Determine the equation of the line using the method of selected points.

(*c*) Determine the equation of the line using computer-assisted methods.

(*d*) Give the average acceleration.

5.3   Below is a collection of data for an iron-constantan thermocouple. Temperature is in degrees Celsius, and the electromotive force (*emf*) is in millivolts.

Temperature, T, °C	Voltage, *emf*, mV
50.0	2.6
100.0	6.7
150.0	8.8
200.0	11.2
300.0	17.0
400.0	22.5
500.0	26.0
600.0	32.5
700.0	37.7
800.0	41.0
900.0	48.0
1 000.0	55.2

(a) Plot the graph using rectangular graph paper with voltage as the independent variable.

(b) Using the method of selected points, find the equation of the line.

(c) Using computer-assisted methods, find the equation of the line.

5.4 There are design specifications for the minimum sight distance (distance to see an approaching vehicle measured along the roadway from the intersection of the two roadways) that a driver stopped at a stop sign must have to safely enter a roadway where vehicles do not stop. Values in the table below are for safe entry to *cross* the roadway (not to turn onto the other roadway but to cross) where vehicles do not stop.

Major roadway design speed, DS, mph	Sight distance, SD, ft
25	240
30	290
35	335
40	385
45	430
50	480
60	575
65	625
70	670
75	720

(a) Plot a graph with design speed as the independent variable.

(b) Determine the equation of the relationship using the method of selected points.

(c) Determine the equation of the relationship using computer-assisted methods.

(d) Predict the slight distance required at 55 mph.

5.5 A spring was tested in Chicago last Thursday. The test of the spring, X-19, produced the following data.

Deflection, D, mm	Load, L, kN
2.25	35.0
12.0	80.0
20.0	120.0
28.0	160.0
35.0	200.0
45.0	250.0
55.0	300.0

(a) Plot the data on rectangular graph paper and determine the equation that expresses the deflection to be expected under a given load. Use both the method of selected points and computer-assisted methods.

(b) Predict the load required to produce a deflection of 75 mm.

(c) What load would be expected to produce a deflection of 120 mm?

5.6 An Acme furnace was tested 45 days ago in your hometown to determine the heat generated, expressed in thousands of British thermal units per cubic foot of furnace volume at varying temperatures. The results are shown in the table.

Heat released, H, 10^3 Btu/ft^3	Temperature, T, °F
0.200	172
0.600	241
2.00	392
4.00	483
8.00	608
20.00	812
40.00	959
80.00	1 305

(a) Plot the data on log-log paper with temperature as the independent variable.

(b) Using the method of selected points, determine the equation that best fits the data.

(c) Using computer-assisted methods, plot the graph and determine the equation of the line.

5.7 The capacity of a 20-cm screw conveyor that is moving dry corn is expressed in liters per second and the conveyor speed in revolutions per minute. A test was conducted in Rock Island, IL, on conveyor model JD172 last week. The results of the test are given below.

Capacity, C, L/s	Angular velocity, V, r/min
3.01	10.0
6.07	21.0
15.0	58.2
30.0	140.6
50.0	245.0
80.0	410.0
110.0	521.0

(a) Plot the data on log-log paper with angular velocity as the independent variable.

(b) Determine the equation that expresses capacity as a function of angular velocity using the method of selected points.

(c) Repeat (a) and (b) using computer-assisted methods.

5.8 Electrical resistance for a given material can be a function of both area/unit thickness and material temperature. Holding temperature constant, a range of areas are tested to determine resistance. The measured resistance recorded in the table is expressed in milliohms per meter of conductor length.

127
Problems

Area, A, mm²	Resistance, R, mV/m
0.05	500
0.1	260
0.2	165
0.5	80
1.0	58
3.0	22
5.0	15
10	9.0

(a) Plot the data on rectangular graph paper with area as the independent variable.

(b) Plot the data on log-log graph paper with area as the independent variable.

(c) Plot the data on semilog graph paper with area as the independent variable.

(d) Compute equations from these three plots using the method of selected points.

(e) Plot and find equations for parts (a), (b), and (c) using computer-assisted methods.

(f) What would be the best curve fit for this application?

5.9 The area of a circle can be expressed by the formula $A = \pi R^2$. If the radius varies from 0.5 to 5 cm, perform the following:

(a) Construct a table of radius versus area mathematically. Use radius increments of 0.5 cm.

(b) Construct a second table of log R versus log A.

(c) Plot the values from (a) on log-log paper and determine the equation of the line.

(d) Plot the values from (b) on rectangular paper and determine the equation of the line.

(e) Repeat parts (c) and (d) using computer-assisted methods.

5.10 The volume of a sphere is $V = 4/3\pi r^3$.

(a) Prepare a table of volume versus radius allowing the radius to vary from 2.0 to 10.0 cm in 1-cm increments.

(b) Plot a graph on log-log paper showing the relation of volume to radius using the values from the table in part (a) with radius as the independent variable.

(c) Verify the equation given above by the method of selected points.

(d) Repeat parts (b) and (c) using computer-assisted methods.

5.11 A 90° triangular weir is commonly used to measure flow rate in a stream. Data on the discharge through the weir were collected and recorded as shown below.

Height, h, m	Discharge, Q, m³/s
1	1.5
2	8
3	22
4	45
5	78
6	124
7	182
8	254

(a) Plot the data on log-log paper with height as the independent variable.

(b) Determine the equation of the line using the method of selected points.

(c) Plot and determine the equation using computer-assisted methods.

5.12 According to government statistics, the average selling price of a home in the United States varied as follows.

Year, Y	Price, P, $
1965	$21 500
1970	$26 600
1975	$42 600
1980	$76 400
1985	$100 800
1990	$149 800
1995	$158 700
2000	$207 000
2005	$292 200
2010	$265 500

(a) Plot the data on rectangular graph paper and find the best equation using the method of selected points.

(b) Plot the data on semilog paper and find the best equation using the method of selected points.

(c) Prepare linear and semilog plots using a computer-assisted method and determine the best equations for each.

(d) Which curve fit, linear or exponential, best fits these data?

5.13 The density of air is known to change with the temperature of the air. In a lab test, the following data were measured and recorded.

Temperature, T, K	Density, D, kg/m³
100	3.5
200	1.7
400	0.85
600	0.6
800	0.45
1 000	0.35
1 200	0.3
1 400	0.25
1 600	0.2

(a) Plot these data on linear, semilog, and log-log paper with temperature as the independent variable.

(b) Determine the equation that best fits these data using the method of selected points.

(c) Repeat parts (a) and (b) using a computer-assisted method.

5.14 Voltage across a capacitor during discharge was recorded as a function of time as shown below.

Time, t, s	Voltage, V, V
6	98
10	62
17	23
25	9.5
32	3.5
38	1.9
42	1.3

(a) Plot the data on semilog paper with time as the independent variable.

(b) Determine the equation of the line best representing the points using the method of selected points.

(c) Repeat parts (a) and (b) using a computer-assisted method.

5.15 When a capacitor is being discharged, the current flows until the voltage across the capacitor is zero. This current flow, when measured as a function of time, resulted in the data given in the following table.

Time, t, s	Current, I, A
0.1	1.81
0.2	1.64
0.3	1.48
0.4	1.34
0.5	1.21
1.0	0.73

(a) Plot the data on semilog paper with time as the independent variable.

(b) Determine the equation of the line best representing the points using the method of selected points.

(c) Repeat parts (a) and (b) using a computer-assisted method.

5.16 The density of water vapor in air changes rapidly with the change in air temperature. Data were recorded from an experimental test and are shown in the following table.

Air Temperature, T, K	Water Vapor Density, D, kg/m^3
400	0.55
450	0.49
500	0.44
550	0.39
600	0.36
650	0.34
700	0.33
750	0.29
800	0.27

(a) Plot the data on linear, semilog, and log-log paper with the air temperature as the independent variable.

(b) By the method of selected points, find the best equation relating water vapor density to air temperature.

(c) Repeat parts (a) and (b) using a computer-assisted method.

5.17 All materials are elastic to some extent. It is desirable that a part compresses when a load is applied to assist in making an airtight seal (e.g., a jar lid). The results in the following table are from a test conducted at the Smith Test Labs in Seattle on a material known as Zecon 5.

Pressure, P, MPa	Relative compression, R, %
1.12	27.3
3.08	37.6
5.25	46.0
8.75	50.6
12.3	56.1
16.1	59.2
30.2	65.0

(a) Plot the data on semilog and log-log paper with pressure as the independent variable.

(b) Using the method of selected points, determine the best equation to fit these data.

(c) Using a computer-assisted method, repeat the steps above.

(d) What pressure would cause compression of 10%?

5.18 The rate of absorption of radiation by metal plates varies with the plate thickness and the nature of the source of radiation. A test was conducted at Ames Labs on October 11, 2005, using a Geiger counter and a constant source of radiation; the results are shown in the following table.

Plate thickness, W, mm	Counter, C, counts per second
0.20	5 500
5.00	3 720
10.0	2 550
20.0	1 320
27.5	720
32.5	480

(a) Plot the data on semilog graph paper with plate thickness as the independent variable.

(b) Find the equation of the relationship between the parameters using the method of selected points.

(c) Repeat parts (a) and (b) using a computer-assisted method.

(d) What would you expect the counts per second to be for a 2-in.-thick plate of the metal used in the test?

5.19 It is expected that power functions represent the surface area and volume of a certain geometric shape. The values of the surface area and volume are given in the table below:

Radius, R, ft	Surface Area, SA, ft^2	Volume, V, ft^3
1	12.6	4.19
2	50.3	33.5
3	113	113
4	200	268
5	314	524
6	450	905
7	616	1 437
8	800	2 145
9	1 018	3 054
10	1 257	4 189

(a) Using a computer-assisted method, determine the equations of SA and V as functions of R.

(b) What is the geometric shape?

5.20 According to the United States Department of Labor, the Consumer Price Index for several household expense items are shown in the table below. The time period 1982–1984 is established as the basis with an index of 100.

Year	Food	Apparel	Housing	Transportation	Medical Care	Total
1995	148.4	132.0	148.5	139.1	220.5	152.4
1996	153.3	131.7	152.8	143.0	228.2	156.9
1997	157.3	132.9	156.8	144.3	234.6	160.5
1998	160.7	133.0	160.4	141.6	242.1	163.0
1999	164.1	131.3	165.9	144.4	250.6	166.6
2000	167.8	129.6	169.6	153.3	260.8	172.2
2001	173.1	127.3	176.4	154.3	272.8	177.1
2002	176.2	124.0	180.3	152.9	285.6	179.9
2003	180.0	120.9	184.8	157.6	297.1	184.0
2004	186.2	120.4	189.5	163.1	310.1	188.9

(*a*) Using a computer-assisted method, plot all of these data on the same graph. Be sure to format the graph according to chapter guidelines.

(*b*) Describe in a couple of paragraphs what the plotted information suggests to you.

5.21 Data from the Federal Reserve, the average prime interest rate, the average home mortgage rate, and the average 6-month CD rate for the years 1972 to 2009 are shown in the table below:

Year	Ave. prime rate, %	Ave. mortgage rate, %	Ave. 6-month CD rate, %
1972	5.25	7.38	5.01
1973	8.03	8.04	9.05
1974	10.81	9.19	10.02
1975	7.86	9.04	6.9
1976	6.84	8.86	5.63
1977	6.83	8.84	5.91
1978	9.06	9.63	8.6
1979	12.67	11.19	11.42
1980	15.26	13.77	12.94
1981	18.87	16.63	15.79
1982	14.85	16.08	12.57
1983	10.79	13.23	9.28
1984	12.04	13.87	10.71
1985	9.93	12.42	8.24
1986	8.33	10.18	6.5
1987	8.21	10.2	7.01
1988	9.32	10.34	7.91
1989	10.87	10.32	9.08
1990	10.01	10.13	8.17
1991	8.46	9.25	5.91
1992	6.25	8.4	3.76
1993	6	7.33	3.28
1994	7.15	8.35	4.96
1995	8.83	7.95	5.98
1996	8.27	7.8	5.47
1997	8.44	7.6	5.73
1998	8.35	6.94	5.44
1999	8	7.43	5.46
2000	9.23	8.06	6.59
2001	6.91	6.97	3.66
2002	4.67	6.54	1.81
2003	4.12	5.82	1.17
2004	4.34	5.84	1.74
2005	6.19	5.86	3.73
2006	7.96	6.41	5.24
2007	8.05	6.34	5.23
2008	5.09	6.04	3.14
2009	3.25	5.04	0.87

(a) Using a computer-assisted method, plot all of these data on the same graph. Be sure to format the graph according to chapter guidelines.

(b) In a short narrative, describe in general terms the relationship among the three interest rates as you see it from your graph.

Source: http://www.federalreserve.gov/releases/h15/data.htm

5.22 Performance data for an experimental truck engine were recorded in a recent laboratory test as shown in the table below.

Engine speed, R, rpm	Rated power output, P, bhp	Full load torque, T, ft-lb	Fuel consumption, F, gal/hr
800	148	959	3.2
900	203	1 155	5.3
1 000	249	1 341	6.3
1 100	330	1 601	8.4
1 200	414	1 762	10.3
1 300	499	2 012	13.5
1 400	545	2 072	16.6
1 500	589	2 049	19.2
1 600	605	2 028	22.9
1 700	644	1 981	27.3
1 800	670	1 919	34.1

As a team

(a) Plot each data set on linear, semilog, and log-log graph paper with engine speed as the independent variable.

(b) Using the method of selected points, compute the best equation fit to these data.

(c) Repeat parts (a) and (b) using computer-assisted methods.

(d) Discuss your results in a form that could be understood by other engineering students who have not solved this problem.

Hint: For data that plot as a convex upward curve, try reversing the independent and dependent variables in a plot before applying a curve fitting method. Once the equation has been found, simply solve for the desired dependent variable as a function of the independent variable.

5.23 As a team, conduct an Internet search for data in a technical field of interest to your team that can be graphed by a computer-assisted method. Find a data set (or sets) of a size that would be difficult to enter by hand, download the data, and directly enter them into your graphing software.

For each set, prepare a graph that follows engineering graphing standards as closely as your software allows. Within the graph, demonstrate the following:

- Multiple curves on a graph complete with a legend
- Two separate *y*-axes

Provide documentation to include:

- Explanation and interpretation of the data you selected
- Source of data
- Hard copy from your software with data and graph

CHAPTER **10**

Statistics

Chapter Objectives

When you complete your study of this chapter, you will able to:

- Analyze a wide variety of data sets using descriptive techniques (mean, mode, variance, standard deviation, and correlation)
- Learn to apply the appropriate descriptive statistical techniques in a variety of situations
- Create graphical representations of individual and grouped data points with graphs and histograms
- Make inferences about the relationship between two variables via linear regression analysis
- Determine the strength of linear relationships by calculating and interpreting the correlation coefficient

10.1 Introduction

Statistics, as used by the engineer, can most logically be called a branch of applied mathematics. It constitutes what some call the science of decision making in a world full of uncertainty. In fact, some degree of uncertainty exists in most day-to-day activities, from a simple coin toss or the outcome of a ball game to the results of an election or the relative efficiency of various production processes.

It would be virtually impossible to understand a great deal of the work done in engineering without having a thorough knowledge of statistics. Numerical data derived from surveys and experiments constitute the raw material upon which interpretations, analyses, and decisions are based; it is essential that engineers learn how to properly use the information derived from such data. Everything concerned even remotely with the collection, processing, analysis, interpretation, and presentation of numerical data belongs to the domain of statistics.

There exist today a number of different and interesting stories about the origin of statistics, but most historians believe it can be traced to two dissimilar areas: games of chance and political science. Figure 10.1 illustrates but one of a multitude of familiar games that are associated with a statistical probability.

Figure 10.1

During the eighteenth century, various games of chance involving the mathematical treatment of errors led to the study of probability and, ultimately, to the foundation of statistics. At approximately the same time, an interest in the description and analysis of the voting of political parties led to the development of methods that today fall under the category of *descriptive statistics,* which is basically designed to summarize or describe important features of a set of data without attempting to infer conclusions that go beyond the data.

Descriptive statistics is an important sector of the entire subject area; it is used whenever a person wishes to represent data derived from observation.

10.2 Frequency Distribution

Imagine that you've been given a very large set of data. Unless the information can be appropriately summarized, it will be very difficult to interpret. That is precisely why statistics is so important. Even though raw data contain a lot of information, it is not very meaningful because people have a limited capacity to absorb, remember, sort, and interpret a collection of disparate information. In order to convey meaning, it is necessary to summarize the data.

A frequency distribution is a systematic collection of data illustrating the number of times a given value or collection of values occurs. Frequency distributions can be graphically represented as data curves, bar graphs, scattergrams, histograms, frequency polygrams, and so forth.

Table 10.1

27.2	13.9	40.1	25.9	17.7
4.1	32.3	32.2	22.9	15.6
15.4	36.4	24.1	5.3	12.1
32.9	24.2	19.2	14.5	28.9
21.3	28.8	27.1	8.7	25.2
15.2	19.1	16.5	17.9	12.3
20.9	22.1	21.2	10.8	11.9
35.2	30.2	30.7	37.1	16.3
19.9	20.8	25.6	30.3	21.6

Table 10.2

Range	Tally	Frequency
4.0–8.9	III	3
9.0–13.9	ℍℕ	5
14.0–18.9	ℍℕ III	8
19.0–23.9	ℍℕ ℍℕ	10
24.0–28.9	ℍℕ IIII	9
29.0–33.9	ℍℕ I	6
34.0–38.9	III	3
39.0–43.9	I	1

Various ways of describing measurements and observations, such as the grouping and classifying of data, are a fundamental part of statistics. In fact, when dealing with a large set of collected numbers, a good overall picture of the data can often be conveyed by proper grouping into classes. The following examples will serve to illustrate this point.

Consider the percentage of body fat in 45 men under the age of 50 listed in Table 10.1. Table 10.2 is one possible numerical arrangement showing percentage of body fat distributed among selected classes. Some information such as the highest and lowest values will be lost once the raw data have been sorted and grouped.

The construction of numerical distributions as in this example normally consists of the following series of steps: select classes into which the data are to be grouped, distribute data into appropriate classes, and count the number of items in each class. Since the last two steps are essentially mechanical processes, our attention will be directed primarily toward the *classification* of data.

Two things must be considered when arranging data into classes: the number of classes into which the data are to be grouped and the range of values each class is to cover. Both these areas are somewhat arbitrary, but they do depend on the nature of the data and the ultimate purpose the distribution is to serve.

The following are guidelines that should be followed when constructing a frequency distribution.

1. Use no fewer than six and no more than 15 classes. The square root of *n*, where *n* is the number of data points, provides an approximate number of classes to consider.

Figure 10.2

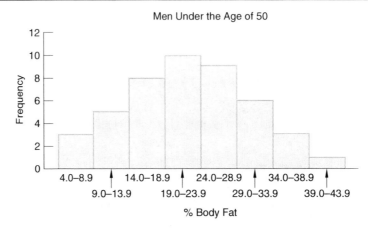

2. Select classes that will accommodate all the data points.
3. Make sure that each data point fits into only one class.
4. Whenever possible, make the class intervals of equal length.

The numbers in the right-hand column of Table 10.2 are called the *class frequencies*, which denote the number of items that are in each class. Since frequency distributions are constructed primarily to condense large sets of data into more easily understood forms, it is logical to display or present that data graphically. The most common form of graphical presentation is called the *histogram*. It is constructed by representing measurements or grouped observations on the horizontal axis and class frequencies along the graduated and calibrated vertical axis. This representation affords a graphical picture of the distribution with vertical bars whose bases equal the class intervals and whose heights are determined by the corresponding class frequencies. Figure 10.2 demonstrates a histogram of the percentage of body fat measures tabulated in Table 10.2.

10.3   Measures of Central Tendency

The solution of many engineering problems in which a large set of data is collected can be facilitated by the determination of single numbers that describe unique characteristics about the data. The most popular measure of this type is called the arithmetic mean or average.

The arithmetic mean, or *mean* of a set of *n* numbers, is defined as the sum of the numbers divided by *n*. In order to develop a notation and a simple formula for arithmetic mean, it is helpful to use an example.

Suppose that the mean height of a starting basketball team is to be determined. Let the height in general be represented by the letter x and the height of each individual player be represented by $x_1, x_2, x_3, x_4,$ and x_5. More generally, there are *n* measurements that are designated $x_1, x_2, \ldots, x_n$. From this notation, the mean can be written as follows:

$$\text{Mean} = \frac{x_1 + x_2 + x_3 + \cdots + x_n}{n}$$

A mathematical notation that indicates the summation of a series of numbers is normally written

$$\sum_{i=1}^{n} x_i$$

which represents $x_1 + x_2 + x_3 + \ldots + x_n$. This notation will be written in the remainder of the chapter as Σx_i but the intended summation will be from 1 to n.

To distinguish between descriptive measures for a population and for a sample we will use different symbols. When a set of all possible observations is used, it is referred to as the *population*. For the mean or average, we will use mu (μ) to represent the mean of a population.

When a portion or subset of that population is used, it is referred to as a *sample*. The notation for arithmetic mean will be $\bar{x}$ (read xbar) when the x values are representative of a random sample and not an entire population.

The standard notations discussed above provide the following common expressions for the arithmetic mean of the population and of a sample:

$$\mu = \frac{\Sigma x_i}{n} \text{ (population)} \tag{10.1a}$$

$$\bar{x} = \frac{\Sigma x_i}{n} \text{ (sample)} \tag{10.1b}$$

where the sum for the population is over all members of the population, whereas for the sample the sum is just the members of the sample.

The mean is a popular measure of central tendency because (1) it is familiar to most people, (2) it takes into account every item, (3) it always exists, (4) it is always unique, and (5) it lends itself to further statistical manipulations.

One disadvantage of the arithmetic mean, however, is that any outlier or gross error in a number can have a pronounced effect on the value of the mean. To avoid this difficulty, it is possible to describe the "center" of a set of data with other kinds of statistical descriptions. One of these is called the *median*, which can be defined as the value of the middle item of data arranged in increasing or decreasing order of magnitude. For example, the median of the five numbers 15, 27, 10, 18, and 22 can be determined by first arranging them in increasing order: 10, 15, 18, 22, and 27. The median or middle number for this series is 18.

If a data set contains an even number of items, there is never a specific middle item, so the median is defined as the mean of the values of the two middle items. For example, the median of the six numbers 5, 9, 11, 13, 16, and 19 is (11 + 13)/2, or 12.

The mean and median of a set of data rarely coincide. Both terms describe the center of a set of data, but in different ways. The median divides the data so that half of all entries are greater than or equal to the median; the mean may be thought of as the center of gravity of the data.

The median, like the mean, has certain desirable properties. It always exists and is always unique. Unlike the mean, the median is not affected by extreme values. If the exclusion of the highest and lowest values causes a significant change in the mean, then the median should be considered as the indicator of central tendency of that data.

In addition to the mean and the median, there is one other average, or center, of a set of data, which we call the *mode*. It is simply the value that occurs with the highest frequency. In the set of numbers 18, 19, 15, 17, 18, 14, 17, 18, 20, 19, 21, and 14, the number 18 is the mode because it appears more often than any of the other values. There may exist more than one mode, for example, if there were an equal number of 18's and 19's in the above data set, there would be two modes; therefore the data set would be bimodal.

An important point for a practicing engineer to remember is that there are any number of ways to suggest the middle, center, or average value of a data set. If comparisons are to be made, it is essential that similar methods be compared. It is only logical to compare the mean of brand A with the mean of brand B, not the mean of one with the median of the other. If one particular item, brand, or process is to be compared with another, the same measures must be used. If the average grade in one section of college calculus is to be compared with the average grade in other sections, the mean of each section would be the important statistic.

10.4 Measures of Variation

It is possible, but not likely, that the mean values of the course grades of different sections of college calculus will be of equal magnitude. However, mean values are only one measure of importance; another is variation.

Measures of variation indicate the degree to which data are dispersed— that is, how much they are spread out or bunched together. Suppose that by coincidence two sections of a college calculus course have exactly the same mean grade values on the first hour exam. It would be of interest to know how far individual scores varied from the mean. Perhaps one class was bunched very closely around the mean, while the other class demonstrated a wide variation, with some very high scores and some very low scores. This situation is typical and is often of interest to the engineer.

It is reasonable to define this variation in terms of how much each number in the sample deviates from the mean value of the sample, that is, $x_1 - \bar{x}$, $x_2 - \bar{x}$, ... $x_n - \bar{x}$. If you wanted an average deviation from the mean you might try adding $x_1 - \bar{x}$ through $x_n - \bar{x}$ and dividing by n. But this does not give a useful result, since the sum of the deviations is always zero. The procedure generally followed is to square each deviation, sum the resulting squares, divide the sum by n, and take the square root. By definition, the formula for the standard deviation of the entire population is

$$\sigma = \left[\frac{\Sigma(x_i - \mu)^2}{n} \right]^{1/2} \text{(population standard deviation)} \qquad (10.2)$$

Statistical procedures used in most engineering applications are concerned with the standard deviation of a sample (s), which can then be used to estimate the standard deviation in the whole population (σ).

To compute the standard deviation of a sample (s), we must alter formula 10.2 in two ways. First we use the mean of the sample ($\bar{x}$) instead of the population mean (μ) and second we replace n in the denominator with $n - 1$. It has been determined that when using just a sample of the population the resulting value of (s) represents a "better" estimate of the true standard deviation of the entire population. To clarify, when a sample size is less than 30, dividing by $n - 1$ has more influence on the calculated value of s. The difference in the calculated value of s when using n or $n - 1$ in the denominator decreases when the sample size is larger.

$$s = \left[\frac{\Sigma(x_i - \bar{x})^2}{n - 1} \right]^{1/2} \text{ (sample standard deviation)} \tag{10.3}$$

Throughout this book, we will use n in the denominator for population standard deviations and $(n - 1)$ in the denominator for all sample standard deviations. Although you may encounter either n or $n - 1$ in the denominator in various textbooks, most calculator and spreadsheet software will use $n - 1$ for sample standard deviations.

An alternate form of Eq. (10.3) that is sometimes easier to use is derived by expanding $(x_i - \bar{x})^2$, substituting for $\bar{x}$ from Eq. (10.1b), and reducing terms. The result is as follows.

$$s = \left[\frac{n(\Sigma x_i^2) - (\Sigma x_i)^2}{n(n - 1)} \right]^{1/2} \text{ (alternate sample standard deviation)} \tag{10.4}$$

Another common measure of variation is actually called the *variance*; it is the square of the standard deviation. Therefore, the sample variance is given by

$$s^2 = \frac{\Sigma(x_i - \bar{x})^2}{n - 1} \tag{10.5}$$

Example Problem 10.1   A Midwestern university campus has 10 540 male students. Using a random selection process, 50 of these students were chosen and weighed to the nearest pound (pound-mass); the raw data were as recorded in Table 10.3. The data were then grouped (Table 10.4), and the histogram in Figure 10.3 was constructed. Calculate the sample mean, sample standard deviation, and sample variance of the data.

Solution   From Eq. (10.1b) the sample mean can be calculated (summary of computations shown in Table 10.5):

$$\bar{x} = \frac{\Sigma x_i}{n} = \frac{8037}{50}$$
$$= 160.74 \text{ lbm} = 161 \text{ lbm}$$

From Eq. (10.3) the sample standard deviation can be determined:

Table 10.3

164	171	154	160	158	150	159	185	168	158
143	159	162	165	160	167	166	164	152	172
177	165	170	155	155	163	180	157	145	160
149	153	137	173	157	175	163	147	156	156
162	167	165	166	162	136	158	170	162	159

Table 10.4

Range	Frequency
136–140	2
141–145	2
146–150	3
151–155	5
156–160	13
161–165	11
166–170	7
171–175	4
176–180	2
181–185	1
	50

$$s = \left[\frac{\Sigma(x_i - \bar{x})^2}{n - 1}\right]^{1/2} = \left[\frac{4\,793.73}{49}\right]^{1/2} = 9.89\,\text{lbm}$$

The sample standard deviation can also be determined from Eq. (10.4):

$$s = \left[\frac{n(\Sigma x_i^2) - (\Sigma x_i)^2}{n(n - 1)}\right]^{1/2} = \left[\frac{50(1\,296\,661) - (8037)^2}{50(49)}\right]^{1/2} = 9.89\,\text{lbm}$$

The sample variance can be calculated by squaring Eq. (10.3):

$$s^2 = \frac{\Sigma(x_i - \bar{x})^2}{n - 1}$$

$$s^2 = \frac{4\,793.74}{49} = 97.8\,\text{lbm}^2$$

By examining the raw data in Example Problem 10.1 we can see the range in variation of values that occurs from a random sample. Certainly we would expect to find both larger and smaller values if all males at the university—that is, the entire population—were weighed. If we were to select additional

Figure 10.3

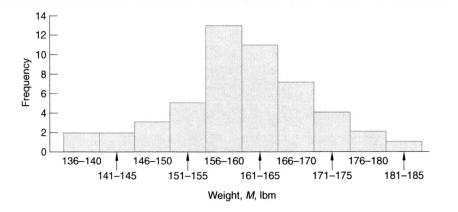

Table 10.5

Mass, x_i, lbm	x_i^2	$x_i - \bar{x}$	$(x_i - \bar{x})^2$
164	26 896	3.26	10.63
143	20 449	−17.74	314.71
177	31 329	16.26	264.39
149	22 201	−11.74	137.83
. . .	. . .	. . .	. . .
156	24 336	−4.74	22.47
159	25 281	−1.74	3.03
8 037	1 296 661	0.00	4 793.73

random values and develop a second sample from the population, we would expect to find a different sample mean and a different sample standard deviation. We would not expect, however, the differences in these measures of central tendency and variation to be significant if the two samples were truly random in nature.

Example Problem 10.2   Interstate Safety Corridors are established on certain roadways with a propensity for strong cross winds, blowing dust, and frequent fatal accidents. A driver is expected to turn on the headlights and pay special attention to the posted speed limit in these corridors. In one such Safety Corridor in northern New Mexico, the posted speed limit is 75 miles per hour. The Department of Public Safety set up a radar checkpoint and the actual speed of 36 vehicles that passed the checkpoint is shown in Table 10.6.

For this data set, use a hand calculation or spreadsheet software to solve parts c, d, and e.
  (a) Make a frequency distribution table using 5 as a class width (e.g., 60.0-64.9)
  (b) Construct a histogram from the frequency distribution
  (c) The sample mean

Table 10.6

70	78	70	80	86	76
85	69	68	61	81	80
71	82	69	71	62	71
75	76	85	72	63	72
65	90	77	89	76	70
66	78	91	69	80	92

Table 10.7

Interval	Frequency
60-64.9	3
65-69.9	6
70-74.9	8
75-79.9	7
80-84.9	5
85-89.9	4
90-94.5	3

(d) The sample standard deviation
(e) The sample variance
(f) If speeding tickets are issued to drivers exceeding 84 mph, what percentage of drivers in this sample would receive tickets?

Solution   A spreadsheet can be used to solve this problem; however, the equations presented in the text material are representative of the theory necessary to determine mean, standard deviation, and variance. A critical step in the use of packaged software is to thoroughly understand how the numbers provided by these packages are calculated.

(a) The data from Table 10.6 was grouped into the frequency distribution shown in Table 10.7.

(b) A histogram was developed using Excel and is shown in Figure 10.4. To determine the sample mean, standard deviation, and variance an Excel spreadsheet was developed in Figure 10.5. This spreadsheet quickly provides the required sums for the equations below. In addition, you may verify that your calculations are correct using the statistical formulas within Excel.

Figure 10.4

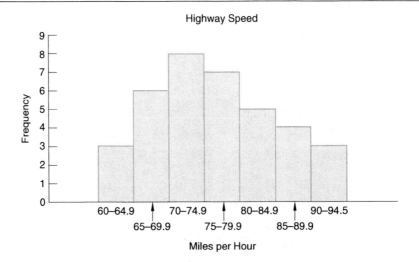

Figure 10.5

	A	B	C
1		Speed	Speed squared
2		70	4 900
3		85	7 225
4		71	5 041
5		75	5 625
6		65	4 225
7		66	4 356
8		78	6 084
9		69	4 761
10		82	6 724
11		76	5 776
12		90	8 100
13		78	6 084
14		70	4 900
15		68	4 624
16		69	4 761
17		85	7 225
18		77	5 929
19		91	8 281
20		80	6 400
21		61	3 721
22		71	5 041
23		72	5 184
24		89	7 921
25		69	4 761
26		86	7 396
27		81	6 561
28		62	3 844
29		63	3 969
30		76	5 776
31		80	6 400
32		76	5 776
33		80	6 400
34		71	5 041
35		72	5 184
36		70	4 900
37		92	8 464
38	Sum	2 716	20 7360
39	Average	75.4444444	Excel software
40	Std Dev	8.3715315	Excel software
41	Variance	70.0825397	Excel software

Excel Spreadsheet—Highway Safety Corridors

(c) The sample mean

$$\bar{x} = \frac{\Sigma x_i}{n} = \frac{2\,716}{36} = 75.44$$

(d) The sample standard deviation

$$s = \left[\frac{n(\Sigma x_i^2) - (\Sigma x_i)^2}{n(n-1)} \right]^{1/2} = \left[\frac{36(207\,360) - (2\,716)^2}{36(35)} \right]^{1/2} = 8.371\,5$$

(e) The sample variance

$$s^2 = 70.082\,5$$

(f) Speeding tickets issued
7/36 drivers are exceeding 84 mph, therefore 19% would be issued
tickets

10.5   Linear Regression

There are many occasions in engineering analysis when the ability to predict or forecast the outcome of a certain event is extremely valuable. The difficulty with most practical applications is the large number of variables that may influence the analysis process. Regression analysis is a study of the relationships among variables. If the situation results in a relationship among three or more variables, the study is called *multiple regression*. There are many problems, however, that can be reduced to a relationship between an independent and a dependent variable. This introduction will limit the subject and treat only two-variable regression analyses.

Of the many equations that can be used for the purposes of prediction, the simplest and most widely used is a linear equation of the form $y = mx + b$, where m and b are constants. Once the constants have been determined, it is possible to calculate a predicted value of y (dependent variable) for any value of x (independent variable).

Before investigating the regression concept in more detail, we must examine how the regression equation is established.

If there is a reason to believe that a relationship exists between two variables, the first step is to collect data. For example, suppose x denotes the age of an automobile in years and y denotes the annual maintenance cost. Thus, a sample of n cars would reveal the age $x_1, x_2, x_3, \ldots, x_n$ and the corresponding annual maintenance cost $y_1, y_2, y_3, \ldots, y_n$.

The next step would be to plot the data on rectangular coordinate paper or by using a spreadsheet. The resulting graph is called a *scatter diagram*.

From the scatter diagram shown in Figure 10.6, it may be possible to construct a straight line that adequately represents the data, in which case a linear relationship exists between the variables. In other cases, the line may be curved, and the relationship between variables will therefore be nonlinear in nature.

Ideally, we would hope to determine the best possible line (straight or curved) through the points. A standard approach to this problem is called the *method of least squares*.

To demonstrate how the process works, as well as to explain the concept of the method of least squares, consider the following situation. A class of 20 students is given a math test and the resulting scores are recorded. Each student's IQ score is also available. Both scores for the 20 students are shown in Table 10.8.

First, the data must be plotted on rectangular coordinate paper (see Figure 10.7). As you can see by observing the plotted data, there is no limit to the number of straight lines that could be drawn through the points. In order to find the line of best fit, it is necessary to state what is meant by "best." The method of least squares requires that the sum of the squares $\Sigma(y - y')^2$ of the vertical deviations from the data points (y) to the straight line (y') be minimized. This vertical deviation $(y - y')^2$ is also called a residual (see Figure 10.8).

Figure 10.6

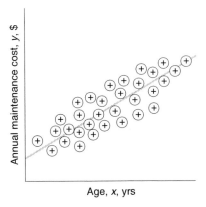

To demonstrate how a least-squared line is fit to data, let us consider this problem further. There are n pairs of numbers $(x_1, y_1), (x_2, y_2), \ldots, (x_n, y_n)$, where $n = 20$, with x and y being IQ and math scores, respectively. Suppose that the equation of the line that best fits the data is of the form

$$y' = mx + b \tag{10.6}$$

where the symbol y' (y prime) is used to differentiate between the observed values of y and the corresponding values calculated by means of the equation of the line. (Note that although y' is sometimes used to represent a derivative in calculus, it is not a derivative here, rather a computed value on the line being sought.) In other words, for each value of x, there exist an observed value (y) and a calculated value (y') obtained by substituting x into the equation $y' = mx + b$.

Table 10.8

Student No.	Math Score	IQ	Student No.	Math Score	IQ
1	85	120	11	100	130
2	62	115	12	85	130
3	60	100	13	77	118
4	95	140	14	63	112
5	80	130	15	70	122
6	75	120	16	90	128
7	90	130	17	80	125
8	60	108	18	100	140
9	70	115	19	95	135
10	80	118	20	75	130

Figure 10.7

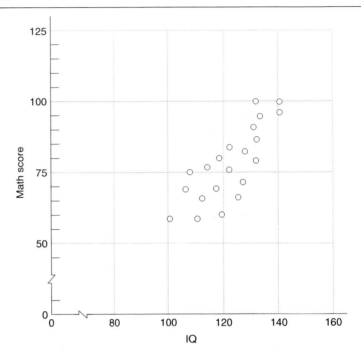

Figure 10.8

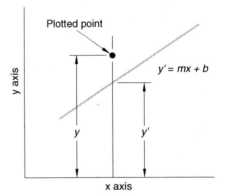

The least-squares criterion requires that the sum of all $(y - y')^2$ terms, as illustrated in Figure 10.8, be the smallest possible. One must determine the constants m and b so that the difference between the observed and the predicted values of y will be minimized.

When this analysis is applied to the linear equation $y = mx + b$, it follows that we wish to minimize the summation of all deviations (residuals):

$$SUM = \Sigma[y_i - (mx_i + b)]^2 \tag{10.7}$$

From the calculus, to minimize *SUM*, the partial derivatives with respect to *m* and *b* must be zero as follows:

$$\frac{\partial(SUM)}{\partial m} = \frac{\partial}{\partial m}\{\Sigma[y_i - (mx_i + b)]^2\} = 0$$

$$\frac{\partial(SUM)}{\partial b} = \frac{\partial}{\partial b}\{\Sigma[y_i - (mx_i + b)]^2\} = 0$$

Performing these partial derivatives gives

$$nb + m\Sigma x_i = \Sigma y_i$$

$$b\Sigma x_i + m\Sigma x_i 2 = \Sigma x_i y_i$$

Solving these two equations simultaneously for *m* and *b* gives

$$m = \frac{n(\Sigma x_i y_i) - (\Sigma x_i)(\Sigma y_i)}{n(\Sigma x_i^2) - (\Sigma x_i)^2} \tag{10.8}$$

$$b = \frac{\Sigma y_i - m(\Sigma x_i)}{n} \tag{10.9}$$

Table 10.9 is a tabulation of the values necessary to determine the constants *m* and *b* for the math score–IQ problem. The independent variable is the IQ, and the dependent variable is the math score.

Substituting the values from Table 10.9 into Eqs. (10.8) and (10.9), we get the following values for the two constants:

$$m = \frac{20(198\ 527) - (2\ 466)(1\ 592)}{20(306\ 124) - (2\ 466)^2}$$

$$= 1.080\ 9$$

$$b = \frac{1\ 592 - (1.080\ 9)(2\ 466)}{20}$$

$$= -53.67$$

The equation of the line relating math score and IQ using the method of least squares becomes

$$\text{Math score} = 1.08\ (\text{IQ}) - 53.67$$

Interesting questions arise from this problem. Can IQ be used to predict success on a math exam and, if so, how well? Regression analysis or estimation of one variable (dependent) from one or more related variables (independent) does not provide information about the strength of the relationship. Later in this chapter we will suggest a method to determine how well an equation developed from the method of least squares describes the strength of the relationship between variables.

The method of least squares as just explained is a most appropriate technique for determining the best-fit line. You should clearly understand that this method as presented is *linear regression* and is valid only for *linear* relationships. The technique of least squares can, however, be applied to power ($y = bx^m$) and exponential ($y = be^{mx}$) relationships if done correctly. The power function can be handled by noting that there is a linear relationship between log *y* and

Table 10.9

Independent Variable		Dependent Variable		
IQ	(IQ)²	Math Score	(Math Score)²	IQ (Math Score)
120	14 400	85	7 225	10 200
115	13 225	62	3 844	7 130
100	10 000	60	3 600	6 000
140	19 600	95	9 025	13 300
130	16 900	80	6 400	10 400
120	14 400	75	5 625	9 000
130	16 900	90	8 100	11 700
108	11 664	60	3 600	6 480
115	13 225	70	4 900	8 050
118	13 924	80	6 400	9 440
130	16 900	100	10 000	13 000
130	16 900	85	7 225	11 050
118	13 924	77	5 929	9 086
112	12 544	63	3 969	7 056
122	14 884	70	4 900	8 540
128	16 384	90	8 100	11 520
125	15 625	80	6 400	10 000
140	19 600	100	10 000	14 000
135	18 225	95	9 025	12 825
130	16 900	75	5 625	9 750
2 466	306 124	1 592	129 892	198 527

$\log x$ ($\log y = m \log x + \log b$, which plots as a straight line on log-log paper). Thus we can apply the method of least squares to the variables $\log y$ and $\log x$ to obtain parameters m and $\log b$.

The exponential function written in natural logarithm form is $\ln y = mx + \ln b$. Therefore, there exists a linear relationship between $\ln y$ and x (this plots as a straight line on semilog paper). The next examples will demonstrate the use of least squares method for power and experimental curves.

Example Problem 10.3   The data in Table 10.10 were obtained from measuring the distance dropped by a falling body with time. We would expect that the distance should be related to the square of the time according to theory (neglecting air friction) $s = 1/2\ gt^2$. Find the equation of the line of best fit.

Solution   The expected form of the equation is $s = bt^m$ or, in logarithmic form, $\log s = m\log t + \log b$. Therefore, if we use $\log t$ in place of x and $\log s$ in place of y in Eqs. (10.8) and (10.9) we can solve for m and $\log b$. (Note carefully that the parameters are m and $\log b$, not m and b.) Refer to Table 10.11.

Substitute into Eq. (10.8):

$$m = \frac{6(5.521\ 9) - (2.857\ 4)(9.855\ 8)}{6(1.774\ 9) - (2.857\ 4)^2}$$

$$= 2.000\ 0$$

Table 10.10

Time t, s	Distance s, m
0	0
1	4.9
2	19.6
3	44.1
4	78.4
5	122.5
6	176.4

Table 10.11

t	s	Independent Variable		Dependent Variable	
		$\log t$	$(\log t)^2$	$\log s$	$(\log t)(\log s)$
1	4.9	0.000 0	0.000 0	0.609 2	0.000 0
2	19.6	0.301 0	0.090 6	1.292 3	0.389 0
3	44.1	0.477 1	0.227 6	1.644 4	0.784 5
4	78.4	0.602 1	0.362 5	1.894 3	1.140 6
5	122.5	0.699 0	0.488 6	2.088 1	1.459 6
6	176.4	0.778 2	0.605 6	2.246 5	1.748 2
		2.857 4	1.774 9	9.855 8	5.521 9

Substitute into Eq. (10.9), using $\log b$, not b:

$$\log b = \frac{9.855\,8 \;-\; (2.000\,0)(2.857\,4)}{6}$$

$$\log b = 0.690\,17$$

$$b = 4.899\,7$$

The equation is then $s = 4.9t^2$

Example Problem 10.4   Using the method of least squares, find the equation that best fits the data shown in Table 10.12.

Solution   This data set produces a straight line when plotted on semilog graph paper; therefore, its equation will be of the form $Q = be^{mV}$ or $\ln Q = mV + \ln b$.

An examination of the equation and the graph paper leads us to the following:

1. Since the line is straight, the method of least squares can be used.
2. Since the abscissa is a uniform scale, the independent variable values (velocity in this problem) may be used without adjustment.
3. Since the ordinate is a log scale, the dependent variable values (fuel consumption) must be the logarithms of the data, not the raw data.

Table 10.12

Fuel Consumption, Q, mm³/s	Velocity, V, m/s
25.2	10.0
44.6	20.0
71.7	30.0
115	40.0
202	50.0
367	60.0
608	70.0

Table 10.13

Independent Variable		Dependent Variable	
v	v²	ln Q	v(ln Q)
10	100	3.226 8	32.27
20	400	3.797 7	75.95
30	900	4.272 5	128.17
40	1 600	4.744 9	189.80
50	2 500	5.308 3	265.41
60	3 600	5.905 4	354.32
70	4 900	6.410 2	448.71
280	14 000	33.665 8	1 494.63

Table 10.13 provides us with the needed values to substitute into Eqs. (10.8) and (10.9). Substitute into Eq. (10.8):

$$m = \frac{7(1\,494.63) - (280)(33.665\,8)}{7(14\,000) - (280)^2}$$

$$= 0.052\,86$$

Substitute into Eq. (10.9), using ln b rather than b:

$$\ln b = \frac{33.665\,8 - (0.052\,86)(280)}{7}$$

$$= 2.695\,0$$

$$b = 14.805$$

The equation becomes $Q = 14.8\,e^{0.053V}$

10.6 Coefficient of Correlation

The technique of finding the best possible straight line to fit experimentally collected data is certainly useful, as previously discussed. The next logical and interesting question is how well such a line actually fits. It stands to reason that if the differences between the observed y's and the calculated y's are small, the sum of squares $\Sigma(y - y')^2$ will be small; and if the differences are large, the sum of squares will tend to be large.

Figure 10.9

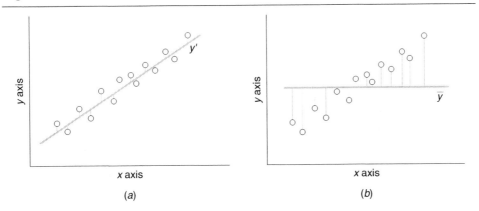

(a)   (b)

Although $\Sigma(y - y')^2$ provides an indication of how well a least-squares line fits particular data, it has the disadvantage that it depends on the units of y. For example, if the units of y are changed from dollars to cents, it will be like multiplying $\Sigma(y - y')^2$ by a factor of 10 000. To avoid this difficulty, the magnitude of $\Sigma(y - y')^2$ is normally compared with $\Sigma(y - y')^2$. This allows the sum of the squares of the vertical deviations from the least-squares line to be compared with the sum of squares of the deviations of the y's from the mean.

To illustrate, Figure 10.9a shows the vertical deviation of the y's from the least-squares line, while Figure 10.9b shows the deviations of the y's from their collective mean. It is apparent that where there is a close fit, $\Sigma(y - y')^2$ is much smaller than $\Sigma(y - y')^2$.

In contrast, consider Figure 10.10. Again, Figure 10.10a shows the vertical deviation of the y's from the least-squares line, and Figure 10.10b shows the deviation of the y's from their mean. In this case, $\Sigma(y - y')^2$ is approximately the same as $\Sigma(y - y')^2$. This would seem to indicate that if the fit is good, as in Figure 10.9, $\Sigma(y - y')^2$ is much less than $\Sigma(y - y')^2$; and if the fit is as poor as in Figure 10.10, the two sums of squares are approximately equal.

Figure 10.10

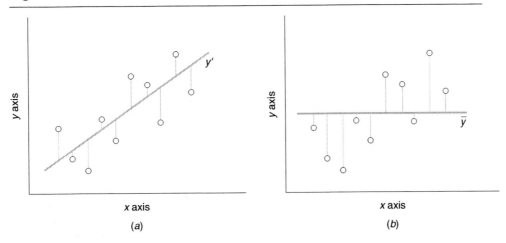

(a)   (b)

The coefficient of correlation puts this comparison on a precise basis:

$$r = \pm \sqrt{1 - \frac{\Sigma(y_i - y')^2}{\Sigma(y_i - \bar{y})^2}} \tag{10.10}$$

If the fit is poor, the ratio of the two sums is close to 1 and r is close to zero. However, if the fit is good, the ratio is close to zero and r is close to +1 or –1. From the equation, it is obvious that the ratio can never exceed 1. Hence, r cannot be less than –1 or greater than +1.

The statistic is used to measure the strength of a linear relationship between any two variables. It indicates the goodness of fit of a line determined by the method of least squares, and this in turn indicates whether a relationship exists between x and y.

Although Eq. (10.10) serves to define the coefficient of correlation, it is seldom used in practice. An alternative form of the formula is

$$r = \frac{n(\Sigma x_i y_i) - (\Sigma x_i)(\Sigma y_i)}{\sqrt{n(\Sigma x_i^2) - (\Sigma x_i)^2}\sqrt{n(\Sigma y_i^2) - (\Sigma y_i)^2}} \tag{10.11}$$

The interpretation of r is not difficult if it is ±1 or zero: When it is zero, the points are scattered and the fit of the regression line is so poor that a knowledge of x does not help in the prediction of y; when it is +1 or –1, all the points actually lie on the straight line, so an excellent prediction of y can be made by using x values. The problem arises when r falls between zero and +1 or zero and –1.

General guidelines for interpreting the correlation coefficient are as follows:

Correlation Coefficient	Correlation Interpretation
0.9 to 1.0	Very high positive
0.7 to 0.9	High positive
0.5 to 0.7	Moderate positive
0.3 to 0.5	Low positive
−0.3 to 0.3	Little, if any
−0.5 to −0.3	Low negative
−0.7 to −0.5	Moderate negative
−0.9 to −0.7	High negative
−1.0 to −0.9	Very high negative

The physical interpretation of r can be explained in the following manner. If the coefficient of correlation is known for a given set of data, then $100r^2\%$ of the variation of the y's can be attributed to differences in x, namely, to the relationship of y with x. If $r = 0.6$ in a given problem, then 36%—that is, $100(0.6^2)$—of the variation of the y's is accounted for (perhaps caused) by differences in $\times$ values. The square of the correlation coefficient (r^2) is called the *coefficient of determination*.

Again consider the problem of IQ and math scores, substituting values from Table 10.9 into the equation for the correlation coefficient.

$$r = \frac{(20)(198\,527) - (2\,466)(1\,592)}{\sqrt{(20)(306\,124) - (2\,466)^2}\sqrt{(20)(129\,892) - (1\,592)^2}}$$

$$= 0.87$$

Computing the coefficient of determination and multiplying by 100 to obtain percent yields

$$100r^2 = 76\%$$

This would indicate that 76% of the variations in math scores can be accounted for by differences in IQ.

One word of caution when using or considering results from linear regression and coefficients of correlation and determination. There is a fallacy in interpreting high values of r or r^2 as implying cause-effect relations. If the increase in television coverage of professional football is plotted against the increase in traffic accidents at a certain intersection over the past 3 years, an almost perfect positive correlation (+1.0) can be shown to exist. This is obviously not a cause-effect relation, so it is wise to interpret the correlation coefficient and coefficient of determination carefully. The variables must have a measure of association if the results are to be meaningful.

The following example problem is intended to illustrate how much of the material presented in this chapter could be used in the solution to a practical engineering problem.

Example Problem 10.5   Water conservation can be a critical matter. Many regions of the country can have a serious lack of water for many years and an excess in other years. One solution to this problem is construction of dams that allows water storage in large reservoirs. The amount of water flowing into a region is a function of the watershed area, annual rainfall, snow melt, and so on. Assume the dam height, discharge area, and spillways must be designed to accommodate a 100-year flood.

Data showing the flow rate (discharge) from a river that is under consideration for the construction of a dam as a function of the recovery time needed to refill the reservoir is given in Table 10.14. These are measurements from the primary watershed of about 5 540 mi^2 located in a southwestern state.

1.   Using the least-squares method, obtain an equation relating the discharge Q to the recovery period P.
2.   Compute the correlation coefficient and interpret the results.
3.   From the derived equation, compute the projected discharge for a 100-year flood.

Solution   A spreadsheet is a convenient tool for this problem. The data were entered in columns A and B as shown in Figure 10.11. Test plots were then done to determine visually whether linear, semilog, or log-log techniques would be most likely to produce a straight line. As shown in Figure 10.12, the log-log plot, although not a perfect straight line, is more nearly so than either the linear plot or the semilog plot. Thus we will use the method of least squares to find an equation of the form $Q = bP^m$ ($\log Q = m\log P + \log b$).

The spreadsheet was then modified (see Fig. 10.11) by adding columns to compute $\log P$, $\log Q$, $(\log P)(\log Q)$, $(\log P)^2$ and $(\log Q)^2$. The sums of each

Table 10.14

Period (years)	Discharge (cfs)	Period (years)	Discharge (cfs)
1	2 480	2.66	5 360
1.09	2 690	2.87	5 600
1.15	2 730	3.11	5 950
1.2	2 780	3.48	6 300
1.41	3 300	3.75	7 300
1.45	3 320	4.18	7 530
1.49	3 350	4.73	8 650
1.55	3 420	5.43	9 000
1.62	3 750	6.39	9 150
1.68	3 800	7.75	10 700
1.72	4 200	9.84	12 000
1.85	4 330	13.5	15 250
1.95	4 470	21.8	21 100
2.06	4 600	33.7	26 870
2.18	4 620	41.5	33 250
2.32	5 110	50.5	34 750
2.48	5 320	55.8	44 800

of columns A through G were also computed. From these sums, the parameter m could be found as follows,

$$m = \frac{n(\Sigma x_i y_i) - (\Sigma x_i)(\Sigma y_i)}{n(\Sigma x_i^2) - (\Sigma x_i)^2}$$

$$= \frac{34(81.329) - (19.765)(130.032)}{34(19.969) - (19.765)^2} = 0.676\,8$$

$$\log b = \frac{\Sigma y_i - m(\Sigma x_i)}{n} = \frac{130.032 - 0.676\,8(19.765)}{34} = 3.431\,1$$

$$b = 2\,698.1$$

and once m has been determined, $\log b$ can be calculated. The parameter b is obtained from the expression $b = 10^{\log b}$.

The least-squares equation is then

$$Q' = 2.7 \times 10^3\, P^{0.677}$$

after rounding the coefficients.

The correlation coefficient was then computed and found to be about 0.997. Squaring this value (coefficient of determination) and multiplying by 100% gives a result of 99.4%, which is an indication of a very good agreement between the data and the prediction line. It suggests that nearly 99% of the variation in the discharge can be accounted for by variation in the return period.

Spreadsheets also provide a mechanism for computing a least-squares curve fit (Excel calls this a trendline) to a data set. Figure 10.13 shows the result of this approach for Example Problem 10.5. The data were plotted as a scatter chart (log-log) and a trendline was added.

Figure 10.11

	A	B	C	D	E	F	G	H
1	P	Q	log P	log Q	(log P)(log Q)	(log P)^2	(log Q)^2	Q'
2	1	2480	0	3.394452	0	0	11.5223022	2698.6
3	1.09	2690	0.037426	3.429752	0.128363617	0.001401	11.7632007	2860.627
4	1.15	2730	0.060698	3.436163	0.208567652	0.003684	11.8072137	2966.243
5	1.2	2780	0.079181	3.444045	0.272703758	0.00627	11.8614446	3052.9
6	1.41	3300	0.149219	3.518514	0.525029528	0.022266	12.3799404	3404.867
7	1.45	3320	0.161368	3.521138	0.568199018	0.02604	12.3984134	3469.925
8	1.49	3350	0.173186	3.525045	0.610489356	0.029993	12.4259409	3534.405
9	1.55	3420	0.190332	3.534026	0.67263719	0.036226	12.4893405	3630.086
10	1.62	3750	0.209515	3.574031	0.748813213	0.043897	12.7736995	3740.213
11	1.68	3800	0.225309	3.579784	0.806558471	0.050764	12.8148506	3833.388
12	1.72	4200	0.235528	3.623249	0.853378278	0.055474	13.1279354	3894.907
13	1.85	4330	0.267172	3.636488	0.971566757	0.071381	13.2240442	4091.729
14	1.95	4470	0.290035	3.650308	1.058715524	0.08412	13.324745	4240.098
15	2.06	4600	0.313867	3.662758	1.14961962	0.098513	13.4157949	4400.49
16	2.18	4620	0.338456	3.664642	1.240321873	0.114553	13.4296008	4572.336
17	2.32	5110	0.365488	3.708421	1.355383282	0.133581	13.7523856	4769.004
18	2.48	5320	0.394452	3.725912	1.469692106	0.155592	13.8824175	4989.127
19	2.66	5360	0.424882	3.729165	1.584453639	0.180524	13.90667	5231.346
20	2.87	5600	0.457882	3.748188	1.716227443	0.209656	14.0489135	5507.334
21	3.11	5950	0.49276	3.774517	1.859932448	0.242813	14.2469783	5814.872
22	3.48	6300	0.541579	3.799341	2.057643982	0.293308	14.4349886	6274.383
23	3.75	7300	0.574031	3.863323	2.217668119	0.329512	14.9252635	6599.759
24	4.18	7530	0.621176	3.876795	2.408173089	0.38586	15.0295393	7102.748
25	4.73	8650	0.674861	3.937016	2.656939181	0.455438	15.5000958	7722.351
26	5.43	9000	0.7348	3.954243	2.905576722	0.539931	15.6360338	8478.208
27	6.39	9150	0.805501	3.961421	3.190928091	0.648832	15.6928571	9465.431
28	7.75	10700	0.889302	4.029384	3.583337854	0.790858	16.2359336	10785.49
29	9.84	12000	0.992995	4.079181	4.050606983	0.986039	16.6397196	12676.49
30	13.5	15250	1.130334	4.18327	4.728491167	1.277654	17.4997466	15700.82
31	21.8	21100	1.338456	4.324282	5.787863932	1.791466	18.6994188	21713.92
32	33.7	26870	1.52763	4.429268	6.766281726	2.333653	19.6184121	29156.33
33	41.5	33250	1.618048	4.521792	7.316476372	2.61808	20.4465997	33566.79
34	50.5	34750	1.703291	4.540955	7.734569174	2.901202	20.6202706	38334.12
35	55.8	44800	1.746634	4.651278	8.124081248	3.050731	21.6343872	41012.03
36	Sum P	Sum Q	Sum log P	Sum log Q	Sum (log P)(log Q)	Sum (log P)^2	Sum (log Q)^2	
37	299.19	327830	19.7654	130.0321	81.32929041	19.96931	501.209098	

Column H was added to compute values of the predicted discharge, Q', for each return period P. The original data ($R^2 = 0.994\ 2$) as well as the predicted curve ($R^2 = 1$) are plotted in Figure 10.13.

To determine the discharge for a 100-year flood, use the least-squares equation.

$$Q' = 2.7 \times 10^3\ P^{0.677}$$

$$Q' = 2.7 \times 10^3 (100)^{0.677}$$

$$= 61 \times 10^3\ \text{cfs}$$

Figure 10.12

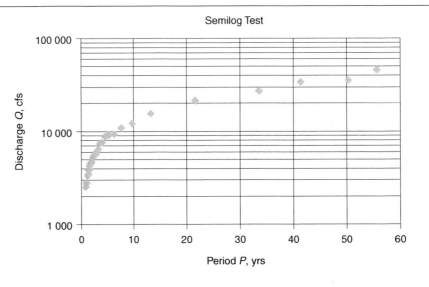

Semilog Test

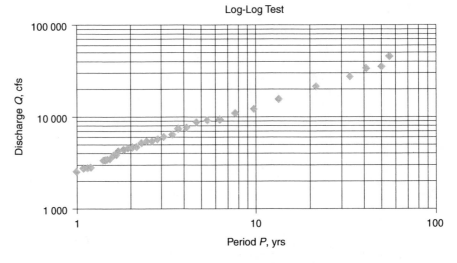

Log-Log Test

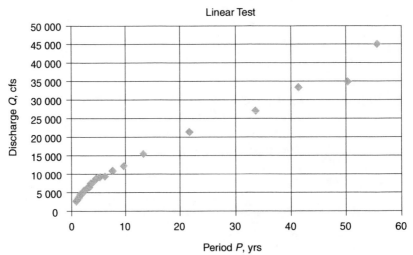

Linear Test

Figure 10.13

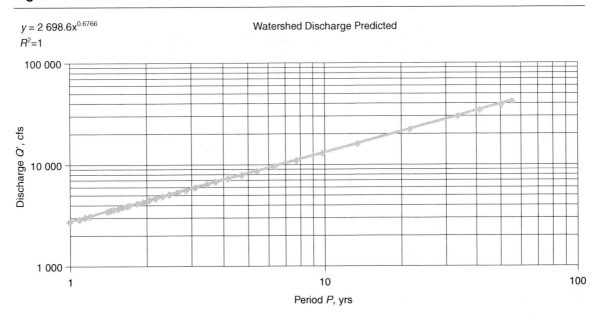

$y = 2\,698.6x^{0.6766}$
$R^2 = 1$

Watershed Discharge Predicted

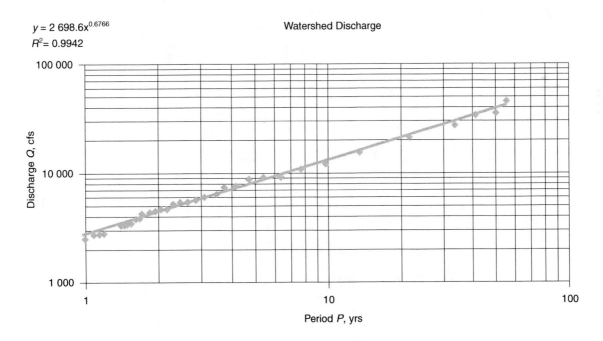

$y = 2\,698.6x^{0.6766}$
$R^2 = 0.9942$

Watershed Discharge

Problems

10.1 The number of home runs hit per game for the Millard girls' softball team are: 1, 2, 4, 3, 2, 4, 3, 0, 1, 2, 3, 5, 2, 1, and 5.
   (a) What is the mean number of home runs hit?
   (b) What is the median?
   (c) What is the mode?

10.2 The temperature, in degrees Celsius, each day over a three-week period was recorded as follows:

17, 18, 20, 22, 21, 19, 16, 15, 18, 20, 21, 21, 22, 21, 19, 20, 19, 17, 16, 16, 17

   (a) Compute the mean, median, and mode.
   (b) Using two-degree intervals starting with 15-16, draw a frequency diagram.

10.3 The following table gives the life expectancy of males and females at birth in the United States, 1979 to 2004.

Year	Male	Female	Year	Male	Female
1979	70.0	77.4	1992	72.1	78.9
1980	70.0	77.5	1993	72.1	78.9
1981	70.4	77.8	1994	72.4	79.0
1982	70.9	78.1	1995	72.5	78.9
1983	71.0	78.1	1996	73.1	79.1
1984	71.2	78.2	1997	73.6	79.4
1985	71.2	78.2	1998	73.8	79.5
1986	71.3	78.3	1999	73.9	79.4
1987	71.5	78.4	2000	74.3	79.7
1988	71.5	78.3	2001	74.4	79.8
1989	71.7	78.5	2002	74.5	79.9
1990	71.8	78.8	2003	74.7	80.0
1991	72.0	78.9	2004	75.2	80.4

Source: NCHS (National Center for Health Statistics)

   (a) Calculate the mean and median, of the life expectancies for men and for women.
   (b) Calculate the standard deviation for the data for men and for women.

10.4 The exam scores of 50 students in a class follow:

92	71	91	53	99	93	88	95	65	67
98	76	65	68	82	91	93	44	77	100
88	87	56	85	60	98	89	70	78	82
78	70	78	89	34	95	67	88	89	78
77	65	88	78	59	50	66	76	91	87

   (a) What is the average (mean) score in the class?
   (b) More students got a _____ score than any other score. (mode)
   (c) What is the median score?
   (d) Compute the standard deviation of the data using equation 10.4 and a calculator or software.

10.5 Survey at least 30 engineering students to obtain each student's total investment in calculators and computers in the past 18 months. The investment figure should include all equipment and software, whether bought personally or received as a gift.
   (a) Find the mean, mode, and median investment.
   (b) Find the standard deviation.

257

Problems

10.6 The output of a gas furnace has large quantities of carbon dioxide, which must be monitored carefully. This table gives the percentage of CO_2 in the output, with samples taken every 9 seconds.

53.8	56	48.4	48.3	51.5	54.4	57.7
53.6	56.8	47.9	47	51.6	56	57
53.5	56.8	47.6	45.8	51.2	56.9	56
53.5	56.4	47.5	45.6	50.5	57.5	54.7
53.4	55.7	47.5	46	50.1	57.3	53.2
53.1	55	47.6	46.9	49.8	56.6	52.1
52.7	54.3	48.1	47.8	49.6	56	51.6
52.4	53.2	49	48.2	49.4	55.4	51
52.2	52.3	50	48.3	49.3	55.4	50.5
52	51.6	51.1	47.9	49.2	56.4	50.4
52	51.2	51.8	47.2	49.3	57.2	
52.4	50.8	51.9	47.2	49.7	58	
53	50.5	51.7	48.1	50.3	58.4	
54	50	51.2	49.4	51.3	58.4	
54.9	49.2	50	50.6	52.8	58.1	

Source: Time Series Data Library

(a) Group these measurements into equal classes, and construct a frequency distribution table for the data. (Use a spreadsheet to help solve this problem.)

(b) Compute the mean, median, and mode of the data.

(c) Compute the standard deviation of the data.

10.7 A farm-implement manufacturer in the Midwest purchases castings from the Omaha Steel foundry. Thirty castings were selected at random and weighed, and their masses were recorded to the nearest kilogram, as shown below:

235	232	228	228	240	231
225	220	218	230	222	229
217	233	222	221	228	228
244	241	238	219	242	222
227	227	229	229	224	227

(a) Group the measurements into a frequency distribution table having six equal classes from 215 to 244.

(b) Construct a histogram of the distribution.

(c) Determine the median, mode, and mean of the data.

10.8 The number of users that were logged into an Internet server was monitored every minute, over a period of 100 minutes. Here are the results:

88	138	140	171	112	91	193
84	146	134	172	104	91	204
85	151	131	172	102	94	208
85	150	131	174	99	101	210
84	148	129	175	99	110	215
85	147	126	172	88	121	222
83	149	126	172	88	135	228
85	143	132	174	84	145	226
88	132	137	174	84	149	222
88	131	140	169	88	156	220
91	139	142	165	89	165	
99	147	150	156	88	171	
104	150	159	142	85	175	
112	148	167	131	86	177	
126	145	170	121	89	182	

Source: Time Series Data Library

(*a*) Group these measurements into 10 equal classes, (81–95, 96–110, etc.) and construct a frequency distribution table for the data.

(*b*) Draw a histogram of the distribution.

(*c*) Find the average number of users during the sample period.

(*d*) Using the histogram, estimate the probability of 141–165 users being logged in at any given time.

10.9 The team earned-run averages for the American and National League baseball teams in 2009 are shown below. Calculate the median, mean, and standard deviation for each league individually and for Major League Baseball as a whole.

American League Team	ERA	National League Team	ERA
Seattle Mariners	3.87	Los Angeles Dodgers	3.41
Chicago White Sox	4.14	San Francisco Giants	3.55
Oakland Athletics	4.26	Atlanta Braves	3.57
New York Yankees	4.26	St Louis Cardinals	3.66
Detroit Tigers	4.29	Chicago Cubs	3.84
Tampa Bay Rays	4.33	Philadelphia Phillies	4.16
Boston Red Sox	4.35	Cincinnati Reds	4.18
Texas Rangers	4.38	Colorado Rockies	4.22
Los Angeles Angels	4.45	Florida Marlins	4.29
Toronto Blue Jays	4.47	San Diego Padres	4.37
Minnesota Twins	4.50	Arizona Diamondbacks	4.42
Kansas City Royals	4.83	New York Mets	4.45
Cleveland Indians	5.06	Houston Astros	4.54
Baltimore Orioles	5.15	Pittsburgh Pirates	4.59
		Milwaukee Brewers	4.83
		Washington Nationals	5.00

10.10 A land-grant university located in the Midwest has an entering freshman class of 1 522 students. A random sample of 150, or approximately 10%, of the entering first-year students' cumulative grade points were recorded. Academic standards require each student to have a first-year grade average of 1.5 or better to return for the sophomore year and 3.5 or better to be eligible for the Dean's list. The grade point averages (GPA) below have been partially grouped.

(a) Determine the mean grade point average and standard deviation for the sample.

(b) Group the data into equal classes and construct a frequency distribution table.

(c) Draw a histogram of the distribution.

GPA	# Students	GPA	# Students	GPA	# Students	GPA	# Students
0	0	1	3	2	7	3	5
0.1	0	1.1	2	2.1	7	3.1	2
0.2	1	1.2	3	2.2	10	3.2	1
0.3	0	1.3	2	2.3	8	3.3	3
0.4	1	1.4	4	2.4	12	3.4	2
0.5	1	1.5	4	2.5	14	3.5	4
0.6	0	1.6	3	2.6	6	3.6	2
0.7	2	1.7	5	2.7	7	3.7	1
0.8	1	1.8	6	2.8	5	3.8	0
0.9	2	1.9	6	2.9	6	3.9	1
						4	1

259
Problems

10.11 The WHO (Wyatt Hiring Organization) would like to predict how the trainees in its sales force will perform. At the beginning of their two-month training course, they are given an aptitude test. Sales records are kept for each trainee over the first year, the results are shown below.

Aptitude Score	Number of Sales
18	54
26	64
28	54
34	62
36	68
42	70
48	76
52	66
54	76
60	74

(a) Plot the data on linear graph paper.
(b) Using the method of least squares, determine the equation of the line.
(c) Draw the line on the curve.
(d) Calculate and interpret the coefficient of correlation.
(e) What level of sales would you expect from an aptitude score of 40, 50, 70?

10.12 All materials are elastic to some degree. It is desirable that certain parts of some designs compress when a load is applied to assist in making the part air- or watertight. The test results in the following table resulted from a test on a material known as Silon Q-177.

Pressure P (MPa)	Relative Compression R (%)
0.1	15
0.2	17
0.3	18
0.4	19
0.5	20
0.6	21
0.7	22
0.8	23
0.9	24
1.0	25.5
1.1	27
1.2	28
1.3	29.7
1.4	31.2
1.5	32.8
2.0	42
2.5	54
3.0	70

(a) Plot the data on semilog paper.
(b) Using the method of least squares, find the equation of the line of best fit.
(c) Draw the line on the curve.
(d) Calculate the coefficient of correlation.
(e) What pressure should be applied to achieve a relative compression of 60%?

10.13 An insurance company is interested in the relationship between the number of licensed vehicles in a state and the number of accidents per year in that state. It collects a random sample of 10 counties within the state:

X, Number of Licensed Vehicles (in thousands)	Y, Number of Accidents (in hundreds)
4	1
10	4
15	5
12	4
8	3
16	4
5	2
7	1
9	4
10	2

(a) Plot the points on linear graph paper.
(b) Find the equation that relates X and Y.
(c) Find the correlation coefficient.
(d) Estimate from the derived equation the number of accidents in the largest county, with 35 000 vehicles.

10.14 The annual flows (lowest one-day flow rate within a calendar year) of two tributaries of a river are expected to be linearly related. Data for a 12-year period are shown below.

Year	North Tributary Flow (cfs)	South Tributary Flow (cfs)
1	225	232
2	354	315
3	201	174
4	372	402
5	246	204
6	324	324
7	216	189
8	210	224
9	195	210
10	264	281
11	276	235
12	183	174

Use a spreadsheet to do the following:
(a) Compute the best-fit line using the method of least squares. Use data for the north tributary as the independent variable.
(b) Plot the data and the prediction equation on the same graph.
(c) Compute the correlation coefficient and interpret it.
(d) If the low flow for the north tributary is 150 cfs, what would you expect the flow for the south tributary to be?

261
Problems

10.15 The capacity of a screw conveyor that is moving dry ground corn is expressed in liters per second and the conveyor speed in revolutions per minute. The results of tests conducted on a new model conveyor are given below:

Capacity C (L/s)	Angular Velocity V (r/min)
3.01	10.0
6.07	21.0
15.0	58.2
30.0	140.6
50.0	245.0
80.0	410.0
110.0	521.0

(a) Plot the data on log-log graph paper.
(b) Using the method of least squares, find the equation of the line of best fit.
(c) Draw the line on the graph.
(d) Calculate the correlation coefficient.
(e) If the angular velocity of the auger was accelerated to 1 000 r/min, how many liters of corn could be moved each second?

10.16 The following table shows the U.S. consumption and production of oil per day in barrels × 1 000 from 1994 to 2008:

Year	U.S. Daily Oil Consumption Barrels × 1 000	U.S. Daily Oil Production Barrels × 1 000
1994	17 719	8 389
1995	17 725	8 322
1996	18 309	8 295
1997	18 621	8 269
1998	18 917	8 011
1999	19 519	7 731
2000	19 701	7 733
2001	19 649	7 669
2002	19 761	7 626
2003	20 033	7 400
2004	20 517	7 241

Source: BP Statistical Review of World Energy June 2005.

(a) Plot the data on linear graph paper.
(b) Find the equation that best describes the data for production and consumption.
(c) Use the equation found in part (b) to predict the expected U.S. oil consumption for the year 2015.
(d) Use the equation found in part (b) to predict the expected U.S. oil production for the year 2015.
(e) Estimate the number of dollars per day the United States will spend on imported oil at $80.00/barrel in 2015.

10.17 A mechanized "swinging hammer" is used to drive bolts into a wall. It is known that at the point of contact, the energy dissipated as heat is proportional to the square of the terminal velocity of the hammer. We have collected the following data:

Terminal Velocity (m/s)	Energy Dissipated (J)
26	2 800
35	4 220
40	5 380
49	8 250
53	10 097

(a) Manually plot the points on a suitable graph.
(b) Determine the mathematical relationship between the variables using the equations from the chapter.
(c) Using a spreadsheet, plot the points on a suitable graph.
(d) Using a spreadsheet, construct a trendline and determine the equation of the curve and the coefficient of determination.
(e) Compare and discuss the results between the two methods.

10.18 Experimental aircraft for the military are to be ranked relative to their Mach number, *Ma*. Mach number is a ratio of the velocity, *V*, of the aircraft to the speed of sound, *c*. The speed of sound, however, is a function of temperature. The theoretical equations for the speed of sound can be expressed as $c = (kRT)^{0.5}$, where

k = specific heat ratio that varies with temperature but has no dimension. However, for this problem assume that it is a constant with a value of 1.4.

R = Gas constant for air (53.33 ft · lbf/lbm · °R)

T = Temperature, °R

Let us imagine that we did not know the equation for the speed of sound but had access to data relating the speed of sound in air to temperature. That set of data is recorded in the table below.

(a) Develop a table using spreadsheet software that will provide the necessary variables for Eqs. (10.16), (10.17), and (10.19).
From the data in part (a) above and the equations presented in the chapter material, determine:
(b) The equation of the line $c = bT^m$
(c) The coefficient of correlation
(d) Using the spreadsheet package, determine the equation of the line and the coefficient of determination.
(e) Does the equation obtained from the data verify the theoretical equation presented for the speed of sound?
(f) What is the numerical value and what are the units on the constant *b*? Recall

$$g_c = \frac{32.2 \text{ lbm} \cdot \text{ft}}{\text{lbf} \cdot \text{s}^2}$$

(g) Three aircraft were measured at the following velocities and temperatures. Determine the Mach number for each from the equation of the curve in part (b):
     1. X101   855 mph at −100 degrees Fahrenheit
     2. X215   548 m/s at −95 degrees Celsius
     3. X912   2 120 ft/s at 520 degrees Rankine

Speed (ft/s)	Temperature Rankine	Speed (ft/s)	Temperature Rankine
100	490	550	1149
150	600	600	1201
200	693	650	1250
250	775	700	1297
300	849	750	1342
350	917	800	1387
400	980	850	1429
450	1040	900	1471
500	1096	950	1511
		1000	1550

CHAPTER **8**

Introduction to Engineering Economics

Chapter Objectives

When you complete your study of this chapter, you will able to:

- Understand that the value of money changes with time
- Distinguish between simple and compound interest
- Prepare a cash-flow diagram
- Compute present worth and future worth of multiple sums of money
- Calculate the equivalent uniform annual cost of a series of amounts
- Recognize and solve problems involving sinking funds and installment loans
- Solve problems with arithmetic and geometric gradients

8.1 Introduction

Engineers often serve as managers or executive officers of businesses and therefore are required to make financial as well as technical decisions. Even in companies where the managers are not engineers, engineers serve as advisers and provide reports and analyses that influence decisions. Also, the amount of capital investment (money spent for equipment, facilities, and so on) in many industries represents a significant part of the cost of doing business. Thus, estimates of the cost of new equipment, facilities, software, and processes must be carefully done if the business is to be successful and earn a profit on its products and services.

A couple of examples will be used to illustrate how an engineer might be involved in the financial decision-making process. Suppose a manufacturing company has decided to upgrade its computer network. The network will connect all parts of the company, such as engineering design, purchasing, marketing, manufacturing, field sales, and accounting. Ten different vendors are invited to submit bids based on the specifications prepared by engineers. The bids will include hardware, software, installation, and maintenance. As an engineer, you will then analyze the bids submitted and rank the 10 vendors' proposals based on predetermined criteria.

This assignment is possible once a method of comparison, such as the equivalent uniform annual cost (EUAC) or the present worth (PW) method is selected. These methods of analysis are discussed later in the chapter. However, they allow us to compare only tangible costs. Intangible items, such as safety or environmental concerns, must also be considered.

Another example of a common engineering task is justification of the purchase of a new machine to reduce the costs of manufacture. This justification is usually expressed as a rate of return on investment or *rate of return* (ROR). Rate of return is defined as the equivalent compound interest rate that must be earned on the investment to produce the same income as the proposed activity. Often the profit comes from the reduction of production costs as a result of the new machine.

Since any venture has some risk involved and the cost reductions expected are only estimated, companies will not choose to invest in new equipment unless there is a promise of a much greater return than could be realized by less risky investments, such as bank deposits or the purchase of treasury notes or government bonds.

In addition to the application of engineering economy methods in your professional life, you will also have applications in your personal life. Major purchases such as a vehicle or a home, as well as investments (e.g., money markets, bonds, treasury notes, company stock) you may make using your own funds, require understanding of the principles you will learn in this chapter. As an example, Table 8.1 is an Excel spreadsheet that shows an annual investment of $1 200 (nominally $100 per month) for 10 years beginning at age 22. This is left at 8% annual compounded interest until age 65. Compare that with starting the same yearly investment at age 32 and continuing until age 65. Of course you may not be able to earn 8% at all times, although over the long term, 8% is a reasonable number. Suppose, however, you could earn only 4%. Table 8.2 shows equal investments earning 8% and 4%, the difference being in one case the investment is made early and in the other the investment is made late. It is clear the 8% compound interest results in much greater accumulation than 4%, just as you would expect. Notice the difference in accumulation between investing early and investing late. Your conclusion should be that to optimize your retirement income you will need to invest (save) just as early as you possibly can.

8.2 Simple and Compound Interest

The idea of interest on an investment is certainly not new. The New Testament of the Christian Bible refers to banks, interest, and return. History records business dealings involving interest at least 40 centuries ago. Early business was largely barter in nature with repayment in kind. It was common during the early years of the development of the United States for people to borrow grain, salt, sugar, animal skins, and other products from each other to be repaid when the commodity was again available. Since most of these items depended on the harvest, annual repayment was the normal process. When it became impossible to repay the loan after a year, the interest was calculated by multiplying the

Table 8.1

Age	Annual Savings	Accumulation	Annual Savings	Accumulation
22	$1,200	$1,296		
23	$1,200	$2,696		
24	$1,200	$4,207		
25	$1,200	$5,840		
26	$1,200	$7,603		
27	$1,200	$9,507		
28	$1,200	$11,564		
29	$1,200	$13,785		
30	$1,200	$16,184		
31	$1,200	$18,775		
32		$20,277	$1,200	$1,296
33		$21,899	$1,200	$2,696
34		$23,651	$1,200	$4,207
35		$25,543	$1,200	$5,840
36		$27,586	$1,200	$7,603
37		$29,793	$1,200	$9,507
38		$32,176	$1,200	$11,564
39		$34,750	$1,200	$13,785
40		$37,530	$1,200	$16,184
41		$40,533	$1,200	$18,775
42		$43,776	$1,200	$21,573
43		$47,278	$1,200	$24,594
44		$51,060	$1,200	$27,858
45		$55,145	$1,200	$31,383
46		$59,556	$1,200	$35,189
47		$64,321	$1,200	$39,300
48		$69,466	$1,200	$43,740
49		$75,024	$1,200	$48,536
50		$81,025	$1,200	$53,714
51		$87,508	$1,200	$59,308
52		$94,508	$1,200	$65,348
53		$102,069	$1,200	$71,872
54		$110,234	$1,200	$78,918
55		$119,053	$1,200	$86,527
56		$128,577	$1,200	$94,745
57		$138,863	$1,200	$103,621
58		$149,973	$1,200	$113,207
59		$161,970	$1,200	$123,559
60		$174,928	$1,200	$134,740
61		$188,922	$1,200	$146,815
62		$204,036	$1,200	$159,856
63		$220,359	$1,200	$173,941
64		$237,988	$1,200	$189,152
65		$257,027	$1,200	$205,580

principal amount by the product of the interest rate and the number of periods (years), now called simple interest.

$$I = Pni \qquad (8.1)$$

where

I = Interest accrued

P = Principal amount

n = Number of interest periods

i = Interest rate per period (as a decimal, not as a percent)

This is an example of a simple interest transaction where interest is calculated using the principal only, ignoring any interest accrued in preceding interest periods. Therefore, if \$1 000 were to be loaned at 7% annual interest for five years, the interest would be

$$I = Pni$$
$$= (1\ 000)(5)(0.07)$$
$$= \$350$$

and the total amount F to be repaid at the end of five years is

$$F = P + I \qquad (8.2)$$
$$= 1\ 000 + 350$$
$$= \$1\ 350$$

It can be seen that

$$F = P + I = P + Pni$$
$$= P\ (1 + ni) \qquad (8.3)$$

As time progressed and business developed, the practice of borrowing became more common, and the use of money replaced the barter system. It also became increasingly more common that money was loaned for longer periods of time. Simple interest was relegated to the single-interest period, and the practice of compounding developed. It can be shown by using Eq. (8.3), $n = 1$, that the amount owed at the end of one period is

$$P + Pi = P(1 + i)$$

The interest generated during the second period is then $(P + Pi)i$. It can be seen that interest is being calculated not only on the *principal* but on the previous interest as well. The sum F at the end of two periods becomes

P	principal amount
$+ Pi$	interest during first period
$+ Pi + Pi^2$	interest during second period
$P + 2Pi + Pi^2$	sum after two periods

This can be factored as follows:

$$P(1 + 2i + i^2) = P(1 + i)^2$$

Table 8.2

Age	Annual Savings	Accumulation (8%)	Accumulation (4%)	Annual Savings	Accumulation (8%)	Accumulation (4%)
22	$1,200	$1,296	$1,248			
23	$1,200	$2,696	$2,546			
24	$1,200	$4,207	$3,896			
25	$1,200	$5,840	$5,300			
26	$1,200	$7,603	$6,760			
27	$1,200	$9,507	$8,278			
28	$1,200	$11,564	$9,857			
29	$1,200	$13,785	$11,499			
30	$1,200	$16,184	$13,207			
31	$1,200	$18,775	$14,984			
32	$1,200	$21,573	$16,831			
33	$1,200	$24,594	$18,752			
34	$1,200	$27,858	$20,750			
35	$1,200	$31,383	$22,828			
36	$1,200	$35,189	$24,989			
37	$1,200	$39,300	$27,237			
38	$1,200	$43,740	$29,574			
39	$1,200	$48,536	$32,005			
40	$1,200	$53,714	$34,534			
41	$1,200	$59,308	$37,163			
42	$1,200	$65,348	$39,898			
43	$1,200	$71,872	$42,741			
44		$77,622	$44,451	$1,200	$1,296	$1,248
45		$83,831	$46,229	$1,200	$2,696	$2,546
46		$90,538	$48,078	$1,200	$4,207	$3,896
47		$97,781	$50,001	$1,200	$5,840	$5,300
48		$105,603	$52,002	$1,200	$7,603	$6,760
49		$114,052	$54,082	$1,200	$9,507	$8,278
50		$123,176	$56,245	$1,200	$11,564	$9,857
51		$133,030	$58,495	$1,200	$13,785	$11,499
52		$143,672	$60,834	$1,200	$16,184	$13,207
53		$155,166	$63,268	$1,200	$18,775	$14,984
54		$167,579	$65,799	$1,200	$21,573	$16,831
55		$180,986	$68,430	$1,200	$24,594	$18,752
56		$195,465	$71,168	$1,200	$27,858	$20,750
57		$211,102	$74,014	$1,200	$31,383	$22,828
58		$227,990	$76,975	$1,200	$35,189	$24,989
59		$246,229	$80,054	$1,200	$39,300	$27,237
60		$265,928	$83,256	$1,200	$43,740	$29,574
61		$287,202	$86,586	$1,200	$48,536	$32,005
62		$310,178	$90,050	$1,200	$53,714	$34,534
63		$334,992	$93,652	$1,200	$59,308	$37,163
64		$361,791	$97,398	$1,200	$65,348	$39,898
65		$390,735	$101,294	$1,200	$71,872	$42,741

The interest during the third period is

$$(P + 2Pi + Pi^2)i = Pi + 2Pi^2 + Pi^3$$

and the sum after three periods is

$P + 2Pi + Pi^2$	sum after second period
$+ Pi + 2Pi^2 + Pi^3$	interest during third period
$P + 3Pi + 3Pi^2 + Pi^3 = P(1 + i)^3$	sum after three periods

This procedure can be generalized to n periods of time and will result in

$$F = P(1 + i)^n \tag{8.4}$$

where F is future worth or the sum generated after n periods.

For compound interest, the interest accrued for each interest period is calculated on the principal plus the total interest accumulated in all previous periods. Thus, compound interest means interest on top of interest. Consider the sum or future worth at the end of five years on a $1 000 loan with 7% annual interest, compounded annually.

$$F = P(1 + i)^n$$
$$= (1\,000)(1.07)^5$$
$$= \$1\,402.55$$

Thus, the sum with annual compounding is $1 402.55, compared with the previous sum of $1 350 when simple interest was used.

Table 8.3 demonstrates the difference between simple and compound interest on a year-by-year basis for the problem just discussed. Care must be exercised in using interest rates and payment periods to make sure that the interest rate used is the rate for the period selected.

Consider calculating the sum after one year. If the annual interest rate is 12% compounded annually, then $i = 0.12$ and $n = 1$. However, when the annual rate is 12%, but it is to be compounded every six months (semiannually), then $i = 0.12/2$ and $n = 2$. This idea can be extended to a monthly compounding period, with $i = 0.12/12$ and $n = 12$, or a daily compounding period, with $i = 0.12/365$ and $n = 365$.

Table 8.3 Principal and Interest Paid on Money Borrowed for Five Years at 7% Annual Interest

Year	Simple Interest		Compound Interest	
	Principal	Interest	Principal	Interest
0 (today)	1000		1000	
1	1000	70.00	1000	70.00
2	1000	70.00	1000	74.90
3	1000	70.00	1000	80.14
4	1000	70.00	1000	85.75
5	1000	70.00	1000	91.76
	$1000 +	350.00	$1000 +	402.55
Total owed		**$1350.00**		**$1402.55**

Example Problem 8.1   What total amount (principal and interest) must be paid at the end of four years if $8 000 is borrowed from a bank at a 12% annual interest rate compounded (a) annually, (b) semiannually, (c) monthly, and (d) daily?

Solution

    (*a*) Compounded annually:

$$F = P(1 + i)^n$$

where

$$i = 0.12$$
$$n = 1 \times 4 = 4 \text{ periods (years)}$$
$$P = \$8\ 000$$
$$F = 8\ 000(1.12)^4$$
$$= \$12\ 588.15$$

    (*b*) Compounded semiannually:

$$F = P(1 + i)^n$$

where

$$i = 0.12/2$$
$$n = 2 \times 4 = 8 \text{ periods}$$
$$P = \$8\ 000$$
$$F = 8\ 000(1.06)^8$$
$$= \$12\ 750.78$$

    (*c*) Compounded monthly:

$$F = P(1 + i)^n$$

where

$$i = 0.12/12$$
$$n = 12 \times 4 = 48 \text{ periods (months)}$$
$$P = \$8\ 000$$
$$F = 8\ 000(1.01)^{48}$$
$$= \$12\ 897.81$$

    (*d*) Compounded daily:

$$F = P(1 + i)^n$$

where

$$i = 0.12/365$$
$$n = 365 \times 4 = 1\ 460 \text{ periods (days)}$$
$$P = \$8\ 000$$
$$F = 8\ 000(1 + 0.12/365)^{1460}$$
$$= \$12\ 927.57$$

Note: Always round the answer to the nearest penny.

As you can see from the example, even though the stated interest is the same, 12% in this case, the change in the compounding period changes the sum. Thus, to compare different alternatives, we must know the *stated* or *nominal* annual interest rate and the compounding period. We can also define an *effective annual rate*, often called *annual percentage rate* (APR), for comparison purposes. The annual percentage rate (APR) is then the interest rate that would have produced the final amount under annual (rather than semiannual, monthly, or other) compounding.

Then, continuing with Example Problem 8.1 part (b), with a nominal interest rate of 12% and semiannual compounding, the APR can be found as follows:

$$F = \$12{,}750.73 = 8{,}000(1 + APR)^4 = 8{,}000\left(1 + \frac{0.12}{2}\right)^8$$

or

$$(1 + APR)^4 = \left(1 + \frac{0.12}{2}\right)^8$$

then

$$APR = \left(1 + \frac{0.12}{2}\right)^2 - 1 = 0.123\,6 \qquad (12.36\% \text{ APR})$$

Considering part (c) with 12% nominal and monthly compounding, the APR is found from

$$\$12\,897.81 = 8\,000(1 + APR)^4 = 8\,000\left(1 + \frac{0.12}{12}\right)^{48}$$

$$APR = \left(1 + \frac{0.12}{12}\right)^{12} - 1 = 0.126\,8 \qquad (12.68\% \text{ APR})$$

Financial institutions sometimes "intentionally confuse" nominal and APR values in their advertising. They may state the nominal rate and simply call it the APR if this makes the rate appear to be a better deal. APR is always going to be larger than nominal interest if the compounding period is less than one year when the APR value is computed as previously defined. Since you know how to compute APR, you can always check it out.

8.3 Cash-Flow Diagram

The transaction described in Example Problem 8.1 for annual compounding can and should be graphically illustrated in a *cash-flow diagram* (Fig. 8.1). Since cash-flow diagrams are very useful in the visualization of any transaction, they will be used throughout this chapter. The following general rules apply:

1. The horizontal line is a time scale. The interval of time is normally given in years, though in some cases other periods may be more meaningful.
2. The arrows signify cash flow. A downward arrow means money out, and an upward arrow means money in.
3. The diagram is dependent on the point of view from which it is constructed—that is, on whether it is the lender's or the borrower's point of view (see Fig. 8.1).

Figure 8.1

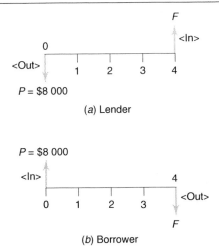

(a) Lender

(b) Borrower

Cash-flow diagram: (a) as seen by the lender; (b) as seen by the borrower.

8.4 Present Worth and Future Worth

It is important to keep in mind that the value of any transaction (loan, investment, and so on) changes with time because of interest. Thus, to express the value of a transaction, you must also give the point in time at which that value is computed. For example, the value of the loan described in Example Problem 8.1 (assuming annual compounding) is $8 000 at year zero but is $12 588.15 four years later. We will examine several methods of stating the value of a transaction.

Present worth (P) is the worth of a monetary transaction at the current time. It is the amount of money that must be invested now in order to produce a prescribed sum at another date.

Future worth (F) is the worth of a monetary transaction at some point in the future. It is an analysis of what the future amount of money will be if we take some particular course of action now.

To illustrate, if you were guaranteed an amount of money (F) four years from today, then P would be the present worth of F, where the interest is i and n = 4 (assuming annual compounding). Since this analysis is exactly the inverse of finding a future sum, we have

$$P = F(1 + i)^{-n} \tag{8.5}$$

As an example, if you can convince a lending institution that you will have a guaranteed amount of money available four years from today, it may be possible to borrow the present worth of that amount. If the guaranteed sum (four years later) is equal to $12 588.15, the present worth at 12% annual interest (compounded annually) is $8 000. (See Fig. 8.2.)

$$P = F(1 + i)^{-n}$$

Figure 8.2

$12 588.15 (Guaranteed)

$8 000 (Available to take out today)

Banker's cash-flow diagram.

where

$$F = \$12\,588.15$$

$$i = 0.12$$

$$n = 4$$

$$P = \frac{12\,588.15}{(1.12)^4}$$

$$= \$8\,000.00$$

In situations that involve economic decisions the following types of questions may arise:

1. Does it pay to make an investment now?
2. What is the current benefit of a payment that will be made at some other date?
3. How does the monthly price paid to lease a computer compare with the future cost of a new computer?
4. How much money do you need to invest annually, beginning at graduation, to accumulate $5 million by the time you retire?

In such cases the answer is found by calculating the present or future worth of the transaction.

Many businesses calculate their present worth each year since the change in their present worth is a measure of the growth of the company. The following example problem will help to demonstrate the concepts just described.

Example Problem 8.2   Listed below are five transactions. Determine their present worth if money is currently valued at 10% annual interest compounded annually. Determine the current net cash equivalent assuming no interest has been withdrawn or paid. Draw a cash-flow diagram for each.

Solution
   (*a*) $1 000 deposited two years ago. (See Fig. 8.3.)

$$F = 1\,000(1.10)^2 = \$1\,210.00$$

   (*b*) $2 000 deposited one year ago. (See Fig. 8.4.)

$$F = 2\,000(1.10)^1 = \$2\,200.00$$

Figure 8.3

$1 000

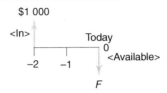

Owner's cash-flow diagram.

Figure 8.4

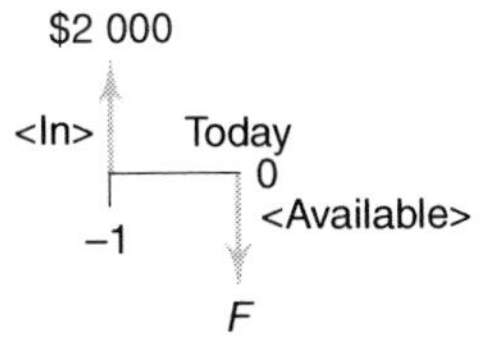

$2 000

Owner's cash-flow diagram.

Note: For parts (a) and (b) we solve for F to bring the value of money deposited one or two years ago to today's equivalent amount.

(c) $3 000 to be received one year from now. (See Fig. 8.5.)

$$P = 3\,000(1.10)^{-1} = \$2\,727.27$$

(d) $4 000 to be paid two years from now (treated as negative for the owner since it must be paid). (See Fig. 8.6.)

$$P = -4000(1.10)^{-2}$$
$$= -3\,305.79$$

Figure 8.5

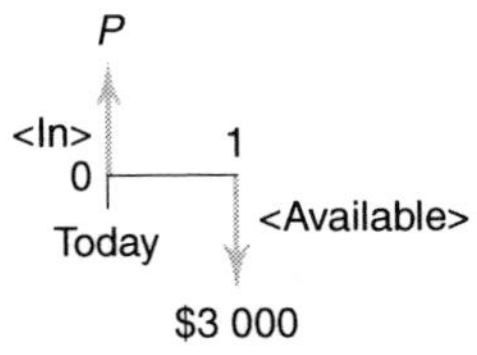

P

$3 000

Owner's cash-flow diagram.

Figure 8.6

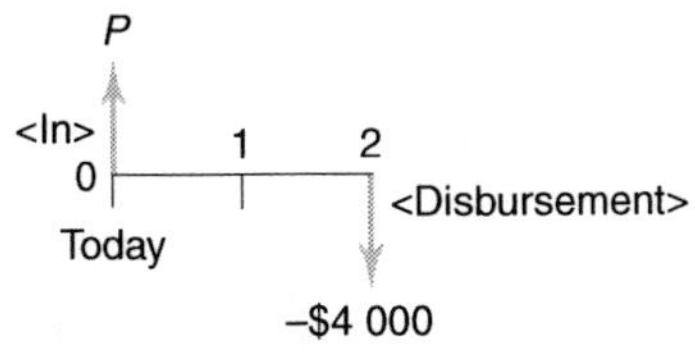

P

−$4 000

Owner's cash-flow diagram.

Figure 8.7

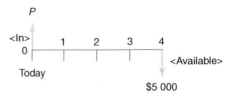

P

\<In\>   1   2   3   4

0

Today

\<Available\>

$5 000

Owner's cash-flow diagram.

(e) $5 000 to be received four years from now. (See Fig. 8.7.)

$$P = 5\,000(1.10)^{-4} = \$3\,415.07$$

Present worth of the five transactions (*note:* the values can be added or subtracted because each value has been computed on the *same* date):

$1 210.00

2 200.00

2 727.27

−3 305.79

3 415.07

Present worth = $6 246.55

Example Problem 8.3   A company can buy a vacant lot and have a new manufacturing plant constructed on the property. The timing and costs of various components for the factory are given in the cash-flow table below. If annual interest is 8% compounded annually, draw a cash-flow diagram and determine the future worth of the costs incurred when the firm begins production at the end of three years.

Year	Activity	Cost
0	Buy land	$ 75 000
1	Design and initial construction costs	150 000
2	Balance of construction costs	1 150 000
3	Setup production equipment	150 000

Solution   See Figure 8.8.
Using Eq. (8.4):

$$F = P(1 + i)^n$$

$$F = \$75\,000(1 + 0.08)^3 + 150\,000(1 + 0.08)^2 + 1\,150\,000(1 + 0.08)^1 + 150\,000$$

$$F = \$94\,478.40 + 174\,960.00 + 1\,242\,000.00 + 150\,000.00$$

$$F = \$1\,661\,438.40$$

In this problem, one must examine the source of the money that is being spent. It is likely from one of two sources: (1) It is money that is borrowed

Figure 8.8

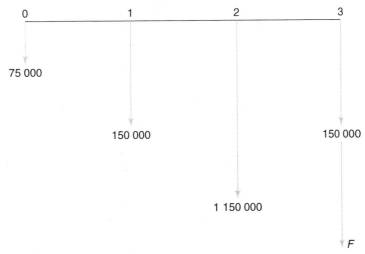

Future worth of the cost of a new manufacturing plant.

from a bank and the company is paying 8% annual interest, or (2) It is money that the company has on hand (profit). If the money is from the second source, then we must explore what other opportunities for investment are being forgone in order to build the new factory.

8.5 Annual Worth and Gradients

With present and future worth analysis, we resolved cash flows into single equivalent cash sums. But we can also state the value of a transaction on an equivalent annual basis.

Annual worth (*A*) is the worth of monetary transactions that have been converted to an equivalent uniform annual cost or benefit (EUAC or EUAB). An *annuity* involves a series of equal payments at regular intervals. The value of such a series will be developed in the following sections from the idea of compound interest. *Consideration of the point in time at which compounding begins will be of prime importance.*

Several forms of annuities will be discussed later in this chapter:

Annual Future Worth (Sinking Fund)
Annual Present Worth (Installment Loan)
Capitalized Cost (Infinite Life)

In many cases, however, annual payments do not occur in equal-amount payment series. For example, as your car ages, you may expect to pay more each year for automobile maintenance. If these costs increase (or decrease) in equal dollar amounts each year, they are referred to as arithmetic gradients (*G*); a formula allows easy computation of equivalent present values for gradient series. Geometric gradients occur in cases where a uniform payment increases (or decreases) by a constant percentage. For example, you may expect your salary to increase by 8% per year for the first five years of your career. If you want to find the present worth of this series of cash flows, you may use one of the formulas derived and demonstrated later in this chapter:

Arithmetic Gradients
Geometric Gradients

8.5.1   Annual Future Worth (Sinking Fund)

A *sinking fund* is an annuity that is designed to produce an amount of money at some future time. It might be used to save for an expenditure that you know is going to occur—for instance, a Christmas gift fund or a new car fund. In business, the fund may be used to provide cash needed to replace obsolete equipment or to upgrade software. The cash-flow diagram for the sinking fund is shown in Figure 8.9.

If an amount A is deposited at the *end* of each period and interest is compounded each period at a rate of i, the sum F will be produced after n periods. Please note that the deposit period and the interest compounding period must be *equal* for the equations being developed to be valid.

It can be seen from Figure 8.9 that the last payment will produce no interest, the payment at period $n - 1$ will produce interest equal to A times i, the payment at period $n - 2$ will produce a sum (interest and principal) of $A(1 + i)^2$, and so on. Hence, the sum produced will be as follows:

Deposit at end of period	Interest generated	Sum due to this payment
n	None	$A(1)$
$n - 1$	$A(i)$	$A(1 + i)$
$n - 2$	$A(1 + i)i$	$A(1 + i)^2$
$n - 3$	$A(1 + i)^2 i$	$A(1 + i)^3$

Thus, for four payments

$$F = A(4 + 6i + 4i^2 + i^3)$$

Figure 8.9

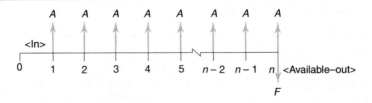

Saver's cash-flow diagram.

If we multiply and divide this expression by i, and then add and subtract 1 from the numerator, F becomes

$$F = A\left[\frac{(4i + 6i^2 + 4i^3 + i^4 + 1) - 1}{i}\right]$$

$$= A\left[\frac{(1 + i)^4 - 1}{i}\right]$$

It can be shown that the general term is

$$F = A\left[\frac{(1 + i)^n - 1}{i}\right] \tag{8.6}$$

Therefore the annual future worth equation, Eq. (8.6), should be used if you want to accumulate a future amount F over n periods, an amount A must be deposited at the end of each period at i interest rate compounded at each period.

Example Problem 8.4 How much money would be accumulated by a sinking fund if $90 is deposited at the end of each month for three years with an annual interest rate of 10% compounded monthly?

Solution (See Fig. 8.10.)

$$F = A\left[\frac{(1 + i)^n - 1}{i}\right]$$

where

$A = \$90$

$i = 0.10/12$ (monthly compounding)

$n = 12 \times 3 = 36$ (# of periods)

$$F = 90\left[\frac{(1 + 0.10/12)^{36} - 1}{0.10/12}\right]$$

$$= \$3\,760.36$$

Figure 8.10

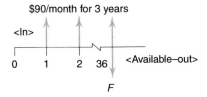

$90/month for 3 years

Saver's cash-flow diagram.

Example Problem 8.5 $10 000 will be needed in eight years to replace a piece of equipment. How much money must be placed annually into a sinking fund that earns 7% interest? Assume the first payment is made today and the last one eight years from today with interest compounded annually.

Solution   (See Fig. 8.11.)

$$F = A\left[\frac{(1 + i)^n - 1}{i}\right]$$

$$A = \frac{F(i)}{(1 + i)^n - 1}$$

$$= \frac{(10\,000)(0.07)}{(1.07)^9 - 1}$$

$$= \$834.86$$

Note that $n = 9$ in this example because nine payments will be made. For the sinking-fund formula to be valid, the time of the initial payment ("today," in the problem) must be considered to be the end of the first period.

8.5.2   Annual Present Worth (Installment Loan)

A second and very popular way that annuities are used to retire a debt is by making periodic payments instead of a single large payment at the end of a given time period. This time-payment plan, offered by most retail businesses and lending institutions, is called an *installment loan*. It is also used to amortize (pay off with a sinking-fund approach) bond issues. A cash-flow diagram for this scheme is illustrated in Figure 8.12.

Figure 8.11

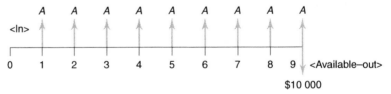

Company's cash-flow diagram.

Figure 8.12

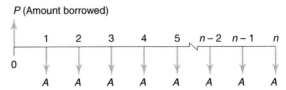

Buyer's cash-flow diagram.

In this case the principal amount P is the size of the debt and A is the amount of the periodic payment that must be made with interest compounded at the end of each period. It can be seen that if P were removed from the time line and F placed at the end of the nth period, the time line would represent a sinking fund. Furthermore, it can be shown that F would also be the value of P placed at compound interest for n periods $[F = P(1 + i)^n]$. Likewise, P can be termed the present worth of the sinking fund that would be accumulated by the deposits. Therefore, since

$$F = P(1 + i)^n \text{ and } F = A\left[\frac{(1 + i)^n - 1}{i}\right]$$

the present worth becomes

$$P = A\left[\frac{(1 + i)^n - 1}{i(1 + i)^n}\right] = A\left[\frac{1 - (1 + i)^{-n}}{i}\right] \tag{8.7}$$

The term within the brackets is known as the present worth of a sinking fund, or the *uniform annual payment present-worth factor*.

It follows that

$$A = P\left[\frac{i(1 + i)^n}{(1 + i)^n - 1}\right] \tag{8.8}$$

where the term in brackets is most commonly called the *capital recovery factor*, or the *uniform annual payment annuity factor*, and is the reciprocal of the uniform annual payment present-worth factor.

A third way use of annuities is when a sum of money is returned in monthly installments at retirement. The formula that applies is Eq. (8.7), and the cash-flow diagram is shown in Figure 8.13.

The problem could be stated as follows: How much money P must be available at retirement so that A dollars can be received for n periods, assuming i interest rate? Equation (8.7) can be solved for the amount of money P that must be accumulated by retirement if an amount A is to be withdrawn for n periods at a given interest rate.

To understand the concept of installment loans and retirement plans, consider the following example problems.

Figure 8.13

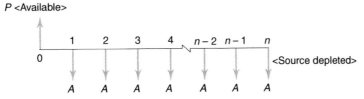

Series of monthly withdrawals.

198
Chapter 8
Introduction to Engineering Economics

Example Problem 8.6 Suppose you borrow \$1 000 from a bank for one year at 9% annual interest compounded monthly. Consider paying the loan back by two different methods:

1. You keep the \$1 000 for one year and pay back the bank at the end of the year in a lump sum. What would you owe? (See Fig. 8.14; note that the time line shown is in years but interest is compounded monthly.)

Solution

$$F = 1\,000(1 + 0.0075)^{12}$$
$$= \$1\,093.81$$

2. The second method is the installment loan. You borrow \$1 000 from the bank and repay it in equal monthly payments. What is the amount of each payment? (See Fig. 8.15.)

Solution

From Eq. (8.8):

$$A = P\left[\frac{i(1 + i)^n}{(1 + i)^n - 1}\right]$$
$$= 1\,000\left[\frac{0.0075(1 + 0.0075)^{12}}{(1 + 0.0075)^{12} - 1}\right]$$
$$= \$87.45$$

Figure 8.14

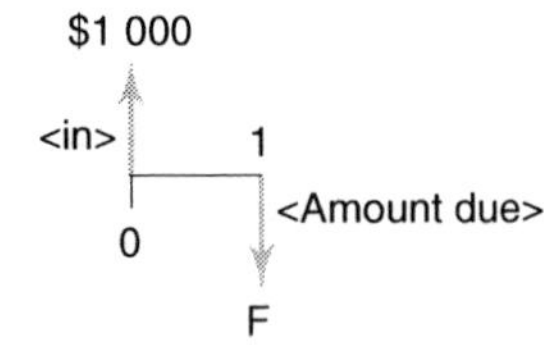

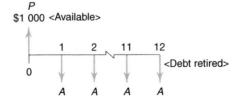

Borrower's cash-flow diagram.

Figure 8.15

Borrower's cash-flow diagram.

Example Problem 8.7   A used automobile that has a total cost of $15 500 is to be purchased in part by trading in an older vehicle for which $6 250 is allowed. The balance will be financed over three years. If the interest rate is 8.5% per year, compounded monthly, what are the monthly payments? The first installment is to be paid at the end of the first month. (See Fig. 8.16.)

Solution   From Eq. (8.8):

$$A = (15\ 500 - 6\ 250)\left[\frac{\dfrac{(0.085)}{12}\left(1 + \dfrac{0.085}{12}\right)^{36}}{\left(1 + \dfrac{0.085}{12}\right)^{36} - 1}\right]$$

$$= \$292.00$$

Another way of expressing the relationship is by saying that $9 250 (that is, $15 500 − $6 250) is the present worth of 36 monthly payments of $292.00, beginning in one month at 8.5% annual interest compounded monthly.

Example Problem 8.8   Suppose that the auto purchase described in Example Problem 8.7 is modified so that no payment is made until six months after the purchase and then a total of 36 monthly payments are made. Now, what is the amount of each monthly payment? (See Fig. 8.17.)

Figure 8.16

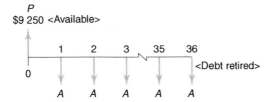

Purchaser's cash-flow diagram.

Figure 8.17

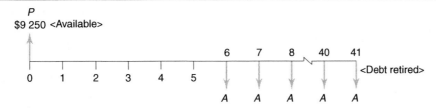

Purchaser's cash-flow diagram.

Solution Balance due after trade-in = \$15 500 − \$6 250 = \$9 250. Balance due after five months = \$9 250$(1 + 0.085/12)^5$ = \$9 582.28. Note that the unpaid balance is compounded for only five months because the first payment marks the end of the first period of the annuity. This is called a *deferred annuity*.

The monthly payment is then

$$A = 9\,582.28 \left[\frac{\frac{(0.085)}{12}\left(1 + \frac{0.085}{12}\right)^{36}}{\left(1 + \frac{0.085}{12}\right)^{36} - 1} \right]$$

$$= \$302.49$$

Example Problem 8.9 Amy and Kevin are purchasing their first home and have arranged for a mortgage of \$200 000 at a fixed annual interest rate of 6.75% compounded monthly for a period of 30 years.

(a) What will be their monthly payment?
(b) At the end of year 10, what amount will be necessary to pay off the loan?
(c) If at the end of the first year they pay an additional sum of \$50 000 on the principal, what is the remaining principal?
(d) If they continue with the monthly payments as found in part (a), how many payments will be necessary to retire the debt following the \$50 000 payment described in part (c)?

Solution

(a) This problem describes a standard installment loan, so Eq. (8.8) applies. (See Fig. 8.18.)

$$A = P\left[\frac{i(1 + i)^n}{(1 + i)^n - 1} \right]$$

$$= 200\,000 \left[\frac{\frac{(0.0675)}{12}\left(1 + \frac{0.0675}{12}\right)^{360}}{\left(1 + \frac{0.0675}{12}\right)^{360} - 1} \right]$$

$$= \$1\,297.20$$

Figure 8.18

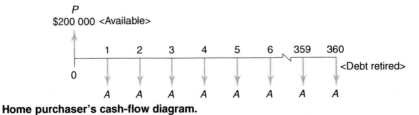

Home purchaser's cash-flow diagram.

Figure 8.19

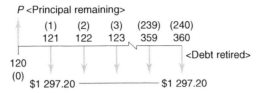

Purchaser's cash-flow diagram for last 240 months.

    (b) The amount necessary to pay off the loan at year 10 is the principal remaining. This can be viewed as the present worth of the monthly payments following year 10. (See Fig. 8.19.) From Eq. (8.7):

$$P = A\left[\frac{(1 + i)^n - 1}{i(1 + i)^n}\right]$$

$$= 1\,297.20\left[\frac{\left(1 + \dfrac{0.0675}{12}\right)^{240} - 1}{\left(\dfrac{0.0675}{12}\right)\left(1 + \dfrac{0.0675}{12}\right)^{240}}\right]$$

$$= \$170\,602.50$$

    (c) The principal remaining at the end of the first year can be found following the procedure in part (b). (See Fig. 8.20.)

$$P = 1\,297.20\left[\frac{\left(1 + \dfrac{0.0675}{12}\right)^{348} - 1}{\left(\dfrac{0.0675}{12}\right)\left(1 + \dfrac{0.0675}{12}\right)^{348}}\right]$$

$$= \$197\,869.08$$

After the lump-sum payment of $50 000 the principal remaining is $197 869.08 − $50 000 = $147 869.08.

    (d) Equation (8.7) applies here with the present worth of $147 869.08, the monthly payment equal to $1 297.20, and the number of payments unknown. (See Fig. 8.21.)

$$147\,869.08 = 1\,297.20\left[\frac{\left(1 + \dfrac{0.0675}{12}\right)^{n} - 1}{\left(\dfrac{0.675}{12}\right)\left(1 + \dfrac{0.0675}{12}\right)^{n} - 1}\right]$$

Figure 8.20

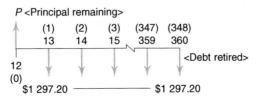

Purchaser's cash-flow diagram for last 29 years.

Figure 8.21

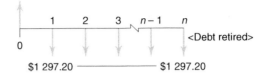

$1 297.20 ——————————— $1 297.20

Purchaser's cash-flow diagram.

Thus

$$(0.64120)\left(1 + \frac{0.0675}{12}\right)^n = \left(1 + \frac{0.0675}{12}\right)^n - 1$$

$$\left(1 + \frac{0.0675}{12}\right)^n = 2.7871$$

Taking the logarithm of both sides, we have

$$n \log\left(1 + \frac{0.0675}{12}\right) = \log 2.787\,1$$

Then

$$n = \frac{\log 2.7871}{\log\left(1 + \frac{0.0675}{12}\right)}$$

$$= 182.73$$

As is often the case, the computed number of periods is not an integer value, meaning that there will be 182 full payments of $1 297.20 followed by a partial payment required to retire the mortgage.

Example Problem 8.10   Suppose following graduation you decide to purchase a vehicle and borrow $15 000 at 8.5% annual interest, compounded monthly, to finance the deal. The agreement requires monthly payments for a period of two years. Use a spreadsheet to calculate your payment schedule and prepare it so that the amount borrowed and the annual interest rate can be changed with simple cell modifications. Include the amount of each payment, the amount of each payment going toward principal and toward interest, the principal remaining after each payment, and a running total of the interest paid.

Solution   *Note:* The spreadsheet application shown in this example is Microsoft Excel. Many other applications can be used with small coding changes.

Figure 8.22

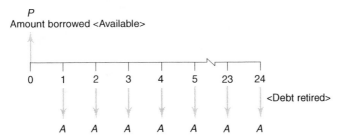

Purchaser's cash-flow diagram.

The cash-flow diagram for you as the purchaser is shown in Figure 8.22. As the problem is described, it fits the installment loan definition.

Table 8.4 shows the cell contents (values and formulas) used to compute the results. Please note the following points:

1. Cell C3 contains the principal amount and can be changed.
2. Cell C4 contains the annual interest rate in percent and can be changed. (Coded as 8.5%; formula view shows as 0.085.)
3. Cell C5 is the loan term in years and can be changed, but will not be changed in this example because the loan term affects the total number of payments and therefore the size of the spreadsheet.
4. A built-in function, PMT, is used in cell C6 to compute the payment based on the monthly interest rate, the number of payments, and the principal amount. Equation (8.7) could have been coded here rather than using the spreadsheet function.
5. Cells B12 through B35 all contain the value computed in C6.
6. The split of the payment into interest and principal is handled by first computing the interest for the first period (cell D12) and then subtracting it from cell B12 to obtain the portion of the payment applied to the principal. Note that cells D12 through D35 depend on the principal at the beginning of the period. The principal at the beginning of the first period is the original amount borrowed.
7. The principal remaining is found by subtracting the portion of the payment going to principal (column C) from the previous principal amount.
8. Finally, the total interest paid is simply a running sum.
9. You should note that this spreadsheet calculates values to greater precision than is displayed and thus there will be places where sums or differences will be off by a penny in the display. This can be prevented by using an option "precision as displayed" which actually changes the data at that point in the spreadsheet to the value displayed. The general result will be that the last payment will then be in error by a few cents.

Table 8.4 Spreadsheet Cell Contents (Values and Formulas)

	A	B	C	D	E	F
1			AUTO FINANCE SCHEDULE			
2						
3	Amount borrowed		15000			
4	Annual interest rate (percent)		0.085			
5	Loan term (years)		2			
6	Monthly payment		=PMT(C4/(12) .C5*12,-C3)			
7						
8			PAYMENT SCHEDULE			
9						
10	Number	Amount paid	Principal	Interest	Principal remaining	Total interest
11	0				=C3	
12	1	=$C$6	=B12-D12	=$C$4/(12)*E11	=E11-C12	=F11+D12
13	2	=$C$6	=B13-D13	=$C$4/(12)*E12	=E12-C13	=F12+D13
14	3	=$C$6	=B14-D14	=$C$4/(12)*E13	=E13-C14	=F13+D14
15	4	=$C$6	=B15-D15	=$C$4/(12)*E14	=E14-C15	=F14+D15
16	5	=$C$6	=B16-D16	=$C$4/(12)*E15	=E15-C16	=F15+D16
17	6	=$C$6	=B17-D17	=$C$4/(12)*E16	=E16-C17	=F16+D17
18	7	=$C$6	=B18-D18	=$C$4/(12)*E17	=E17-C18	=F17+D18
19	8	=$C$6	=B19-D19	=$C$4/(12)*E18	=E18-C19	=F18+D19
20	9	=$C$6	=B20-D20	=$C$4/(12)*E19	=E19-C20	=F19+D20
21	10	=$C$6	=B21-D21	=$C$4/(12)*E20	=E20-C21	=F20+D21
22	11	=$C$6	=B22-D22	=$C$4/(12)*E21	=E21-C22	=F21+D22
23	12	=$C$6	=B23-D23	=$C$4/(12)*E22	=E22-C23	=F22+D23
24	13	=$C$6	=B24-D24	=$C$4/(12)*E23	=E23-C24	=F23+D24
25	14	=$C$6	=B25-D25	=$C$4/(12)*E24	=E24-C25	=F24+D25
26	15	=$C$6	=B26-D26	=$C$4/(12)*E25	=E25-C26	=F25+D26
27	16	=$C$6	=B27-D27	=$C$4/(12)*E26	=E26-C27	=F26+D27
28	17	=$C$6	=B28-D28	=$C$4/(12)*E27	=E27-C28	=F27+D28
29	18	=$C$6	=B29-D29	=$C$4/(12)*E28	=E28-C29	=F28+D29
30	19	=$C$6	=B30-D30	=$C$4/(12)*E29	=E29-C30	=F29+D30
31	20	=$C$6	=B31-D31	=$C$4/(12)*E30	=E30-C31	=F30+D31
32	21	=$C$6	=B32-D32	=$C$4/(12)*E31	=E31-C32	=F31+D32
33	22	=$C$6	=B33-D33	=$C$4/(12)*E32	=E32-C33	=F32+D33
34	23	=$C$6	=B34-D34	=$C$4/(12)*E33	=E33-C34	=F33+D34
35	24	=$C$6	=B35-D35	=$C$4/(12)*E34	=E34-C35	=F34+D35

Table 8.5 shows the resulting values. Once the spreadsheet is prepared, you could readily change the amount borrowed and/or the interest rate to learn how the payment schedule would change.

Example Problem 8.11 Modify the spreadsheet developed in Example Problem 8.10 so that the following series of payments (always greater than or equal to the minimum payment for a two-year loan except for the final one) can be made:

Table 8.5 Spreadsheet Values for Example Problem 8.10

	A	B	C	D	E	F
1			AUTO FINANCE SCHEDULE			
2						
3	Amount borrowed		$15,000			
4	Annual interest rate(percent)		8.50%			
5	Loan term (years)		2			
6	Monthly payment		$681.84			
7						
8			PAYMENT SCHEDULE			
9						
10	Number	Amount paid	Principal	Interest	Principal remaining	Total interest
11	0				$15,000.00	
12	1	$681.84	$575.59	$106.25	$14,424.41	$106.25
13	2	$681.84	$579.66	$102.17	$13,844.75	$208.42
14	3	$681.84	$583.77	$98.07	$13,260.98	$306.49
15	4	$681.84	$587.90	$93.93	$12,673.08	$400.42
16	5	$681.84	$592.07	$89.77	$12,081.01	$490.19
17	6	$681.84	$596.26	$85.57	$11,484.75	$575.76
18	7	$681.84	$600.48	$81.35	$10,884.27	$657.11
19	8	$681.84	$604.74	$77.10	$10,279.53	$734.21
20	9	$681.84	$609.02	$72.81	$9,670.51	$807.02
21	10	$681.84	$613.34	$68.50	$9,057.17	$875.52
22	11	$681.84	$617.68	$64.15	$8,439.49	$939.68
23	12	$681.84	$622.06	$59.78	$7,817.44	$999.46
24	13	$681.84	$626.46	$55.37	$7,190.98	$1,054.83
25	14	$681.84	$630.90	$50.94	$6,560.08	$1,105.77
26	15	$681.84	$635.37	$46.47	$5,924.71	$1,152.23
27	16	$681.84	$639.87	$41.97	$5,284.84	$1,194.20
28	17	$681.84	$644.40	$37.43	$4,640.44	$1,231.64
29	18	$681.84	$648.97	$32.87	$3,991.47	$1,264.51
30	19	$681.84	$653.56	$28.27	$3,337.91	$1,292.78
31	20	$681.84	$658.19	$23.64	$2,679.72	$1,316.42
32	21	$681.84	$662.85	$18.98	$2,016.87	$1,335.40
33	22	$681.84	$667.55	$14.29	$1,349.32	$1,349.69
34	23	$681.84	$672.28	$9.56	$677.04	$1,359.25
35	24	$681.84	$677.04	$4.80	$0.00	$1,364.04

1. $681.84	**10.** $900.00
2. $681.84	**11.** $700.00
3. $700.00	**12.** $800.00
4. $681.84	**13.** $1 000.00
5. $1 000.00	**14.** $681.84
6. $681.84	**15.** $1 000.00
7. $1 000.00	**16.** $1 500.00
8. $1 000.00	**17.** $1 000.00
9. $1 500.00	**18.** $569.25

Assume that any amount paid that is greater than $681.84 will be applied toward the principal and that no prepayment penalty is added.

Solution   Table 8.6 shows the cell contents for this case. Column B is no longer constant and the specific value must be placed in the cells since no pattern of payments is evident. Column E is modified to test whether there is principal remaining. If not, a value of zero is entered in the cell. Finally, Table 8.7 provides the numerical solution to the problem.

Table 8.6   Spreadsheet Cell Contents for Example Problem 8.11

	A	B	C	D	E	F
1			AUTO FINANCE SCHEDULE			
2						
3	Amount borrowed		1500			
4	Annual interest rate (percent)		0.085			
5	Loan term (years)		2			
6	Monthly payment (minimum)		=PMT(C4/(12), C5*12,-C3)			
7						
8			PAYMENT SCHEDULE			
9						
10	Number	Amount paid	Principal	Interest	Principal remaining	Total interest
11	0				=C3	
12	1	681.84	=B12-D12	=$C$4/(12)*E11	=IF(B12>0, E11-C12, 0)	=F11+D12
13	2	681.84	=B13-D13	=$C$4/(12)*E12	=IF(B13>0, E14-C13, 0)	=F12+D13
14	3	700	=B14-D14	=$C$4/(12)*E13	=IF(B14>0, E15-C14, 0)	=F13+D14
15	4	681.84	=B15-D15	=$C$4/(12)*E14	=IF(B15>0, E16-C15, 0)	=F14+D15
16	5	1000	=B16-D16	=$C$4/(12)*E15	=IF(B16>0, E17-C16, 0)	=F15+D16
17	6	681.84	=B17-D17	=$C$4/(12)*E16	=IF(B17>0, E18-C17, 0)	=F16+D17
18	7	1000	=B18-D18	=$C$4/(12)*E17	=IF(B18>0, E19-C18, 0)	=F17+D18
19	8	1000	=B19-D19	=$C$4/(12)*E18	=IF(B19>0, E18-C19, 0)	=F18+D19
20	9	1500	=B20-D20	=$C$4/(12)*E19	=IF(B20>0, E19-C20, 0)	=F19+D20
21	10	900	=B21-D21	=$C$4/(12)*E20	=IF(B21>0, E22-C21, 0)	=F20+D21
22	11	700	=B22-D22	=$C$4/(12)*E21	=IF(B22>0, E23-C22, 0)	=F21+D22
23	12	800	=B23-D23	=$C$4/(12)*E22	=IF(B23>0, E24-C23, 0)	=F22+D23
24	13	1000	=B24-D24	=$C$4/(12)*E23	=IF(B24>0, E25-C24, 0)	=F23+D24
25	14	681.84	=B25-D25	=$C$4/(12)*E24	=IF(B25>0, E26-C25, 0)	=F24+D25
26	15	1000	=B26-D26	=$C$4/(12)*E25	=IF(B26>0, E27-C26, 0)	=F25+D26
27	16	1500	=B27-D27	=$C$4/(12)*E26	=IF(B27>0, E28-C27, 0)	=F26+D27
28	17	1000	=B28-D28	=$C$4/(12)*E27	=IF(B28>0, E29-C28, 0)	=F27+D28
29	18	569.25	=B29-D29	=$C$4/(12)*E28	=IF(B29>0, E28-C29, 0)	=F28+D29
30	19		=B30-D30	=$C$4/(12)*E29	=IF(B30>0, E29-C30, 0)	=F29+D30
31	20		=B31-D31	=$C$4/(12)*E30	=IF(B31>0, E30-C31, 0)	=F30+D31
32	21		=B32-D32	=$C$4/(12)*E31	=IF(B32>0, E31-C32, 0)	=F31+D32
33	22		=B33-D33	=$C$4/(12)*E32	=IF(B33>0, E32-C33, 0)	=F32+D33
34	23		=B34-D34	=$C$4/(12)*E33	=IF(B34>0, E33-C34, 0)	=F33+D34
35	24		=B35-D35	=$C$4/(12)*E34	=IF(B35>0, E34-C35, 0)	=F34+D35

Table 8.7 Spreadsheet Values for Example Problem 8.11

	A	B	C	D	E	F
1			AUTO FINANCE SCHEDULE			
2						
3	Amount borrowed		$15,000			
4	Annual interest rate (percent)		8.50%			
5	Loan term (years)		2			
6	Monthly payment		$681.84			
7						
8			PAYMENT SCHEDULE			
9						
10	Number	Amount paid	Principal	Interest	Principal remaining	Total interest
11	0				$15,000.00	
12	1	$681.84	$575.59	$106.25	$14,424.41	$106.25
13	2	$681.84	$579.66	$102.17	$13,844.75	$208.42
14	3	$700.00	$601.93	$98.07	$13,242.81	$306.49
15	4	$681.84	$588.04	$93.80	$12,654.77	$400.29
16	5	$1000.00	$910.36	$89.64	$11,744.41	$489.93
17	6	$681.84	$598.65	$83.19	$11,145.76	$573.12
18	7	$1000.00	$921.05	$78.95	$10,224.71	$652.07
19	8	$1000.00	$927.57	$72.43	$9,297.13	$724.49
20	9	$1500.00	$1,434.15	$65.85	$7,862.99	$790.35
21	10	$900.00	$844.30	$55.70	$7,018.69	$846.05
22	11	$700.00	$650.28	$49.72	$6,368.40	$895.76
23	12	$800.00	$754.89	$45.11	$5,613.51	$940.87
24	13	$1000.00	$960.24	$39.76	$4,653.27	$980.63
25	14	$681.84	$648.88	$32.96	$4,004.39	$1,013.59
26	15	$1000.00	$971.64	$28.36	$3,032.76	$1,041.96
27	16	$1500.00	$1,478.52	$21.48	$1,554.24	$1,063.44
28	17	$1000.00	$988.99	$11.01	$565.25	$1,074.45
29	18	$569.25	$565.25	$4.00	$0.00	$1,078.45
30	19		$0.00	$0.00	$0.00	$1,078.45
31	20		$0.00	$0.00	$0.00	$1,078.45
32	21		$0.00	$0.00	$0.00	$1,078.45
33	22		$0.00	$0.00	$0.00	$1,078.45
34	23		$0.00	$0.00	$0.00	$1,078.45
35	24		$0.00	$0.00	$0.00	$1,078.45

Example Problem 8.12   Estimate the amount of money you will need to save for retirement. Assume that you want to continue to receive 80% of your current (just prior to retirement) take-home pay ($8 200/month) for 30 years and that you can earn 12% interest on your retirement funds.

Solution   The cash-flow diagram is shown in Figure 8.23.

Eighty percent of $8 200 = $6 560/month

Number of periods = 30 years × 12 months per year = 360 months

Interest (i) = 0.12/12 = 0.01

$$P = 6\,560\left[\frac{1 - (1 + 0.01)^{-360}}{0.01}\right]$$

$P = \$637\,752.23$

Note: This calculation does not include taxes collected by federal and state governments. You should plan on saving an additional 35 to 50% to cover tax payments.

8.5.3 Capitalized Cost (Infinite Life Analysis)

Capitalized cost (CC) refers to the present worth (P) of a project or investment that is assumed to last forever. Public works projects like dams, railroads, and irrigation systems are typical capitalized-cost calculations. Investments requiring perpetual (infinite) payments such as endowed scholarships or trusts also rely on capitalized-cost calculations.

Capitalized cost can be used to extend the retirement planning problem in Example Prob. 8.12. Suppose that you want the monthly amount (A) to continue after your death to be disbursed to your heirs. Begin with Eq. 8.7:

$$P = A\left[\frac{1 - (1 + i)^{-n}}{i}\right]$$

and consider that, as n approaches infinity (∞), the numerator becomes 1, yielding

$$P = \frac{A}{i} \tag{8.9}$$

We can restate the problem by asking what amount of money P must be available at retirement so that an amount A can be withdrawn each month and never affect the principal amount P.

Figure 8.23

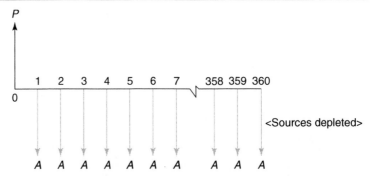

Monthly withdrawals of $6 560 for 360 months.

If we use the compound interest formula, that is, $F = P(1 + i)^n$, and find the amount of interest generated for one month (here that is equal to A), then $F = P + A = P(1 + i)^1$. If we solve this equation for P, then

$$P = \frac{A}{i}$$

Given an interest rate earned by the annuity (say, $i = 0.12/12$) and a fixed monthly income (say, $A = \$6\,560$), $P = \$656\,000$.

Example Problem 8.13   Recalculate Example Problem 8.12 assuming annual interest of 7% and desired perpetual monthly income of $6 560.

Solution (See Fig. 8.24.)

$$P_{CC} = \frac{A}{i} = \frac{6\,560}{(0.07/12)} = \$1\,124\,571.43$$

Example Problem 8.14   A wealthy alum from your institution wishes to provide ten $5 000 scholarships to deserving engineering students starting next year and to continue giving the same number of scholarships and the same dollar amount of scholarship money every year forever. Assuming that 8% interest can be earned annually, how much money would this alum need to turn over to the university today?

Solution Ten scholarships at $5 000 each = $50 000 per year = A

$$P = \frac{A}{i} = \frac{50\,000}{(0.08)} = \$625\,000$$

Note in this problem the $50 000 amount is spent only once a year (not every month as in previous examples), thus the interest rate is the annual 8%.

8.5.4 Arithmetic Gradients

Now consider the case where annual cash flows do not occur in equal amounts for every period. An arithmetic gradient is a cash-flow series which either

Figure 8.24

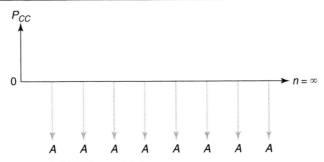

Capitalized cost of a $6 560 monthly income.

Figure 8.25

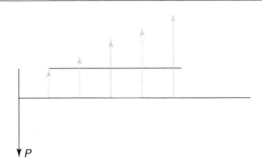

increases or decreases uniformly. That is, income or payments change by the same amount each interest period. The amount of the increase or decrease is the gradient (G). Consider the cash-flow series shown in Figure 8.25.

Cash flows can be resolved into two components with present-worth values of P′ and P″ as shown in Figure 8.26.

We already have an equation for P′ (Equation 8.7) and we can use the present worth equation to derive an equation for P″. The result is

$$P'' = G\left[\frac{(1 + i)^n - in - 1}{i^2(1 + i)^n}\right] \tag{8.10}$$

So, the overall present worth for the arithmetic gradient is $P = P' + P''$ or

$$P = A\left[\frac{1 - (1 + i)^{-n}}{i}\right] + G\left[\frac{(1 + i)^n - in - 1}{i^2(1 + i)^n}\right]$$

Note in Figure 8.26 that the gradient factor begins in period 2 and P″ is located in period zero. Equation 8.10 takes into account that there are $(n - 1)$ terms containing G.

Figure 8.26

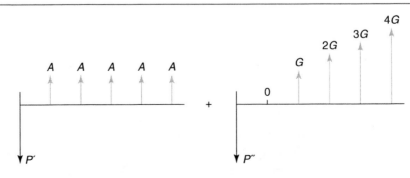

Example Problem 8.15   The annual receipts from operation of a gravel pit are expected to decrease until the pit closes. If next year's receipts are $11 200, and the second year's receipts are $9 800, determine the following:
  (a) How many years will it be before the income stream is zero?
  (b) Draw a cash-flow diagram to depict the situation.
  (c) What is the present worth of the income assuming an annual interest rate of 11%?

Solution
  (a) Number of years remaining = [First-year receipts/annual decrease (gradient)] = [$11 200/($11 200 − $9 800)] = 8 years
Thus, there would be zero income in year 9.
  (b) See Figure 8.27.

  (c) $P = A\left[\dfrac{1-(1+i)^{-n}}{i}\right] - G\left[\dfrac{(1+i)^{n}-in-1}{i^{2}(1+i)^{n}}\right]$

  $P = 11\,200\left[\dfrac{1-(1+0.11)^{-8}}{0.11}\right]$

  $-\,1\,400\left[\dfrac{(1+0.11)^{8}-0.11(8)-1}{(0.11)^{2}(1+0.11)^{8}}\right]$

  $P = 57\,636.57 - 21\,314.50 = \$36\,323.97$

Notice that the value of n in the gradient factor is 8, not 7. The gradient factor is derived based on $(n-1)$ terms containing G. In the case, there are seven terms containing G, thus $(n-1)=7$, so $n=8$.

Example Problem 8.16   A manufacturing plant installed a new machining cell. It is expected that initial tooling, adjustments, and repair costs will be high but that the costs will decline for several years. The project costs are shown below:

Year	Costs
1	$2 400
2	$1 800
3	$1 200
4	$600

Figure 8.27

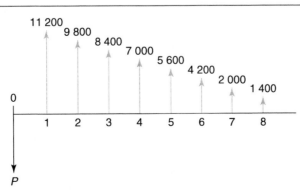

Arithmetic gradient for receipts at gravel pit.

(a) Draw a cash-flow diagram to depict this situation.

(b) What is the present worth of these projected costs if annual interest is 10%?

Solution

(a) See Figure 8.28.

(b) $P = A\left[\dfrac{1 - (1 + i)^{-n}}{i}\right] - G\left[\dfrac{(1 + i)^n - in - 1}{i^2(1 + i)^n}\right]$

$P = 2\,400\left[\dfrac{1 - (1 + 0.10)^{-4}}{0.10}\right] - 600\left[\dfrac{(1 + 0.10)^4 - 0.10(4) - 1}{(0.10)^2(1 + 0.10)^4}\right]$

$P = 7\,607.68 - 2\,626.87 = \$4\,980.81$

8.5.5 Geometric Gradients

Oftentimes, cash flows change by a constant percentage or uniform rate, g, in consecutive payment periods. This type of cash flow is called a geometric gradient series. An example of this is the maintenance costs for an automobile that begin at $150 the first year and are expected to increase at a uniform rate of 10% per year for the next four years. The general cash-flow diagram for geometric gradients is shown in Figure 8.29.

Just as we did for the arithmetic gradient, we can use the present-worth equation to derive two equations to find the present worth of this unique series of annual payments. Care must be taken to apply the appropriate formula based on whether the interest rate is equal (or not equal) to the annual rate of increase of the gradient (g).

$$P = A\left[\dfrac{1 - (1 + g)^n(1 + i)^{-n}}{i - g}\right] \text{ where } i \neq g \qquad (8.11)$$

$$P = A[n(1 + i)^{-1}] \text{ where } i = g \qquad (8.12)$$

Figure 8.28

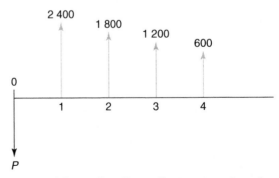

Arithmetic gradient for machining-cell tooling, adjustment, and repair costs.

Figure 8.29

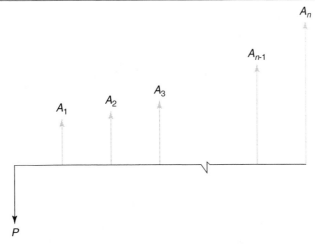

Geometric gradient cash flow.

Example Problem 8.17   The maintenance for an automobile is estimated to be $150 in the first year and is expected to increase at a uniform rate of 10% per year. What is the present worth of the cost of the first five years of maintenance if an 8% annual interest rate is assumed?

Solution   See Figure 8.30 for the cash-flow diagram.
See Table 8.8 for a year-by-year calculation of the present value (P).

Figure 8.30

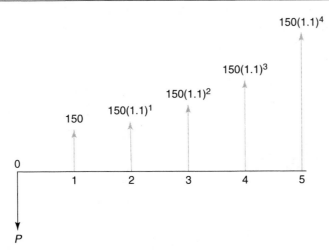

Geometric gradient for automobile maintenance.

Table 8.8   Automobile Maintenance Costs (Geometric Gradient)

Year		Cash Flow, $	Convert to P	P, $ (Maintenance)
1	$150	150.00	$150(1 + 0.08)^{-1}$	138.89
2	$150.00 + 10\%(150.00) = 150(1 + 0.10)^1$	165.00	$165(1 + 0.08)^{-2}$	141.46
3	$165.00 + 10\%(165.00) = 150(1 + 0.10)^2$	181.50	$181.50(1.08)^{-3}$	144.08
4	$181.50 + 10\%(181.50) = 150(1 + 1.10)^3$	199.65	$199.65(1.08)^{-4}$	146.75
5	$199.65 + 10\%(199.65) = 150(1 + 0.10)^4$	219.62	$219.62(1.08)^{-5}$	149.47
				720.65

$$P = A\left[\frac{1 - (1 + g)^n(1 + i)^{-n}}{i - g}\right]$$

$$P = 150\left[\frac{1 - (1 + 0.10)^5(1 + 0.08)^{-5}}{0.08 - 0.10}\right]$$

$$P = 150(4.8043) = \$720.65$$

Example Problem 8.18   Recalculate Example Problem 8.17 using a 10% annual interest rate.

Solution (See Fig. 8.30.) *Note:* The cash-flow diagram is identical to the one for Example Problem 8.17; only the interest rate has changed.

Using Eq. (8.12):

$$P = A[n(1 + i)^{-1}]$$
$$P = 150[5(1 + 0.10)^{-1}]$$
$$P = \$681.82$$

Example Problem 8.19   The utility bill for a small paper recycling center is expected to increase by $528 per year. If the utility cost in year 1 was $4 000, what is the equivalent uniform annual worth through year 8 if the interest rate is 15% per year?

Solution (See Fig. 8.31.)

Since we are to solve for the annual worth, we can first find the present worth of the gradient:

$$P = G\left[\frac{(1 + i)^n - in - 1}{i^2(1 + i)n}\right]$$

$$P = 528\left[\frac{(1 + 0.15)^8 - (0.15)(8) - 1}{(0.15)^2(1 + 0.15)^8}\right]$$

$$P = 528(12.4807) = \$6\ 589.82$$

Figure 8.31

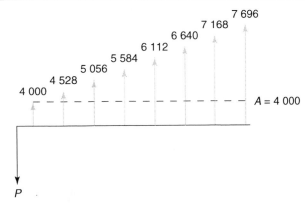

Arithmetic gradient cash flow for utility bill.

Then we can find the annual equivalent of this present worth:

$$A = 6\,589.82 \left[\frac{0.15(1.15)^8}{(1.15)^8 - 1} \right]$$

$$A = \$1\,468.54$$

Finally, we add the initial $4 000 annual cost to the value just calculated to find the equivalent annual worth:

$$A = 4\,000 + 1\,468.54 = \$5\,468.54$$

Thus, for the eight years we are interested in, the variable cost of utilities can be resolved into an equivalent uniform annual cost (EUAC = $5 468.54).

8.6   Summary Table

Table 8.9 summarizes the equations used in this chapter.

Problems

8.1   Determine the difference in interest earned on $5 000 for 15 years at 6% simple interest to that earned when the interest is compounded annually.

8.2   What is the present worth of $1 000 payable in five years, if money is thought to be worth (*a*) 5%, (*b*) 15%, (*c*) 25%?

8.3   How much must be invested now to grow to $30 000 in seven years if the annual interest rate is 8.0% compounded (*a*) annually, (*b*) semiannually, (*c*) monthly?

8.4   Compute the unknown values for each of the following cash-flow diagrams (time shown in years and interest compounded annually).

(*a*) Figure 8.32   (*b*) Figure 8.33
(*c*) Figure 8.34   (*d*) Figure 8.35

Table 8.9 Summary Table

Find/Given	Sample Cash-Flow Diagram	Formula Name/Eq. No.	Formula
To find F Given P		Compound Amount Eq. (8.2)	$F = P(1 + i)^n$
To find P Given F		Present Worth Eq. (8.3)	$P = F(1 + i)^{-n}$
To find F Given A		Future Compound Amount Eq. (8.6)	$F = A\left[\dfrac{(1 + i)^n - 1}{i}\right]$
To find A Given F		Sinking Fund Eq. (8.5)	$A = F\left[\dfrac{i}{(1 + i)^n - 1}\right]$
To find A Given P		Capital Recovery Eq. (8.8)	$A = P\left[\dfrac{i(1 + i)^n}{(1 + i)^n - 1}\right]$
To find P Given A		Present Compound Amount Eq. (8.7)	$P = A\left[\dfrac{(1 + i)^n - 1}{i(1 + i)^n}\right]$
To find P Given G (Arithmetic)		Arithmetic Gradient Present Worth Eq. (8.10)	$P = G\left[\dfrac{(1 + i)^n - in - 1}{i^2(1 + i)^n}\right]$
To find P Given G (Geometric)		Geometric Gradient Present Worth Eq. (8.11) when $i \neq g$ Eq. (8.12) when $i = g$	$P = A\left[\dfrac{1 - (1 + g)^n(1 + i)^{-n}}{i - g}\right]$ $P = A\left[n(1 + i)^{-1}\right]$

8.5   Your real estate taxes are $3 600 per year with one-half due April 1 and the remainder due October 1 each year. What single sum of money must you place in an account earning 5.25% interest 15 months before the first payment is due in order to accumulate enough money to pay each tax bill? Assume monthly compounding.

217
Problems

Figure 8.32

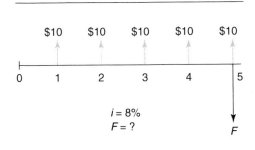

$i = 8\%$
$F = ?$

Figure 8.33

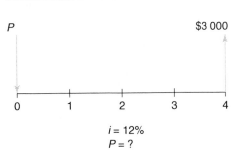

$i = 12\%$
$P = ?$

Figure 8.34

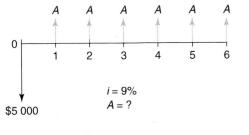

$i = 9\%$
$A = ?$

Figure 8.35

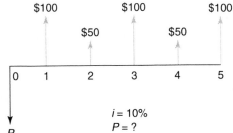

$i = 10\%$
$P = ?$

8.6   Your hometown has been given $1 000 000 from the estate of a citizen. The gift stipulates that the money cannot be used for five full years but must be invested. If the money is invested at 6.7% annual interest, how much will be available in five years if it is compounded (*a*) annually, (*b*) semiannually, (*c*) daily?

8.7   If the interest rate is 6.8% per year, how long will it take for an investment to double in value with semiannual, monthly, and daily compounding? Is the time to double a linear function of the compounding period?

8.8   You have just made an investment that will repay $976.12 at the end of each month; the first payment is one month from today and the last one is six years from today (thereby depleting the account).
   (*a*)   If the interest rate is 6.5% per year compounded monthly, what amount did you invest?
   (*b*)   If you can refuse all the payments and allow the money to earn at the same rate as stated, how much will you have at the end of six years?

8.9   You have made an investment that will yield $5 000 exactly 10 years from today. If the current interest rate is 6.2% compounded quarterly, what is your investment worth today?

8.10 Your parents have agreed to lend you $30 000 to help with your college expenses. They do not expect you to repay the loan or any interest until you have finished school (five years) and worked for 10 years. At the end of 15 years, they will require a lump-sum payment of $60 000.

(*a*) What equivalent annual interest rate are your parents charging for the use of their money?

(*b*) If your parents cannot lend you money and you have to borrow $30 000 at 6.6% annual interest, what would the lump-sum payment be at the end of 15 years?

8.11 You just borrowed $2 500 and have agreed to repay the bank $560 at the end of each of the next five years. What is the annual interest rate of the loan?

8.12 A firm purchased some equipment at a price of $50 000. The equipment resulted in an annual net savings of $2 000 per year during the 10 years it was used. At the end of 10 years, the equipment was sold for $40 000. Draw a cash-flow diagram that depicts this situation. Assuming $i = 8\%$, what was the equivalent cost to the company of this transaction on the purchase date?

8.13 Today you have a savings account of $15 620. Based on an annual interest rate of 4.2%, what equal amount can you withdraw from the account at the end of each month for three years and leave $4 000 in the account? If you could earn 6.0% interest, what would be the value of your monthly withdrawals?

8.14 On March 1 of this year you borrowed $75 000 toward materials for a product you hope to have on the market in November of this year. You have agreed upon an annual interest rate of 8.2% compounded monthly. You also have agreed to begin repaying the debt on December 1, making equal monthly payments until the loan is repaid on April 1 next year. What are your monthly payments?

8.15 Referring to Problem 8.14, suppose that you are unable to make the monthly payments and your creditor agrees to allow you to make a single payment on April 1 next year. How much will you owe at that time?

8.16 What uniform annual payment is equivalent to the following payment schedule if the interest rate is 7.5 percent, compounded annually?

(*a*) $600 at the end of the first year

(*b*) $800 at the end of the second year

(*c*) $1 200 at the end of the third year

(*d*) $2 000 at the end of the fourth year

(*e*) $2 400 at the end of the fifth year

8.17 If sales at your company are doubling every five years, what is the annual rate of increase? What annual rate of increase would be necessary for sales to double in four years? Three years?

8.18 You have $200 000 to invest, and you have decided to purchase bonds that will mature in six years. You have narrowed your choices to two types of bonds. The first class pays 8.75% annual interest. The second class pays 5.4% annual interest but is tax-free, both federal and state. Your income bracket is such that your highest income tax rate is 31% federal and the state income tax is 9%. Which is the better investment for you at this time? Assume that all conditions remain unchanged for the six-year period.

8.19 The average age of engineering students when they graduate is a little over 23 years. Let's assume that the working career of most engineers is exactly 40 years (retiring at 63). How much would an engineer need to save each month to have $3 million saved by the end of his or her working career? Assume $i = 7.0\%$ compounded monthly.

8.20 Assume that when you graduate you will owe a total of $29 500 in student loans. Assume that the interest rate is 7.5%, compounded monthly, and that the entire amount must be repaid within 10 years. Draw the cash-flow diagram that describes this situation. Determine what your minimum monthly payment will be.

8.21 On your 23rd birthday you open a 401K account (retirement account). At that time and on each succeeding birthday up to and including your 60th birthday, you deposit $2 000. During this period the interest rate on the account remains constant at 6.8%. No further payments are made, and beginning one month after your 65th birthday you begin withdrawing equal payments (the annual interest rate is the same as before). How much will you withdraw each month if the account is to be depleted with the last check on your 85th birthday? Assume annual compounding up to your 65th birthday and monthly compounding thereafter.

8.22 You wish to retire at age 66 and at the end of each month thereafter, for 30 years, to receive $5 000. Assume that you begin making monthly payments into an account at age 24. You continue these payments until age 66. If the interest rate is constant at 7.5%, how much must you deposit monthly between ages 24 and 66?

8.23 Your aunt has decided to give most of her wealth to charity and to retain for herself only enough money to provide for her living. She feels that $4 000 per month will provide for her needs. She will establish a trust fund at a bank that will pay 6% interest, compounded monthly. She has also arranged that upon her death, the balance in the account is to be paid to you. If she opens the trust fund and deposits enough money to withdraw her $4 000 a month forever, how much will you receive when your aunt dies?

8.24 You have borrowed as follows:

January 1, 2008	$52 000
July 1, 2009	$35 000
January 1, 2010	$30 000

The agreed-upon annual interest rate was 7.50% compounded semiannually. How much did you owe on July 1, 2010?
You agreed to make the first of 15 monthly payments on October 1, 2010. Assume the interest rate was still 7.50% but was compounded monthly. How much was each of the 15 payments?

8.25 Compute the unknown values for each of the following cash-flow diagrams (time shown in years and interest compounded annually).

(*a*) Figure 8.36   (*b*) Figure 8.37
(*c*) Figure 8.38   (*d*) Figure 8.39

Figure 8.36

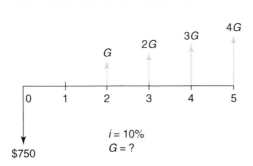

i = 10%
G = ?

Figure 8.37

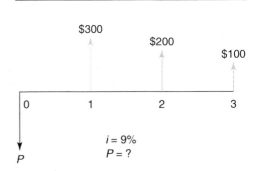

i = 9%
P = ?

Figure 8.38

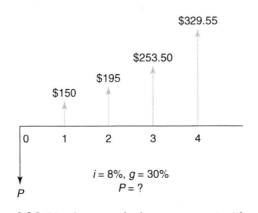

i = 8%, g = 30%
P = ?

Figure 8.39

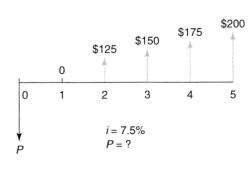

i = 7.5%
P = ?

8.26 You have reached an agreement with an auto dealer regarding a new car. She has offered you a trade-in allowance of $8 500 on your old car for a new one that she has "reluctantly" reduced to only $19 995 (before trade-in). She has further agreed upon a contract that requires you to pay $315.22 each of the next 48 months, beginning one month from today. What is your interest rate, expressed as an annual percentage? Give your answer to the nearest 0.01%. With your instructor's approval, write a computer program or use a spreadsheet to solve the problem.

8.27 You have been assigned the task of estimating the annual cost of operating and maintaining a new assembly line in your plant. Your calculations indicate that during the first four years the cost will be $400 000 per year; the next five years will cost $520 000 per year; and the following six years will cost $600 000 per year. If the interest rate is constant at 8.2% over the next 15 years, what will be the equivalent uniform annual cost (EUAC) of operation and maintenance?

8.28 You are buying a new home for $385 000. You have an agreement with the savings and loan company to borrow the needed money if you pay 15% in cash and monthly payments for 30 years at an interest rate of 6.25% compounded monthly.

(*a*) What monthly payments will be required?

(*b*) How much principal reduction will occur in the first payment?

(*c*) Prepare a spreadsheet that will show each payment, how much of each will go to principal and how much to interest, the current balance, and the cumulative interest paid.

(d) Repeat steps (*a*), (*b*), and (*c*) for interest rates of 6.50, 6.75, 7.00, 7.25, and 7.50%. Work as a team if approved by your instructor.

8.29 If you had started a savings account that paid 4.5%, compounded monthly, and your payments into the account were the monthly payments for 6.25% interest as in Problem 8.28, how long would you have had to make payments in order to purchase the home for cash? (Assume the same down-payment amount was available as in Problem 8.28.)

8.30 Your bank pays 2.25% on Christmas Club accounts. How much must you put into an account weekly beginning on January 2 in order to accumulate $1 000 on December 4? Assume weekly compounding and a non-leap year.

8.31 You can purchase a treasury note today for 94.2% of its face value of $20 000. Every six months you will receive an interest payment at the annual rate of 4.88% of face value. You can then invest your interest payments at the annual rate of 5.0% compounded semiannually. If the note matures six years from today, how much money will you receive from all the investments? Express this also as an annual rate of return.

8.32 What is the present worth of each of the following assets and liabilities and your net present worth?
(*a*) You deposited $2 000 exactly four years ago.
(*b*) You have a checking account with a current balance of $1 427.22.
(*c*) You must pay $3 500 exactly four years from now.
(*d*) Today you just made the 29th of 36 monthly payments of $142.60.
(*e*) You will receive $12 000 exactly six years from now.
Assume all annual interest rates are 5.5%. Assume monthly compounding in figuring part (*d*) and annual compounding for the rest.

8.33 Smith Fabrication has estimated that the purchase of a milling machine costing $160 000 will reduce the firm's fabrication expenses by $13 000 per month during a two-year period. If the milling machine has zero salvage value in two years, what is the firm's expected annual rate of return on investment? (*Rate of return* is the equivalent interest rate that must be earned on the investment to produce the same income as the proposed project. What would be the rate of return if the salvage value for 50% of the purchase price? If approved by your instructor, write a computer program or use a spreadsheet to solve the problem. Repeat for expense reductions of $13 500, $14 000, $14 500 $15 000 and $15 500 per month.

8.34 Engineers at Specialty Manufacturing are writing a justification report to support the purchase of a DNC milling center (mill, controller, microcomputer, installation, etc.). They have learned that the total initial cost will be $90 000. The labor savings and improved product quality will result in an estimated benefit to the company of $2 400 each month over a 10-year time period. If the salvage value of the center is about $12 000 in 10 years, what annual rate of return (annual percentage) on investment did the engineers calculate? Write a computer program or use a spreadsheet if assigned by your instructor. Repeat for estimated benefits of $2 600, $2 800, $3 000, $3 200 and $3 400 per month.

8.35 In payment for engineering services rendered, you have been offered the choice of (a) a lump sum payment of $8 000 to be paid five years from now, or (b) five yearly payments of $1 000 that begin one year from now and increase by $300 per year. Draw the cash-flow diagrams for parts (a) and (b). If $i = 10\%$ compounded annually, which option should you select?

8.36 What present expenditure is warranted for business that is expected to produce a savings of $8 000 per year that will decrease by $800 per year for nine years with an interest rate of 10%? Draw a cash-flow diagram that depicts this situation.

8.37 You have decided to invest a fixed percentage of your salary in the stock market at the end of each year. This year (today) you will invest $3 000. For the next five years, you expect that your salary will increase at an 8% annual rate and you will increase your savings at 8% per year. Thus, there will be a total of six investments ($3 000 today plus five more).

   (*a*) What is the present worth of your investment if the stock market yields a 15% annual rate?

   (*b*) What is the present worth of your investment if the market yields only 8%?

8.38 Many new engineering graduates purchase and finance new cars. Automobiles are typically financed for four years with monthly payments made to the lending agency. Assume you will need to borrow $18 000 with 48 monthly payments at 6.5% annual interest.

   (*a*) Write a computer program or prepare a spreadsheet to produce the mortgage table below:

Payment number	Monthly payment	Amount to principal	Amount to interest	Cumulative interest	Current balance
1	$xxx.xx	$xxx.xx	$xxx.xx	$xxx.xx	$xxx.xx
2	$xxx.xx	$xxx.xx	$xxx.xx	$xxx.xx	$xxx.xx
3	.	.	.	.	.
.	.	.	.	.	.
.	.	.	.	.	.
.	.	.	.	.	.

   (*b*) If you decided to pay the loan off at the end of 10 months, what amount is needed? At the end of 20 months? At the end of 40 months?

   (*c*) What is the cumulative interest paid in the first 12 payments? Second 12? Third 12? Last 12?

   (*d*) Repeat parts (*a*), (*b*), and (*c*) assuming the interest rate is 8.5% instead of 6.5%. The amount borrowed remains the same.

   (*e*) Repeat parts (*a*), (*b*), and (*c*) assuming you find it necessary to borrow $20 000. The interest rate is still 6.5%.

   (*f*) What is the result if you borrow $20 000 and the interest rate is 8.5%?

8.39 Many of you will eventually purchase a house. Few will have the total cash on hand, so it will be necessary to borrow money from a home loan agency. Often you can borrow the money at a fixed annual interest for, say, 15 or 30 years. Monthly payments are made to the lending agency. Write a computer program or use a spreadsheet to prepare mortgage tables similar to the one described in Problem 8.38 for the following situations:

   (*a*) $80 000 at 7% interest for 15 years

   (*b*) $80 000 at 6.25% interest for 15 years

   (*c*) $200 000 at 7% interest for 15 years

   (*d*) $200 000 at 7% interest for 30 years

   (*e*) Other cases as may be assigned

   (*f*) Critically examine the monthly payments and the cumulative interest amount produced by changing from a 30-year loan to a 15-year loan, all other parameters being constant.

CHAPTER **9**

Economics: Decision Making

Chapter Objectives

When you complete your study of this chapter, you will able to:

- Make considered economical decisions based on comparing alternatives

9.1 Economic Decision Making

An engineer makes use of engineering economy principals in a very practical way. They are used to analyze a situation so that an intelligent decision can be made. Normally, several alternatives are available, each having some strong attributes. The task is to compare each alternative and to select the one that appears superior, all things considered.

The most obvious method of comparing costs is to determine the total cost of each alternative. An immediate problem arises in that the various costs occur at different times, so the *total number of dollars spent is not a valid method of comparison*. You have seen that the present worth of an expenditure can be calculated. If this is done for all costs, the present worth of buying, operating, and maintaining two or more alternatives can then be compared. Simply stated, the present worth is the sum of money needed now to buy, maintain, and operate a facility for a given interest rate. The alternatives must obviously be compared for the same length of time, and replacements due to short-life expectancies must be considered.

A second method, preferred by those who work with annual budgets, is to calculate the *equivalent uniform annual cost* of each. The approach is similar to the present worth method, but the numerical value is in essence the annual contribution to a sinking fund that would produce a sum identical to the present worth placed at compound interest.

Many investors approach decisions on the basis of the profit that a venture will produce in terms of percent per year. The purchase of a piece of equipment, a parcel of land, or a new product line is thus viewed favorably only if it appears that it will produce an annual profit greater than the money could earn if invested elsewhere. The acceptable return fluctuates with the money market. Since there is doubt about the amount of the profit, and certainly there is a chance of a loss, it would not be prudent to proceed if the prediction of return was not considerably above "safe" investments such as bonds.

The example that follows illustrates the use of these two methods (present worth and average annual cost) and includes a third technique called *future worth* that provides a check.

Each method compares money at the same point in time or over the same time period. Each method is different yet each yields the same conclusion.

Example Problem 9.1   Consider the purchase of two computer-aided design (CAD) systems. Assume the annual interest rate is 12%.

	System 1	**System 2**
Initial cost	100 000	65 000
Maintenance & operating cost	4 000/year	8 000/year
Salvage	18 000 after 5 years	5 000 after 5 years

Using each of the three methods below, compare the two CAD systems and offer a recommendation:

1. Annual cost
2. Present worth
3. Future worth

Solution

1. Annual cost

(See Fig. 9.1.)

System 1

(a) Initial cost

$$A = P\left[\frac{i(1 + i)^n}{(1 + i)^n - 1}\right]$$

$P = 100\ 000$
$i = 0.12$
$n = 5$
$A = \$27\ 740.97/\text{year}$

(b) Maintenance and operating costs $MC = 4\ 000/\text{year}$

System 2

(a) Initial cost

$$A = P\left[\frac{i(1 + i)^n}{(1 + i)^n - 1}\right]$$

$P = 65\ 000$
$i = 0.12$
$n = 5$
$A = \$18\ 031.63/\text{year}$

(b) Maintenance and operating costs $MC = 8\ 000/\text{year}$

Figure 9.1

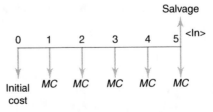

Company's cash-flow diagram (*MC = maintenance cost*).

(*c*) Salvage

$$F = A\left[\frac{(1 + i)^n - 1}{i}\right]$$

$$A = \left[\frac{F(i)}{(1 + i)^n - 1}\right]$$

$F = 18\ 000$
$i = 0.12$
$n = 5$
$A = \$(-)2\ 833.38/\text{year}$

(*c*) Salvage

$$F = A\left[\frac{(1 + i)^n - 1}{i}\right]$$

$$A = \left[\frac{F(i)}{(1 + i)^n - 1}\right]$$

$F = 5\ 000$
$i = 0.12$
$n = 5$
$A = \$(-)787.05/\text{year}$

System 1 (annual-cost analysis)	System 2 (annual-cost analysis)
+27 740.97	+18 031.63
+4 000.00	+8 000.00
(−)2 833.38	(−) 787.05
$28 907.59	$25 244.58

Conclusion: System 2 is less expensive.

2. Present worth

System 1

(*a*) Initial cost = $100 000

(*b*) Maintenance and operating costs

$$P = A\left[\frac{(1 + i)^n - 1}{i(1 + i)^n}\right]$$

$A = \$4\ 000$
$i = 0.12$
$n = 5$
$P = \$14\ 419.11$

(*c*) Salvage

$P = F(1 + i)^{-n}$
$F = 18\ 000$
$i = 0.12$
$n = 5$
$P = \$(-)10\ 213.68$

System 2

(*a*) Initial cost = $65 000

(*b*) Maintenance and operating costs

$$P = A\left[\frac{(1 + i)^n - 1}{i(1 + i)^n}\right]$$

$A = \$8\ 000$
$i = 0.12$
$n = 5$
$P = \$28\ 838.21$

(*c*) Salvage

$P = \text{F}(1 + i)^{-n}$
$F = 5\ 000$
$i = 0.12$
$n = 5$
$P = \$(-)2\ 837.13$

System 1 (present-worth analysis)	System 2 (present-worth analysis)
$100 000.00	$ 65 000.00
14 419.11	28 838.21
(−)10 213.68	(−)2 837.13
$104 205.43	$ 91 001.08

Conclusion: System 2 is less expensive.

3. Future worth

System 1	**System 2**
(*a*) Initial cost = $100 000	(*a*) Initial cost = $65 000

System 1:
(*a*) Initial cost = $100 000
$F = P(1 + i)^n$
$P = \$100\ 000$
$i = 0.12$
$n = 5$
$F = \$176\ 234.17$

System 2:
(*a*) Initial cost = $65 000
$F = P(1 + i)^n$
$P = \$65\ 000$
$i = 0.12$
$n = 5$
$F = \$114\ 552.21$

(*b*) Maintenance and operating costs
$$F = A\left[\frac{(1 + i)^n - 1}{i}\right]$$
$A = \$4\ 000$
$F = \$25\ 411.39$

(*b*) Maintenance and operating costs
$$F = A\left[\frac{(1 + i)^n - 1}{i}\right]$$
$A = \$8\ 000$
$F = \$50\ 822.78$

(*c*) Salvage = $(−)18 000

(*c*) Salvage = $(−)5 000

System 1 (future-cost analysis)

$176 234.17
25 411.39
(−)18 000.00
$183 645.56

System 2 (future-cost analysis)

$114,552.21
50 822.78
(−)5 000.00
$160 374.99

Conclusion: System 2 is less expensive.

Example Problem 9.2   A major potentiometer manufacturer is considering two alternatives for new production machines with capacity to produce 20 000 units per day. One alternative is for a high-capacity automated production machine capable of producing 20 000 units per day when operated for three shifts per day. A quarter-time employee would be assigned to monitor the machine (employee would monitor other machines at the same time). With the three-shift schedule this would be equivalent to a three-quarter-time employee.

A second alternative would be to use two manually operated machines, each capable of 10 000 units per day assuming three-shift operation. Here, a total of six employees (2 per shift, 3 shifts) would be needed.
The following data have been estimated:

	Alternative 1	**Alternative 2**
Cost to purchase	$500 000	$100 000
Number of machines required	1	2
Number of employees required	0.75	6
Expected life of machine	10 yr	10 yr
Interest rate	8%	8%
Annual maintenance cost per machine	$30 000	$10 000
Salvage value at 10 years per machine	$100 000	$20 000

Figure 9.2

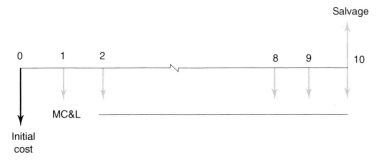

Company's cash-flow diagram
(MC&L = maintenance cost and labor)

If labor costs (including wages, benefits, etc.) are \$40 000 per employee per year, recommend which alternative is best using the equivalent uniform annual cost method.

Solution: Refer to Fig. 9.2

Alternative 1	**Alternative 2**
(a) Initial cost (annualized)	(a) Initial cost (annualized)

Alternative 1

(a) Initial cost (annualized)

$$A = P\left[\frac{i(1 + i)^n}{(1 + i)^n - 1}\right]$$

$P = \$500\ 000$
$i = 0.08$
$n = 10$
$A = \$74\ 514.74$

(b) Maintenance \$30 000

(c) Labor costs \$30 000

(d) Salvage value

$$A = \frac{F(i)}{[(1 + i)^n - 1]}$$

$F = \$100\ 000$
$i = 0.08$
$n = 10$
$A = -6\ 902.95$

Alternative 2

(a) Initial cost (annualized)

$$A = P\left[\frac{i(1 + i)^n}{(1 + i)^n - 1}\right]$$

$P = \$200\ 000$
$i = 0.08$
$n = 10$
$A = \$29\ 805.90$

(b) Maintenance \$20 000

(c) Labor costs \$240 000

(d) Salvage value

$$A = \frac{F(i)}{[(1 + i)^n - 1]}$$

$F = \$40\ 000$
$i = 0.08$
$n = 10$
$A = -2\ 761.18$

Alternative 1 (EUAC)	Alternative 2 (EUAC)
$74 514.74	$29 805.90
$30 000	$20 000
$30 000	$240 000
−$6 902.95	−$2 761.18
$127 611.79	$287 044.72

Clearly alternative 1 results in the lowest EUAC and would be recommended for implementation. The labor costs dominated all other costs in this example. If the EUAC for the two alternatives differed by only a few thousand dollars, and remembering that the numbers in the analysis are necessarily estimates, then other factors would have to be included in order to make a final recommendation.

9.2 Depreciation and Taxes

As demonstrated in Example Problem 9.1, economic decision analysis is concerned with judging the economic desirability of alternative investment proposals and policies. The desirability of a venture is measured in terms of the difference between income and costs, receipts and disbursements, or some other measure of profit. One additional topic we have not yet discussed is taxes. Income taxes represent additional costs and are therefore levies on a company's profit. In fact, businesses can expect to pay federal, state, and local governments 35–50% of the company's net income.

The U.S. government taxes individuals and businesses to support its processes, such as lawmaking, domestic and foreign economic policymaking, infrastructure (roads, dams, etc.), even the making and issuing of money itself.

The tax codes are a complex set of rules that outline appropriate deductions, calculations, and acceptable depreciation. Depreciation is defined as a reduction in value of a property such as a machine, building, or a vehicle because, with the passage of time, the value of most physical property suffers a reduction. Depreciation, while not a cash-flow item itself, results in a positive cash flow (savings) of income tax payments by decreasing the net income on which taxes are based.

For our purposes in this chapter, we define taxes as simply another disbursement similar to operating costs, maintenance, labor and materials, etc. While income taxes are important to the bottom line of a company, the details go beyond the scope of this text. Further study in this area is advised, as the after-tax consequences of an economic decision are critical.

Problems

9.1 Your company is trying to reduce energy costs for one of its warehouses by improving its insulation. Two options are being considered and it is up to you to recommend either urethane foam or fiberglass insulation. Use a 12-year analysis period and an interest rate of 14%. The initial cost of the foam will be $37 000 and it will have to be painted every three years at a cost of $3 000. The energy savings is expected to be $6 500 per year. Alternatively, fiberglass batts can be installed for $14 000 with no maintenance costs. Fiberglass batts will likely save $2 600 per year in energy costs.

9.2 Two machines are being considered to do a certain task. Machine A costs $24 000 new and $2 600 to operate and maintain each year. Machine B costs $32 000 new and $1 200 to operate and maintain each year. Assume that both will be worthless after eight years and that the interest rate is 10.0%. Determine by the equivalent uniform annual cost method which alternative is the better buy.

9.3 Two workstations are being considered by your company. Workstation 1 costs $12 000 new and $1 300 to operate and maintain each year. Workstation 2 costs $15 000 new and $600 to operate and maintain each year. Assume both will be worthless after six years and that the interest rate is 9.0%. Determine by the equivalent uniform annual cost method which alternative is the better buy.

9.4 Assume you needed $10 000 on April 1, 2006, and two options were available:

(a) Your banker would lend you the money at an annual interest rate of 7.0%, compounded monthly, to be repaid on September 1, 2006.

(b) You could cash in a certificate of deposit (CD) that was purchased earlier. The cost of the CD purchased September 1, 2005, was $10 000. If left in the savings and loan company until September 1, 2006, the CD's annual interest is 3.8% compounded monthly. If the CD is cashed in before September 1, 2006, you lose all interest for the first three months and the interest rate is reduced to 1.9%, compounded monthly, after the first three months.

Which option is better and by how much? (Assume an annual rate of 3.6%, compounded monthly, for any funds for which an interest rate is not specified.)

9.5 Two machines are being considered for purchase. The Sande 10 costs $36 000 new and is estimated to last five years. The cost to replace the Sande 10 will increase by 4% each year. Annual operation and maintenance costs are $2 400. It will have a trade-in (salvage) value of $3 000. The Sande 20 costs $76 000 to buy, but will last 10 years and will have a trade-in (salvage) value of $4 000. The cost of operation and maintenance is $1 400 per year.

Compare the two machines and state the basis of your comparison. Include a cash-flow diagram for each alternative. Assume all interest rates at 6% per year unless otherwise stated.

9.6 Two systems are being considered for the same task. System 1 costs $63 000 new and is estimated to last four years. It will then have a salvage or trade-in value of $4 500. The cost to replace system 1 will be 3.5% more each year than it was the year before. It will cost $4 200 per year to operate and maintain system 1, payable at the end of each year. System 2 costs $120 000 to buy and will last eight years. It will have a salvage or trade-in value of $6 000. The cost to operate and maintain system 2 will be $2 400 per year, payable at the end of each year. Assume the task will be performed for eight years. Compare the two systems, state your basis of comparison, and include a cash-flow diagram. All interest rates are 7.0% per year unless otherwise stated.

9.7 Compare two units, A and B. A has a new cost of $42 000, a life expectancy of 14 years, a salvage value of $4 000, and an annual operating cost of $3 000. B has a new cost of $21 000, a life expectancy of 7 years, a salvage value of $2 000, and an operating cost of $5 000. Assume an annual interest rate of 7 percent. Which of the two units would you recommend? What initial cost of machine A would make the two machines identical in overall cost?

9.8 One of two machines, alpha and beta, is to be purchased to provide for a new production operation in a factory. Machine alpha costs $10 000 and machine beta, $15 000. However, machine beta will result in an annual savings in operating costs of $800 over machine alpha. Which machine would you recommend purchasing and why, if each has a useful life of 10 years and money is worth 9 percent? Assume that both machines will be worthless at the end of 10 years. What value of annual savings of machine beta over machine alpha would result in each being equally desirable?

9.9 Your small company is considering whether to buy a new automobile or to lease it. You have determined that to purchase a new vehicle it will cost $21 000. After 8 years of use, the vehicle can be sold for $4 500. The cost to lease the same vehicle is found to be $3 000 per year for a 4-yr lease after a delivery payment of $2 000. It is expected that the annual operating and maintenance will cost about $1 800 whether the vehicle is purchased or leased. Should you buy or lease? Use present worth analysis to justify your answer. Assume the interest rate is 8% compounded annually.

9.10 A chemical plant is considering three different pieces of equipment to perform a process within the plant. You have gathered the following data:

	Machine 1	**Machine 2**	**Machine 3**
Initial cost	$150 000	$70 000	$39 000
Annual O/M	$1 900	$8 500	$11 000
Salvage value	$18 000	$9 000	$5 500
Life expectancy, years	6	4	3

Which machine would you recommend be purchased using an equivalent equal annual cost method? Interest rate is expected to be 8 percent. (O/M means operating and maintenance costs.)

APPENDIX **A**

Part 1 Unit Conversions

Multiply:	By:	To Obtain:
acres	4.356×10^4	ft^2
acres	$4.046\ 9 \times 10^{-1}$	ha
acres	$4.046\ 9 \times 10^3$	m^2
amperes	1	C/s
ampere hours	3.6×10^3	C
angstroms	1×10^{-8}	cm
angstroms	$3.937\ 0 \times 10^{-9}$	in
atmospheres	1.013 3	bars
atmospheres	$2.992\ 1 \times 10^1$	in of Hg
atmospheres	$1.469\ 6 \times 10^1$	lbf/in^2
atmospheres	7.6×10^2	mm of Hg
atmospheres	$1.013\ 3 \times 10^5$	Pa
barrels (petroleum, US)	4.2×10^1	gal (US liquid)
bars	$9.869\ 2 \times 10^{-1}$	atm
bars	$2.953\ 0 \times 10^1$	in of Hg
bars	$1.450\ 4 \times 10^1$	lbf/in^2
bars	1×10^5	Pa
Btu	$7.776\ 5 \times 10^2$	ft · lbf
Btu	$3.927\ 5 \times 10^{-4}$	hp · h
Btu	$1.055\ 1 \times 10^3$	J
Btu	$2.928\ 8 \times 10^{-4}$	kWh
Btu per hour	$2.160\ 1 \times 10^{-1}$	ft · lbf/s
Btu per hour	$3.927\ 5 \times 10^{-4}$	hp
Btu per hour	$2.928\ 8 \times 10^{-1}$	W
Btu per minute	$7.776\ 5 \times 10^2$	ft · lbf/min
Btu per minute	$2.356\ 5 \times 10^{-2}$	hp
Btu per minute	$1.757\ 3 \times 10^{-2}$	kW
bushels (US)	1.244 5	ft^3
bushels (US)	$3.523\ 9 \times 10^1$	L
bushels (US)	$3.523\ 9 \times 10^{-2}$	m^3
candelas	1	lm/sr
candelas per square foot	$3.381\ 6 \times 10^{-3}$	lamberts
centimeters	1×10^8	Å
centimeters	$3.280\ 8 \times 10^{-2}$	ft
centimeters	$3.937\ 0 \times 10^{-1}$	in
centipoises	1×10^{-2}	g/(cm · s)
circular mils	$5.067\ 1 \times 10^{-6}$	cm^2
circular mils	$7.854\ 0 \times 10^{-7}$	in^2
coulombs	1	A · s
cubic centimeters	$6.102\ 4 \times 10^{-2}$	in^3

411

Multiply:	By:	To Obtain:
cubic centimeters	$3.531\ 5 \times 10^{-5}$	ft^3
cubic centimeters	$2.641\ 7 \times 10^{-4}$	gal (US liquid)
cubic centimeters	1×10^{-3}	L
cubic centimeters	$3.381\ 4 \times 10^{-2}$	oz (US fluid)
cubic centimeters per gram	$1.601\ 8 \times 10^{-2}$	ft^3/lbm
cubic centimeters per second	$2.118\ 9 \times 10^{-3}$	ft^3/min
cubic centimeters per second	$1.585\ 0 \times 10^{-2}$	gal (US liquid)/min
cubic feet	$2.295\ 7 \times 10^{-5}$	acre · ft
cubic feet	$8.035\ 6 \times 10^{-1}$	bushels (US)
cubic feet	$7.480\ 5$	gal (US liquid)
cubic feet	1.728×10^{3}	in^3
cubic feet	$2.831\ 7 \times 10^{1}$	L
cubic feet	$2.831\ 7 \times 10^{-2}$	m^3
cubic feet per minute	$7.480\ 5$	gal (US liquid)/min
cubic feet per minute	$4.719\ 5 \times 10^{-1}$	L/s
cubic feet per pound-mass	$6.242\ 8 \times 10^{1}$	cm^3/g
cubic feet per second	$4.488\ 3 \times 10^{2}$	gal (US liquid)/min
cubic feet per second	$2.831\ 7 \times 10^{1}$	L/s
cubic inches	$4.650\ 3 \times 10^{-4}$	bushels (US)
cubic inches	$1.638\ 7 \times 10^{1}$	cm^3
cubic inches	$4.329\ 0 \times 10^{-3}$	gal (US liquid)
cubic inches	$1.638\ 7 \times 10^{-2}$	L
cubic inches	$1.638\ 7 \times 10^{-5}$	m^3
cubic inches	$5.541\ 1 \times 10^{-1}$	oz (US fluid)
cubic meters	$8.107\ 1 \times 10^{-4}$	acre · ft
cubic meters	$2.837\ 8 \times 10^{1}$	bushels (US)
cubic meters	$3.531\ 5 \times 10^{1}$	ft^3
cubic meters	$2.641\ 7 \times 10^{2}$	gal (US liquid)
cubic meters	1×10^{3}	L
cubic yards	$2.169\ 6 \times 10^{1}$	bushels (US)
cubic yards	$2.019\ 7 \times 10^{2}$	gal (US liquid)
cubic yards	$7.645\ 5 \times 10^{2}$	L
cubic yards	$7.645\ 5 \times 10^{-1}$	m^3
dynes	1×10^{-5}	N
dynes per square centimeter	$9.869\ 2 \times 10^{-7}$	atm
dynes per square centimeter	1×10^{-6}	bars
dynes per square centimeter	$1.450\ 4 \times 10^{-5}$	lbf/in^2
dyne centimeters	$7.375\ 6 \times 10^{-8}$	ft · lbf
dyne centimeters	1×10^{-7}	N · m
ergs	1	dyne · cm
fathoms	6	ft
feet	3.048×10^{1}	cm
feet	1.2×10^{1}	in
feet	3.048×10^{-4}	km
feet	3.048×10^{-1}	m
feet	$1.893\ 9 \times 10^{-4}$	mi
feet	$6.060\ 6 \times 10^{-2}$	rods
feet per second	$1.097\ 3$	km/h
feet per second	$1.828\ 8 \times 10^{1}$	m/min
feet per second	$6.818\ 2 \times 10^{-1}$	mi/h
feet per second squared	3.048×10^{-1}	m/s^2

Multiply:	By:	To Obtain:
foot-candles	1	lm/ft^2
foot-candles	$1.076\ 4 \times 10^1$	lux
foot pounds-force	$1.285\ 9 \times 10^{-3}$	Btu
foot pounds-force	$1.355\ 8 \times 10^7$	dyne · cm
foot pounds-force	$5.050\ 5 \times 10^{-7}$	hp · h
foot pounds-force	$1.355\ 8$	J
foot pounds-force	$3.766\ 2 \times 10^{-7}$	kWh
foot pounds-force	$1.355\ 8$	N · m
foot pounds-force per hour	$2.143\ 2 \times 10^{-5}$	Btu/min
foot pounds-force per hour	$2.259\ 7 \times 10^5$	ergs/min
foot pounds-force per hour	$5.050\ 5 \times 10^{-7}$	hp
foot pounds-force per hour	$3.766\ 2 \times 10^{-7}$	kW
furlongs	6.6×10^2	ft
furlongs	$2.011\ 7 \times 10^2$	m
gallons (US liquid)	$1.336\ 8 \times 10^{-1}$	ft^3
gallons (US liquid)	2.31×10^2	in^3
gallons (US liquid)	$3.785\ 4$	L
gallons (US liquid)	$3.785\ 4 \times 10^{-3}$	m^3
gallons (US liquid)	1.28×10^2	oz (US fluid)
gallons (US liquid)	8	pt (US liquid)
gallons (US liquid)	4	qt (US liquid)
grams	$2.204\ 6 \times 10^{-3}$	lbm
grams per centimeter second	1	poises
grams per cubic centimeter	$6.242\ 8 \times 10^1$	lbm/ft^3
hectares	$2.471\ 1$	acres
hectares	1×10^2	ares
hectares	$1.076\ 4 \times 10^5$	ft^2
hectares	1×10^4	m^2
horsepower	$2.546\ 1 \times 10^3$	Btu/h
horsepower	5.5×10^2	ft · lbf/s
horsepower	$7.457\ 0 \times 10^{-1}$	kW
horsepower	$7.457\ 0 \times 10^2$	W
horsepower hours	$2.546\ 1 \times 10^3$	Btu
horsepower hours	1.98×10^6	ft · lbf
horsepower hours	$2.684\ 5 \times 10^6$	J
horsepower hours	$7.457\ 0 \times 10^{-1}$	kWh
hours	6×10^1	min
hours	3.6×10^3	s
inches	2.54×10^8	Å
inches	2.54	cm
inches	$8.333\ 3 \times 10^{-2}$	ft
inches	1×10^3	mils
inches	$2.777\ 8 \times 10^{-2}$	yd
joules	$9.478\ 2 \times 10^{-4}$	Btu
joules	$7.375\ 6 \times 10^{-1}$	ft · lbf
joules	$3.725\ 1 \times 10^{-7}$	hp · h
joules	$2.777\ 8 \times 10^{-7}$	kWh
joules	1	W · s
joules per second	$5.690\ 7 \times 10^{-2}$	Btu/min
joules per second	1×10^7	ergs/s
joules per second	$7.375\ 6 \times 10^{-1}$	ft · lbf/s

Multiply:	By:	To Obtain:
joules per second	$1.341\,0 \times 10^{-3}$	hp
joules per second	1	W
kilograms	2.204 6	lbm
kilograms	$6.852\,2 \times 10^{-2}$	slugs
kilograms	1×10^{-3}	t
kilometers	$3.280\,8 \times 10^{3}$	ft
kilometers	$6.213\,7 \times 10^{-1}$	mi
kilometers	$5.399\,6 \times 10^{-1}$	nmi (nautical mile)
kilometers per hour	$5.468\,1 \times 10^{1}$	ft/min
kilometers per hour	$9.113\,4 \times 10^{-1}$	ft/s
kilometers per hour	$5.399\,6 \times 10^{-1}$	knots
kilometers per hour	$2.777\,8 \times 10^{-1}$	m/s
kilometers per hour	$6.213\,7 \times 10^{-1}$	mi/h
kilowatts	$3.414\,4 \times 10^{3}$	Btu/h
kilowatts	1×10^{10}	ergs/s
kilowatts	$7.375\,6 \times 10^{2}$	ft · lbf/s
kilowatts	1.341 0	hp
kilowatts	1×10^{3}	J/s
kilowatt hours	$3.414\,4 \times 10^{3}$	Btu
kilowatt hours	$2.655\,2 \times 10^{6}$	ft · lbf
kilowatt hours	1.341 0	hp · h
kilowatt hours	3.6×10^{6}	J
knots	1.687 8	ft/s
knots	1.150 8	mi/h
liters	$2.837\,8 \times 10^{-2}$	bushels (US)
liters	$3.531\,5 \times 10^{-2}$	ft^3
liters	$2.641\,7 \times 10^{-1}$	gal (US liquid)
liters	$6.102\,4 \times 10^{1}$	in^3
liters per second	2.118 9	ft^3/min
liters per second	$1.585\,0 \times 10^{1}$	gal (US liquid)/min
lumens	$7.957\,7 \times 10^{-2}$	candle power
lumens per square foot	1	foot-candles
lumens per square meter	$9.290\,3 \times 10^{-2}$	foot-candles
lux	1	lm/m^2
meters	1×10^{10}	Å
meters	3.280 8	ft
meters	$3.937\,0 \times 10^{1}$	in
meters	$6.213\,7 \times 10^{-4}$	mi
meters per minute	1.666 7	cm/s
meters per minute	$5.468\,1 \times 10^{-2}$	ft/s
meters per minute	6×10^{-2}	km/h
meters per minute	$3.239\,7 \times 10^{-2}$	knots
meters per minute	$3.728\,2 \times 10^{-2}$	mi/h
microns	1×10^{4}	Å
microns	$3.280\,8 \times 10^{-6}$	ft
microns	1×10^{-6}	m
miles	5.28×10^{3}	ft
miles	8	furlongs
miles	1.609 3	km
miles	$8.689\,8 \times 10^{-1}$	nmi (nautical mile)
miles per hour	$4.470\,4 \times 10^{1}$	cm/s

Multiply:	By:	To Obtain:
miles per hour	8.8×10^1	ft/min
miles per hour	1.466 7	ft/s
miles per hour	1.609 3	km/h
miles per hour	$8.689\ 8 \times 10^{-1}$	knots
miles per hour	$2.682\ 2 \times 10^1$	m/min
nautical miles	1.150 8	mi
newtons	1×10^5	dynes
newtons	$2.248\ 1 \times 10^{-1}$	lbf
newton meters	1×10^7	dyne · cm
newton meters	$7.375\ 6 \times 10^{-1}$	ft · lbf
ounces (US fluid)	$2.957\ 4 \times 10^1$	cm^3
ounces (US fluid)	$7.812\ 5 \times 10^{-3}$	gal (US liquid)
ounces (US fluid)	1.804 7	in^3
ounces (US fluid)	$2.957\ 4 \times 10^{-2}$	L
pascals	$9.869\ 2 \times 10^{-6}$	atm
pascals	$2.088\ 5 \times 10^{-2}$	lbf/ft^2
pascals	$1.450\ 4 \times 10^{-4}$	lbf/in^2
poises	1	g/(cm · s)
pounds-force	4.448 2	N
pounds-mass	$4.535\ 9 \times 10^2$	g
pounds-mass	$4.535\ 9 \times 10^{-1}$	kg
pounds-mass	$3.108\ 1 \times 10^{-2}$	slugs
pounds-mass	$4.535\ 9 \times 10^{-4}$	t
pounds-mass	5×10^{-4}	tons (short)
pounds-force per square foot	$4.725\ 4 \times 10^{-3}$	atm
pounds-force per square foot	$4.788\ 0 \times 10^1$	Pa
pounds-force per square inch	$6.804\ 6 \times 10^{-2}$	atm
pounds-force per square inch	$6.894\ 8 \times 10^{-2}$	bars
pounds-force per square inch	2.036 0	in of Hg
pounds-force per square inch	$5.171\ 5 \times 10^1$	mm of Hg
pounds-force per square inch	$6.894\ 8 \times 10^3$	Pa
pounds-mass per cubic foot	$1.601\ 8 \times 10^{-2}$	g/cm^3
pounds-mass per cubic foot	$1.601\ 8 \times 10^1$	kg/m^3
radians	$5.729\ 6 \times 10^1$	°
radians	$1.591\ 5 \times 10^{-1}$	r (revolutions)
radians per second	9.549 3	r/min
slugs	$1.459\ 4 \times 10^1$	kg
slugs	$3.217\ 4 \times 10^1$	lbm
square centimeters	$1.076\ 4 \times 10^{-3}$	ft^2
square centimeters	$1.550\ 0 \times 10^{-1}$	in^2
square feet	$2.295\ 7 \times 10^{-5}$	acre
square feet	$9.290\ 3 \times 10^2$	cm^2
square feet	$9.290\ 3 \times 10^{-6}$	ha
square feet	$9.290\ 3 \times 10^{-2}$	m^2
square meters	$1.076\ 4 \times 10^1$	ft^2
square meters	$1.550\ 0 \times 10^3$	in^2
square miles	6.4×10^2	acres
square miles	$2.787\ 8 \times 10^7$	ft^2
square miles	$2.590\ 0 \times 10^2$	ha
square miles	2.590 0	km^2
square millimeters	$1.076\ 4 \times 10^{-5}$	ft^2

416

Appendix A
Part 1 Unit
Conversions

Multiply:	By:	To Obtain:
square millimeters	$1.550\,0 \times 10^{-3}$	in^2
stokes	1	cm^2/s
stokes	$1.550\,0 \times 10^{-1}$	in^2/s
tons (long)	2.24×10^3	lbm
tons (long)	$1.016\,0$	t
tons (long)	1.12	tons (short)
tons (metric)	$9.017\,2 \times 10^{-1}$	tons (short)
tons (short)	2×10^3	lbm
watts	$3.414\,4$	Btu/h
watts	1×10^7	ergs/s
watts	$4.425\,4 \times 10^1$	ft · lbf/min
watts	$1.341\,0 \times 10^{-3}$	hp
watts	1	J/s
watt hours	$3.414\,4$	Btu
watt hours	$2.655\,2 \times 10^3$	ft · lbf
watt hours	$1.341\,0 \times 10^{-3}$	hp · h

Part 2 Unit Prefixes

Multiple and submultiple	Prefix	Symbol
$1\ 000\ 000\ 000\ 000 = 10^{12}$	tera	T
$1\ 000\ 000\ 000 = 10^{9}$	giga	G
$1\ 000\ 000 = 10^{6}$	mega	M
$1\ 000 = 10^{3}$	kilo	k
$100 = 10^{2}$	hecto	h
$10 = 10$	deka	da
$0.1 = 10^{-1}$	deci	d
$0.01 = 10^{-2}$	centi	c
$0.001 = 10^{-3}$	milli	m
$0.000\ 001 = 10^{-6}$	micro	μ
$0.000\ 000\ 001 = 10^{-9}$	nano	n
$0.000\ 000\ 000\ 001 = 10^{-12}$	pico	p
$0.000\ 000\ 000\ 000\ 001 = 10^{-15}$	femto	f
$0.000\ 000\ 000\ 000\ 000\ 001 = 10^{-18}$	atto	a

Part 3 Physical Constants

Avogadro's number $= 6.022\ 57 \times 10^{23}/\text{mol}$

Density of dry air at 0°C, 1 atm $= 1.293\ \text{kg/m}^3$

Density of water at 3.98°C $= 9.999\ 973 \times 10^2\ \text{kg/m}^3$

Equatorial radius of the earth $= 6\ 378.39\ \text{km} = 3\ 963.34\ \text{mi}$

Gravitational acceleration (standard) at sea level $= 9.806\ 65\ \text{m/s}^2 = 32.174\ \text{ft/s}^2$

Gravitational constant $= 6.672 \times 10^{-11}\ \text{N} \cdot \text{m}^2/\text{kg}^2$

Heat of fusion of water, 0°C $= 3.337\ 5 \times 10^5\ \text{J/kg} = 143.48\ \text{Btu/lbm}$

Heat of vaporization of water, 100°C $= 2.259\ 1 \times 10^6\ \text{J/kg} = 971.19\ \text{Btu/lbm}$

Mass of hydrogen atom $= 1.673\ 39 \times 10^{-27}\ \text{kg}$

Mean density of the earth $= 5.522 \times 10^3\ \text{kg/m}^3 = 344.7\ \text{lbm/ft}^3$

Molar gas constant $= 8.314\ 4\ \text{J/(mol} \cdot \text{K)}$

Planck's constant $= 6.625\ 54 \times 10^{-34}\ \text{J/Hz}$

Polar radius of the earth $= 6\ 356.91\ \text{km} = 3\ 949.99\ \text{mi}$

Velocity of light in a vacuum $= 2.997\ 9 \times 10^8\ \text{m/s}$

Velocity of sound in dry air at 0°C $= 331.36\ \text{m/s} = 1\ 087.1\ \text{ft/s}$

Part 4 Approximate Specific Gravities and Densities

Material	Specific Gravity	Average Density lbm/ft³	Average Density kg/m³
Gases (0°C and 1 atm)			
Air		0.080 18	1.284
Ammonia		0.048 13	0.771 0
Carbon dioxide		0.123 4	1.977
Carbon monoxide		0.078 06	1.251
Ethane		0.084 69	1.357
Helium		0.011 14	0.178 4
Hydrogen		0.005 611	0.089 88
Methane		0.044 80	0.717 6
Nitrogen		0.078 07	1.251
Oxygen		0.089 21	1.429
Sulfur dioxide		0.182 7	2.927
Liquids (20°C)			
Alcohol, ethyl	0.79	49	790
Alcohol, methyl	0.80	50	800
Benzene	0.88	55	880
Gasoline	0.67	42	670
Heptane	0.68	42	680
Hexane	0.66	41	660
Octane	0.71	44	710
Oil	0.88	55	880
Toluene	0.87	54	870
Water	1.00	62.4	1 000
Metals (20°C)			
Aluminum	2.55–2.80	165	2 640
Brass, cast	8.4–8.7	535	8 570
Bronze	7.4–8.7	510	8 170
Copper, cast	8.9	555	8 900
Gold, cast	19.3	1 210	19 300
Iron, cast	7.04–7.12	440	7 050
Iron, wrought	7.6–7.9	485	7 770
Iron ore	5.2	325	5 210
Lead	11.3	705	11 300
Manganese	7.4	462	7 400
Mercury	13.6	849	13 600
Nickel	8.9	556	8 900
Silver	10.4–10.6	655	10 500
Steel, cold drawn	7.83	489	7 830
Steel, machine	7.80	487	7 800

Appendix A
Part 4 Approximate
Specific Gravities
and Densities

Material	Specific Gravity	Average Density	
		lbm/ft³	kg/m³
Steel, tool	7.70	481	7 700
Tin, cast	7.30	456	7 300
Titanium	4.5	281	4 500
Uranium	18.7	1 170	18 700
Zinc, cast	6.9−7.2	440	7 050

Nonmetallic Solids (20°C)

Material	Specific Gravity	Average Density	
		lbm/ft³	kg/m³
Brick, common	1.80	112	1 800
Cedar	0.35	22	350
Clay, damp	1.8−2.6	137	2 200
Coal, bituminous	1.2−1.5	84	1 350
Concrete	2.30	144	2 300
Douglas fir	0.50	31	500
Earth, loose	1.2	75	1 200
Glass, common	2.5−2.8	165	2 650
Gravel, loose	1.4−1.7	97	1 550
Gypsum	2.31	144	2 310
Limestone	2.0−2.9	153	2 450
Mahogany	0.54	34	540
Marble	2.6−2.9	172	2 750
Oak	0.64−0.87	47	750
Paper	0.7−1.2	58	925
Rubber	0.92−0.96	59	940
Salt	0.8−1.2	62	1 000
Sand, loose	1.4−1.7	97	1 550
Sugar	1.61	101	1 610
Sulfur	2.1	131	2 100

NSPE Code of Ethics for Engineers

Preamble

Engineering is an important and learned profession. As members of this profession, engineers are expected to exhibit the highest standards of honesty and integrity. Engineering has a direct and vital impact on the quality of life for all people. Accordingly, the services provided by engineers require honesty, impartiality, fairness, and equity, and must be dedicated to the protection of the public health, safety, and welfare. Engineers must perform under a standard of professional behavior that requires adherence to the highest principles of ethical conduct.

I. Fundamental Canons

Engineers, in the fulfillment of their professional duties, shall:

1. Hold paramount the safety, health, and welfare of the public.
2. Perform services only in areas of their competence.
3. Issue public statements only in an objective and truthful manner.
4. Act for each employer or client as faithful agents or trustees.
5. Avoid deceptive acts.
6. Conduct themselves honorably, responsibly, ethically, and lawfully so as to enhance the honor, reputation, and usefulness of the profession.

II. Rules of Practice

1. Engineers shall hold paramount the safety, health, and welfare of the public.
    a. If engineers' judgment is overruled under circumstances that endanger life or property, they shall notify their employer or client and such other authority as may be appropriate.
    b. Engineers shall approve only those engineering documents that are in conformity with applicable standards.
    c. Engineers shall not reveal facts, data, or information without the prior consent of the client or employer except as authorized or required by law or this Code.
    d. Engineers shall not permit the use of their name or associate in business ventures with any person or firm that they believe is engaged in fraudulent or dishonest enterprise.

NOTE: In regard to the question of application of the Code to corporations vis-à-vis real persons, business form or type should not negate nor influence conformance of individuals to the Code. The Code deals with professional services, which services must be performed by real persons. Real persons in turn establish and implement policies within business structures. The Code is clearly written to apply to the Engineer, and it is incumbent on members of NSPE to endeavor to live up to its provisions. This applies to all pertinent sections of the Code.

    e. Engineers shall not aid or abet the unlawful practice of engineering by a person or firm.

    f. Engineers having knowledge of any alleged violation of this Code shall report thereon to appropriate professional bodies and, when relevant, also to public authorities, and cooperate with the proper authorities in furnishing such information or assistance as may be required.

2. Engineers shall perform services only in the areas of their competence.

    a. Engineers shall undertake assignments only when qualified by education or experience in the specific technical fields involved.

    b. Engineers shall not affix their signatures to any plans or documents dealing with subject matter in which they lack competence, nor to any plan or document not prepared under their direction and control.

    c. Engineers may accept assignments and assume responsibility for coordination of an entire project and sign and seal the engineering documents for the entire project, provided that each technical segment is signed and sealed only by the qualified engineers who prepared the segment.

3. Engineers shall issue public statements only in an objective and truthful manner.

    a. Engineers shall be objective and truthful in professional reports, statements, or testimony. They shall include all relevant and pertinent information in such reports, statements, or testimony, which should bear the date indicating when it was current.

    b. Engineers may express publicly technical opinions that are founded upon knowledge of the facts and competence in the subject matter.

    c. Engineers shall issue no statements, criticisms, or arguments on technical matters that are inspired or paid for by interested parties, unless they have prefaced their comments by explicitly identifying the interested parties on whose behalf they are speaking, and by revealing the existence of any interest the engineers may have in the matters.

4. Engineers shall act for each employer or client as faithful agents or trustees.

    a. Engineers shall disclose all known or potential conflicts of interest that could influence or appear to influence their judgment or the quality of their services.

    b. Engineers shall not accept compensation, financial or otherwise, from more than one party for services on the same project, or for services pertaining to the same project, unless the circumstances are fully disclosed and agreed to by all interested parties.

    c. Engineers shall not solicit or accept financial or other valuable consideration, directly or indirectly, from outside agents in connection with the work for which they are responsible.

    d. Engineers in public service as members, advisors, or employees of a governmental or quasi-governmental body or department shall not participate in decisions with respect to services solicited or provided by them or their organizations in private or public engineering practice.

    e. Engineers shall not solicit or accept a contract from a governmental body on which a principal or officer of their organization serves as a member.

5. Engineers shall avoid deceptive acts.

    a. Engineers shall not falsify their qualifications or permit misrepresentation of their or their associates' qualifications. They shall not misrepresent or exaggerate their responsibility in or for the subject matter of prior assignments. Brochures or other presentations incident to the solicitation of employment shall not misrepresent pertinent facts concerning employers, employees, associates, joint venturers, or past accomplishments.

   b.   Engineers shall not offer, give, solicit, or receive, either directly or indirectly, any contribution to influence the award of a contract by public authority, or which may be reasonably construed by the public as having the effect or intent of influencing the awarding of a contract. They shall not offer any gift or other valuable consideration in order to secure work. They shall not pay a commission, percentage, or brokerage fee in order to secure work, except to a bona fide employee or bona fide established commercial or marketing agencies retained by them.

III.   Professional Obligations

1.   Engineers shall be guided in all their relations by the highest standards of honesty and integrity.
   a.   Engineers shall acknowledge their errors and shall not distort or alter the facts.
   b.   Engineers shall advise their clients or employers when they believe a project will not be successful.
   c.   Engineers shall not accept outside employment to the detriment of their regular work or interest. Before accepting any outside engineering employment, they will notify their employers.
   d.   Engineers shall not attempt to attract an engineer from another employer by false or misleading pretenses.
   e.   Engineers shall not promote their own interest at the expense of the dignity and integrity of the profession.
2.   Engineers shall at all times strive to serve the public interest.
   a.   Engineers shall seek opportunities to participate in civic affairs; career guidance for youths; and work for the advancement of the safety, health, and well-being of their community.
   b.   Engineers shall not complete, sign, or seal plans and/or specifications that are not in conformity with applicable engineering standards. If the client or employer insists on such unprofessional conduct, they shall notify the proper authorities and withdraw from further service on the project.
   c.   Engineers shall endeavor to extend public knowledge and appreciation of engineering and its achievements.
   d.   Engineers shall strive to adhere to the principles of sustainable development[1] in order to protect the environment for future generations.
3.   Engineers shall avoid all conduct or practice that deceives the public.
   a.   Engineers shall avoid the use of statements containing a material misrepresentation of fact or omitting a material fact.
   b.   Consistent with the foregoing, engineers may advertise for recruitment of personnel.
   c.   Consistent with the foregoing, engineers may prepare articles for the lay or technical press, but such articles shall not imply credit to the author for work performed by others.

---

1. "Sustainable development" is the challenge of meeting human needs for natural resources, industrial products, energy, food, transportation, shelter, and effective waste management while conserving and protecting environmental quality and the natural resource base essential for future development.

4. Engineers shall not disclose, without consent, confidential information concerning the business affairs or technical processes of any present or former client or employer, or public body on which they serve.

   a. Engineers shall not, without the consent of all interested parties, promote or arrange for new employment or practice in connection with a specific project for which the engineer has gained particular and specialized knowledge.

   b. Engineers shall not, without the consent of all interested parties, participate in or represent an adversary interest in connection with a specific project or proceeding in which the engineer has gained particular specialized knowledge on behalf of a former client or employer.

5. Engineers shall not be influenced in their professional duties by conflicting interests.

   a. Engineers shall not accept financial or other considerations, including free engineering designs, from material or equipment suppliers for specifying their product.

   b. Engineers shall not accept commissions or allowances, directly or indirectly, from contractors or other parties dealing with clients or employers of the engineer in connection with work for which the engineer is responsible.

6. Engineers shall not attempt to obtain employment or advancement or professional engagements by untruthfully criticizing other engineers, or by other improper or questionable methods.

   a. Engineers shall not request, propose, or accept a commission on a contingent basis under circumstances in which their judgment may be compromised.

   b. Engineers in salaried positions shall accept part-time engineering work only to the extent consistent with policies of the employer and in accordance with ethical considerations.

   c. Engineers shall not, without consent, use equipment, supplies, laboratory, or office facilities of an employer to carry on outside private practice.

7. Engineers shall not attempt to injure, maliciously or falsely, directly or indirectly, the professional reputation, prospects, practice, or employment of other engineers. Engineers who believe others are guilty of unethical or illegal practice shall present such information to the proper authority for action.

   a. Engineers in private practice shall not review the work of another engineer for the same client, except with the knowledge of such engineer, or unless the connection of such engineer with the work has been terminated.

   b. Engineers in governmental, industrial, or educational employ are entitled to review and evaluate the work of other engineers when so required by their employment duties.

   c. Engineers in sales or industrial employ are entitled to make engineering comparisons of represented products with products of other suppliers.

8. Engineers shall accept personal responsibility for their professional activities, provided, however, that engineers may seek indemnification for services arising out of their practice for other than gross negligence, where the engineer's interests cannot otherwise be protected.

   a. Engineers shall conform with state registration laws in the practice of engineering.

   b. Engineers shall not use association with a nonengineer, a corporation, or partnership as a "cloak" for unethical acts.

9. Engineers shall give credit for engineering work to those to whom credit is due, and will recognize the proprietary interests of others.

   a. Engineers shall, whenever possible, name the person or persons who may be individually responsible for designs, inventions, writings, or other accomplishments.

b. Engineers using designs supplied by a client recognize that the designs remain the property of the client and may not be duplicated by the engineer for others without express permission.

c. Engineers, before undertaking work for others in connection with which the engineer may make improvements, plans, designs, inventions, or other records that may justify copyrights or patents, should enter into a positive agreement regarding ownership.

d. Engineers' designs, data, records, and notes referring exclusively to an employer's work are the employer's property. The employer should indemnify the engineer for use of the information for any purpose other than the original purpose.

e. Engineers shall continue their professional development throughout their careers and should keep current in their specialty fields by engaging in professional practice, participating in continuing education courses, reading in the technical literature, and attending professional meetings and seminars.

—As Revised January 2006

"By order of the United States District Court for the District of Columbia, former Section 11(c) of the NSPE Code of Ethics prohibiting competitive bidding, and all policy statements, opinions, rulings or other guidelines interpreting its scope, have been rescinded as unlawfully interfering with the legal right of engineers, protected under the antitrust laws, to provide price information to prospective clients; accordingly, nothing contained in the NSPE Code of Ethics, policy statements, opinions, rulings or other guidelines prohibits the submission of price quotations or competitive bids for engineering services at any time or in any amount."

Statement by NSPE Executive Committee

In order to correct misunderstandings which have been indicated in some instances since the issuance of the Supreme Court decision and the entry of the Final Judgment, it is noted that in its decision of April 25, 1978, the Supreme Court of the United States declared: "The Sherman Act does not require competitive bidding."
It is further noted that as made clear in the Supreme Court decision:

1. Engineers and firms may individually refuse to bid for engineering services.
2. Clients are not required to seek bids for engineering services.
3. Federal, state, and local laws governing procedures to procure engineering services are not affected, and remain in full force and effect.
4. State societies and local chapters are free to actively and aggressively seek legislation for professional selection and negotiation procedures by public agencies.
5. State registration board rules of professional conduct, including rules prohibiting competitive bidding for engineering services, are not affected and remain in full force and effect. State registration boards with authority to adopt rules of professional conduct may adopt rules governing procedures to obtain engineering services.
6. As noted by the Supreme Court, "nothing in the judgment prevents NSPE and its members from attempting to influence governmental action . . ."

Part 1 Selected Algebra Topics

F1.1   Introduction

This appendix includes material on exponents and logarithms, simultaneous equations, and the solution of equations by approximation methods. The material can be used for reference or review. The reader should consult an algebra textbook for more detailed explanations of additional topics for study.

F1.2   Exponents and Radicals

The basic laws of exponents are stated subsequently along with an illustrative example.

Law	Example
$a^m a^n = a^{m+n}$	$x^5 x^{-2} = x^3$
$\dfrac{a^m}{a^n} = a^{m-n} \quad a \neq 0$	$\dfrac{x^5}{x^3} = x^2$
$(a^m) = a^{mn}$	$(x^{-2})^3 = x^{-6}$
$(ab)^m = a^m b^m$	$(xy)^2 = x^2 y^2$
$\left(\dfrac{a}{b}\right)^m = \dfrac{a^m}{b^m} \quad b \neq 0$	$\left(\dfrac{x}{y}\right)^2 = \dfrac{x^2}{y^2}$
$a^{-m} = \dfrac{1}{a^m} \quad a \neq 0$	$x^{-3} = \dfrac{1}{x^3}$
$a^0 = 1 \; a \neq 0$	$2(3x^2)^0 = 2(1) = 2$
$a^1 = a$	$(3x^2)^1 = 3x^2$

These laws are valid for positive and negative integer exponents and for a zero exponent, and can be shown to be valid for rational exponents. Some examples of fractional exponents are illustrated here. Note the use of radical ($\sqrt{}$) notation as an alternative to fractional exponents.

Law	Example
$a^{m/n} = \sqrt[n]{a^m}$	$x^{2/3} = \sqrt[3]{x^2}$
$\dfrac{\sqrt[n]{a}}{\sqrt[n]{b}} = \sqrt[n]{\dfrac{a}{b}} \quad b \neq 0$	$\dfrac{\sqrt[3]{16}}{\sqrt[3]{2}} = \sqrt[3]{8} = 2$
$a^{1/2} = \sqrt[2]{a^1} = \sqrt{a} \quad a \geq 0$	$\sqrt{25} = 5 \;\; (\text{not} \pm 5)$

F1.3   Exponential and Power Functions

Functions involving exponents occur in two forms—power and exponential. The power function contains the base as the variable and the exponent is a rational number. An exponential function has a fixed base and variable exponent.

The simplest exponential function is of the form

$$y = b^x \qquad b \geq 0$$

where b is a constant. Note that this function involves a power but is fundamentally different from the power function $y = x^b$.

The inverse of a function is an important concept for the development of logarithmic functions from exponential functions. Consider a function $y = f(x)$. If this function could be solved for x, the result would be expressed as $x = g(y)$. For example, the power function $y = x^2$ has as its inverse $x = \pm\sqrt{y}$. Note that in $y = x^2$, y is a single-valued function of x, whereas the inverse is a double-valued function. For $y = x^2$, x can take on any real value, whereas the inverse $x = \pm\sqrt{y}$ restricts y to only positive values or zero. This result is important in the study and application of logarithmic functions.

F1.4   The Logarithmic Function

The definition of a logarithm may be stated as follows:

A number L is said to be the logarithm of a positive real number N to the base b (where b is real, positive, and different from 1), if L is the exponent to which b must be raised to obtain N.

Symbolically, the logarithm function is expressed as

$$L = \log_b N$$

for which the inverse is

$$N = b^L$$

For instance,

$$\log_2 8 = 3 \qquad \text{since } 8 = 2^3$$
$$\log_{10} 0.01 = -2 \qquad \text{since } 0.01 = 10^{-2}$$
$$\log_5 5 = 1 \qquad \text{since } 5 = 5^1$$
$$\log_b 1 = 0 \qquad \text{since } 1 = b^0$$

Several properties of logarithms and exponential functions can be identified when plotted on a graph.

Example problem F1.1

Plot graphs of $y = \log_2 x$ and $x = 2^y$ that are inverse functions.

Solution

Since $y = \log_2 x$ and $x = 2^y$ are equivalent by definition, they will graph into the same line. Choosing values of y and computing x from $x = 2^y$ yields Figure F1.1.

Figure F1.1

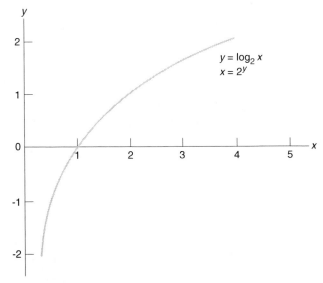

The logarithmic function.

Some properties of logarithms that can be generalized from Figure F1.1 are

1. $\log_b x$ is not defined for negative or zero values of x.
2. $\log_b 1 = 0$.
3. If $x > 1$, then $\log_b x > 0$.
4. If $0 < x < 1$, then $\log_b x < 0$.

Other properties of logarithms that can be proved as a direct consequence of the laws of exponents are, with P and Q being real and positive numbers,

1. $\log_b PQ = \log_b P + \log_b Q$.
2. $\log_b \dfrac{P}{Q} = \log_b P - \log_b Q$.
3. $\log_b (P)^m = m \log_b P$.
4. $\log_b \sqrt[n]{P} = \dfrac{1}{n} \log_b P$.

The base b, as stated in the definition of a logarithm, can be any real number greater than 0 but not equal to 1 since 1 to any power remains 1. When using logarithmic notation, the base is always indicated, with the exception of base 10, in which case the base is frequently omitted. In the expression $y = \log x$, the base is understood to be 10. A somewhat different notation is used for the natural (Naperian) logarithms discussed in Sec. F1.5.

Sometimes it is desirable to change the base of logarithms. The procedure is shown by the following example.

Example problem F1.2

Given that $y = \log_a N$, find $\log_b N$.

Solution

$$y = \log_a N$$

$$N = a^y \qquad \text{(inverse function)}$$

$$\log_b N = y \log_b a \qquad \text{(taking logs to base } b\text{)}$$

$$\log_b N = (\log_a N)(\log_b a) \qquad \text{(substitution for } y\text{)}$$

$$= \frac{\log_a N}{\log_a b} \qquad \left(\text{since } \log_b a = \frac{1}{\log_a b}\right)$$

F1.5   Natural Logarithms and e

In advanced mathematics the base e is usually chosen for logarithms to achieve simpler expressions. Logarithms to the base e are called natural, or Naperian, logarithms. The constant e is defined in the calculus as

$$e = \lim_{n \to 0}(1 + n)^{1/n} = 2.7182818284000\ldots$$

For purposes of calculating e to a desired accuracy, an infinite series is used.

$$e = \sum_{n \to 0}^{\infty} \frac{1}{n!}$$

The required accuracy is obtained by summing sufficient terms. For example,

$$\sum_{n=0}^{6} \frac{1}{n!} = 1 + 1 + \frac{1}{2} + \frac{1}{6} + \frac{1}{24} + \frac{1}{120} + \frac{1}{720}$$

$$= 2.718\,055$$

which is accurate to four significant figures.

Natural logarithms are denoted by the symbol ln, and all the properties defined previously for logarithms apply to natural logarithms. The inverse of $y = \ln x$ is $x = e^y$. The following examples illustrate applications of natural logarithms.

Example problem F1.3

$$\ln 1 = 0 \qquad \text{since } e^0 = 1$$
$$\ln e = 1 \qquad \text{since } e^1 = e$$

Example problem F1.4

Solve for x:

$$2^x = 3^{x-1}$$

Specify your answer to four significant figures.

Taking natural logarithms of both sides of the equation and using a calculator for evaluation of numerical quantities,

$$x \ln 2 = (x - 1)\ln 3$$

$$\frac{x}{x - 1} = \frac{\ln 3}{\ln 2} = 1.585\,0$$

$$x = 2.709 \text{ (four significant figures)}$$

This problem could have been solved by choosing any base for taking logarithms. However, in general, base e or 10 should be chosen so that a scientific calculator can be used for numerical work.

F1.6   Simultaneous Equations

Several techniques exist for finding the common solution to a set of n algebraic equations in n unknowns. A formal method for solution of a system of linear equations is known as Cramer's rule, which requires a knowledge of determinants.

A second-order determinant is defined and evaluated as

$$\begin{vmatrix} a_1 b_1 \\ a_2 b_2 \end{vmatrix} = a_1 b_2 - a_2 b_1$$

A third-order determinant is defined and evaluated as

$$\begin{vmatrix} a_1 b_1 c_1 \\ a_2 b_2 c_2 \\ a_3 b_3 c_3 \end{vmatrix} = a_1 \begin{vmatrix} b_2 c_2 \\ b_3 c_3 \end{vmatrix} - a_2 \begin{vmatrix} b_1 c_1 \\ b_3 c_3 \end{vmatrix} + a_3 \begin{vmatrix} b_1 c_1 \\ b_2 c_2 \end{vmatrix}$$

where the second-order determinants are evaluated as indicated previously. The procedure may be extended to higher-order determinants.

Cramer's rule for a system of n equations in n unknowns can be stated as follows:

1. Arrange the equations to be solved so that the unknowns x, y, z, and so forth appear in the same order in each equation; if any unknown is missing from an equation, it is to be considered as having a coefficient of zero in that equation.
2. Place all terms that do not involve the unknowns in the right member of each equation.
3. Designate by D the determinant of the coefficients of the unknowns in the same order as they appear in the equations. Designate by D_i the determinant obtained by replacing the elements of the ith column of D by the terms in the right member of the equations.
4. Then if $D \neq 0$ the values of the unknowns x y, z, and so forth, are given by

$$x = \frac{D_1}{D} \qquad y = \frac{D_2}{D} \qquad z = \frac{D_3}{D} \cdots$$

Example problem F1.5

Solve the following system of equations that have already been written in proper form for application of Cramer's rule.

$$3x + y - z = 2$$

$$x - 2y + z = 0$$

$$4x - y + z = 3$$

Solution

$$x = \frac{\begin{vmatrix} 2 & 1 & -1 \\ 0 & -2 & 1 \\ 3 & -1 & 1 \end{vmatrix}}{\begin{vmatrix} 3 & 1 & -1 \\ 1 & -2 & 1 \\ 4 & -1 & 1 \end{vmatrix}} = \frac{2\begin{vmatrix} -2 & 1 \\ -1 & 1 \end{vmatrix} - 1\begin{vmatrix} 0 & 1 \\ 3 & 1 \end{vmatrix} + (-1)\begin{vmatrix} 0 & -2 \\ 3 & -1 \end{vmatrix}}{3\begin{vmatrix} -2 & 1 \\ -1 & 1 \end{vmatrix} - 1\begin{vmatrix} 1 & 1 \\ 4 & 1 \end{vmatrix} + (-1)\begin{vmatrix} 1 & -2 \\ 4 & -1 \end{vmatrix}}$$

$$= \frac{2(-2 + 1) - 1(0 - 3) - 1(0 + 6)}{3(-2 + 1) - 1(1 - 4) - 1(-1 + 8)}$$

$$= \frac{2(-1) - 1(-3) - 1(6)}{3(-1) - 1(-3) - 1(7)}$$

$$= \frac{-5}{-7}$$

$$= \frac{5}{7}$$

The reader may verify the solutions $y = 6/7$ and $z = 1$.

There are several other methods of solution for systems of equations that are illustrated by the following examples.

Example problem F1.6

Solve the system of equations:

$$9x^2 - 16y^2 = 144$$

$$x - 2y = 4$$

Solution

The common solution represents the intersection of a hyperbola and straight line. The method used is substitution. Solving the linear equation for x yields

$$x = 2y + 4$$

Substitution into the second-order equation gives

$$9(2y + 4)^2 - 16y^2 = 144$$

which reduces to

$$20y^2 + 144y = 0$$

Factoring gives

$$4y(5y + 36) = 0$$

which yields

$$y = 0, \frac{-36}{5}$$

Substitution into the linear equation $x = 2y + 4$ gives the corresponding values of x:

$$x = 4, -\frac{52}{5}$$

The solutions thus are the coordinates of intersection of the line and the hyperbola:

$$(4.0), \left(-\frac{52}{5}, -\frac{36}{5}\right)$$

which can be verified by graphical construction.

Example problem F1.7

Solve the system of equations:

(a) $3x - y = 7$

(b) $x + z = 4$

(c) $y - z = -1$

Solution

Systems of equations similar to these arise frequently in engineering applications. Obviously they can be solved by Cramer's rule. However, a more rapid solution can be obtained directly by elimination.

From Eq. (*c*),

$$y = z - 1$$

From Eq. (*a*)

$$y = 7 - 3x$$

From Eq. (*b*)

$$x = 4 - z$$

Successive substitution yields

$$z - 1 = 7 - 3x$$
$$z - 1 = 7 - 3(4 - z)$$
$$-2z = -4$$
$$z = +2$$

Continued substitution gives

$$y = 1$$
$$x = 2$$

452

Appendix F
Part 1 Selected
Algebra Topics

Every system of equations first should be investigated carefully before a method of solution is chosen so that the most direct method, requiring the minimum amount of time, is used.

F1.7   Approximate Solutions

Many equations developed in engineering applications do not lend themselves to direct solution by standard methods. These equations must be solved by approximation methods to the accuracy dictated by the problem conditions. Experience is helpful in choosing the numerical technique for solution.

Example problem F1.8

Find to three significant figures the solution to the equation

$$2 - x = \ln x$$

Solution

One method of solution is graphical. If the equations $y = 2 - x$ and $y = \ln x$ are plotted, the common solution would be the intersection of the two lines. This would not likely give three-significant-figure accuracy, however. A more accurate method requires use of a scientific calculator or computer.

Table F1.1   Solution of $2 - x = \ln x$

x	1	2	1.5	1.6	1.55	1.56	1.557
$2 - x$	1	0	0.500	0.400	0.450	0.440	0.443
$\ln x$	0	0.693	0.405	0.470	0.438	0.445	0.443

Inspection of the equation reveals that the desired solution must lie between 1 and 2. It is then a matter of setting up a routine that will continue to bracket the solution between two increasingly accurate numbers. Table F1.1 shows the intermediate steps and indicates that the solution is $x = 1.56$ to three significant figures.

Computer spreadsheets and solvers or a programmable calculator could be used easily to determine a solution by the method just described. The time available and equipment on hand always will influence the numerical technique to be used.

Answers to Selected Problems

Chapter 4

4.1 $\alpha = 55°$, $B_y = 6.0$ m, $\mathbf{B} = 1.0 \times 10^1$ m
4.3 $XZ = 4.2 \times 10^4$ m
4.6 $\mathbf{R} = 19$ cm $\leftarrow$ horizontal
4.8 Height $= 6.2 \times 10^2$ m
4.11 $AB = 156.8$ m, $\angle ABC = 130.0°$
4.16 1.1 cm
4.20 Heading must be S 12.0°W, actual ground speed $= 587$ km/h
4.22 (a) 13 790 more revolutions
(b) 5861 more revolutions
4.25 (a) 0 m/s
(b) 11.5 m
(c) 15 m/s downward
(d) 31.8 m/s
(e) 4.77 s
4.27 Shortest height of the tank $= 32.26$ cm
4.30 Refractive index of the glass, $n_b = 1.58$

Chapter 5

5.2 (c) $V = 0.27\, t - 0.4$
(d) 0.27 m/s^2
5.4 (c) $P = 0.71\, Q - 17$
(d) 9.27 kW
5.6 (c) $H = 4 \times 10^8\, T^3$
5.8 (e) Linear: $R = -27\, A + 206$
Exponential: $R = 152\, e^{-0.35A}$
Power: $R = 51\, A^{-0.75}$
(f) Power curve
5.12 (c) Linear: $P = 6432\, Y - 1.2648 \times 10^7$
Exponential: $P = 5.784 \times 10^{-53}\, e^{0.0663Y}$
(d) Exponential
5.14 (c) $V = 198\, e^{-0.12t}$
5.16 (c) Linear: $D = -0.0007T + 0.7824$
Exponential: $D = 1.0463\, e^{-0.0017T}$
Power: $D = 215.9\, T^{-0.9974}$
Power best
5.18 (c) $C = 5503.8\, e^{-0.0742W}$
(d) 127 counts/second

Chapter 6

6.2 (b) 5
(f) exact conversion
(h) 4

6.3 (*c*) 2.64×10^8

6.4 (*c*) 1400 lbm

6.5 (*d*) 168 cm^3

6.6 (*a*) 205–215 lb/in^2

     (*b*) 82–92 lb/in^2

Chapter 7

7.1 (*a*) 1.60×10^2 kW

    (*b*) 390 ha

    (*c*) 1.057×10^3 m^3

    (*d*) 64.6 m/s

    (*e*) 9.90×10^2 km/hr

    (*f*) 1.1×10^3 kg

    (*g*) 70.3 kg

    (*h*) 652 m

    (*i*) 1.637×10^4 L

    (*j*) 2.470×10^3 km

7.4 (*a*) 10.8×10^3 J

    (*b*) 1.01×10^5 Pa

    (*c*) 8.850×10^3 m

    (*d*) 48.7 g/cm^3

    (*e*) 373K

7.7 (*a*) m = 116 kg

    (*b*) m = 146 kg

7.10 Vol = 1 330 in^3

    Mass = 0.048 2 lbm

    #gal = 8.09 gal

7.13 Time = 14 min

7.16 (*a*) H = 43.0×10^3 ft

     (*b*) Dia = 60.8 ft

7.19

CD	cos θ	θ	> OAB	Area	Length	Vol, ft^3	Vol, gal	Mass, kg
0	1	0	0	0	25	0	0	0
1	0.8	36.87	73.74	4.09		102.19	764.4	2 111.3
2	0.6	53.13	106.26	11.18		279.56	2 091.3	5 776
3	0.4	66.42	132.84	19.82		495.42	3 706	10 236
4	0.2	78.46	156.93	29.34		733.42	5 486.4	15 153
5	0	90	180	39.27		981.75	7 344	20 284
6				49.2		1 230.07	9 201.6	25 415
7				58.72		1 468.07	10 982	30 332
8				67.36		1 683.94	12 597	34 792
9				74.45		1 861.31	13 924	38 457
10				78.54		1 963.5	14 688	40 569

7.22 Vol = 3.5×10^9 ft^3

7.25 $C_{\text{New}} = \dfrac{288.8\,\text{gal}}{\text{h} \cdot \text{in}^{2.5}} \dfrac{\text{h}}{3600\,\text{s}} \dfrac{\text{ft}^3}{7.48\,\text{gal}} \dfrac{12^{2.5}\,\text{in}^{2.5}}{\text{ft}^{2.5}} = 5.35\,\text{ft}^{0.5}/\text{s}$

L, in	H, in	Q, gal/h	Q, ft^3/s
1	2	817	0.03
2	4	4 621	0.17
3	6	12 733	0.47
4	8	26 139	0.97
5	10	45 663	1.7
6	12	72 031	2.68
7	14	105 898	3.93
8	16	147 866	5.49
9	18	198 494	7.37
10	20	258 311	9.59
11	22	327 811	12.17
12	24	407 470	15.13
13	26	497 738	18.48
14	28	599 049	22.25
15	30	711 820	26.43
16	32	836 454	31.06

Chapter 8

8.2 (*a*) $783.53
(*b*) $497.18
(*c*) $327.68
8.4 (*a*) $58.67
(*b*) $1906.55
(*c*) $1114.60
(*d*) $303.60
8.6 (*a*) $1 382 999.74
(*b*) $1 390 288.11
(*c*) $1 397 897.40
8.8 (*a*) $58 068.06
(*b*) 85 675.19
8.10 (*a*) 4.73%
(*b*) $78 249.10
8.12 $18 052.10 Firm lost money
8.14 $16 166.07
8.16 $1 331.16
8.19 $1142.94
8.21 $3488.21
8.23 $800 000
8.24 $114 022.10, $8087.22
8.26 14.19%
8.28 (*a*) $2014.93
(*b*) $310.50
8.30 $20.62
8.32 (*a*) $2477.65 (asset)
(*b*) $1427.22 (asset)
(*c*) $2825.26 (liability)
(*d*) $980.15 (liability)
(*e*) $8702.95 (asset)
Net worth = $8802.41
8.33 76.1%

8.35 Select option b
8.37 (*a*) $15 473.27
(*b*) $18 000.00

Chapter 9

9.1 Foam: $4522.29 (net cost)
Fiberglass: 716.76 (net savings) (select)
9.2 Choose workstation 2
9.3 Choose Sande 10

Chapter 10

10.1 (*a*) 2.53
(*b*) 2
(*c*) 2
10.4 (*a*) 78.72
(*b*) 88
(*c*) 78
(*d*) 14.93
10.7 (*a*)

215–219	3
220–224	6
225–229	11
230–234	4
235–239	2
240–244	4

(*b*)

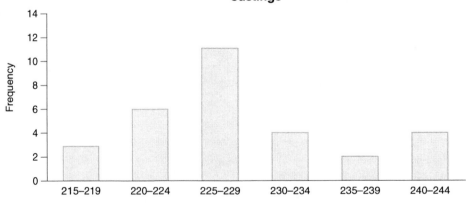

(*c*) Mean = 228.53
Mode = 228
Median = 228

10.12 $R = 15.293e^{0.5085p}$

y = 15.293e$^{0.5085x}$
R^2 = 0.997 8

Test Results for SILON Q-177

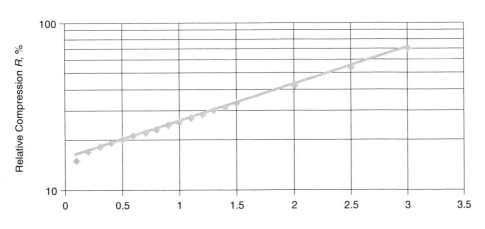

(*b*) 15.293
(*c*) y = 15.293e$^{0.5085x}$
(*d*) r = 0.9989
(*e*) pressure = 2.72 MPa

10.15

y = 2.859 7x$^{1.125\ 7}$
R^2 = 0.998 7

Conveyor Capacity

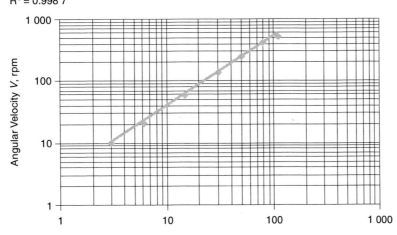

(*d*) r = 0.999 3
(*e*) C = 6 814 L/s = 6800 L/s

Answers to
Selected Problems

Chapter 11

11.1 (*a*) 15.9%

     (*b*) 0.1%

     (*c*) 95.4%

     (*d*) 50%

11.4 (*a*) 23.3%

     (*b*) 74.5%

     (*c*) 82.8%

11.5 21 190 cans

11.7 (*a*) 1714

     (*b*) 259

     (*c*) 14.29%

     (*d*) 139

11.8 $40K \pm 5K$ $p = 0.1587$

     $35K \pm 15K$ $p = 0.2514$

Chapter 12

12.1 F_X = 156 lbf →

     F_y = 99.4 lbf ↑

12.7 R = 42 kN   34°

12.10 Resultant T = 85 kN   36   77

12.13 F_1 = 1200 N   5 2

     F_2 = 1180 N   1 2

12.20 M_A = 4460 ft lbf

     M_B = 18 400 ft lbf

12.22 Unknown force S = 30 lbf ↓

     Location is 3.2 ft left of B

12.25 A = 6.3 kN ↑

     B = 5.4 kN   130°

12.29 A = 2.9 kN   190°

     B = 2.2 kN ↑

12.31 A = 360 lbf   28°

     B = 420 lbf   42°

12.34 Cable tension T = 2090 lbf   160°

     Reaction at A A = 2030 lbf   14°

Chapter 13

13.1 Minimum area for stress: $A = 271$ mm^2
Minimum area for elongation: $A = 235$ mm^2
Therefore: $A_{min} = 271$ mm^2
13.2 Required diameter: $d = 2.6$ cm
Choose next largest commercial size
13.7 Maximum load for stress: $L = 33$ kN
Maximum load for deformation: $L = 49$ kN
Therefore: $L_{max} = 33$ kN

Chapter 14

14.1 $A = 1260$ kg
$B = 872$ kg
14.3 106 lb
14.6 291 kg
14.10 Product = 0.3 t/h; alcohol = 80%; water = 14%; inert = 6%
14.13 Total input to evaporator = 19 t/h
Feed rate to crystallizer/filter = 17 t/h
Water removed by evaporator = 2.0 t/h
14.16 Dirty solvent produced = 12.7 t
Percent solvent in discard = 91%
Percent toxic removed in discard = 92.6%
14.19 40% concentrate req'd = 35 lb; 98% concentrate req'd = 215 lb
14.23 44 lbm
14.25 Feed rate = 99 t/h
Refuse composition: coal = 10%; ash = 45%; water = 13%
14.28 Flow rate of processed livers = 2000 lbm/h
Percent oil in processed livers = 1.0%
Percent ether in processed livers = 48%
Percent inert material in processed livers = 51%

Chapter 15

No solutions

Chapter 16

16.2 $V = 59.0$ mph
16.4 $d = 660$ ft
16.8 $V = 91$ mph
16.11 $V = 54.7$ ft/s
16.16 $u_2 - u_1 = 4.08$ kJ/kg
16.19 The efficiency of the invention is 42%, which is greater than the Carnot
Efficiency of 35.4%; therefore it is not a reasonable claim.
16.20 $T_H = 319°C$
16.23 (*a*) 70 hp
(*b*) 61.3 kW
16.26 # homes = 38 900
16.28 (*a*) 97.6%
(*b*) 3.432 kWh
(*c*) $0.34

Chapter 17

17.2 1.9×10^5 C

17.4 $I = 1.07$ A, $R = 7.03$ Ω

17.6 $P = 50$ W, $R = 3.2$ Ω

17.8 (*b*) $R_E = 52$ Ω

    (*c*) $I = 1.8$ A

    (*d*) $E_1 = 22$ V, $E_2 = 27$ V, $E_3 = 46$ V

17.10 (*b*) $R_E = 6.81$ Ω

    (*c*) $I = 0.881$ A

    (*d*) $I_1 = 0.50$ A, $P_1 = 3.00$ W

    $I_2 = 0.375$ A, $P_2 = 2.25$ W

    $I_3 = 6.0 \times 10^{-3}$ A, $P_3 = 0.036$ W

17.12 Current through 15-Ω resistor $= 1.3$ A

    Voltage across 15-Ω resistor $= 2.0 \times 10^2$ V

    Fraction of power consumed by 25-Ω resistor $= 17\%$

17.14 Charging current $= 3$ A

    Back-emf $= 1.2 \times 10^2$ V

17.16 (*a*) $I_{18H} = 2.22$ A, $I_{18V} = 4.44$ A, $I_{24} = 1.67$ A, $I_{12} = 2.00$ A, $I_8 = 2.00$ A

    (*b*) 533 W

    (*c*) 40.0 V

    (*d*) 48 W

17.18 (*a*) $I_1 = 11.1$ A, $I_2 = 10.6$ A, $I_3 = 21.7$ A, $P_{2.5} = 283$ W, $P_{1.5} = 183$ W, $P_{5.0} = 2.35$ kW

    (*b*) $I_1 = 18.0$ A, $I_2 = 6.00$ A, $I_3 = 24.0$ A, $P_{2.5} = 90.0$ W, $P_{1.5} = 486$ W, $P_{5.0} = 2.88$ kW

17.20 $I_{15Bat} = 1.17$ A, $I_{12Bat} = 0.83$ A, $I_{5.0V} = 2.00$ A, $I_{2.0} = 1.00$ A, $I_{5.0H} = 1.00$A, $I_{6.0} = 0.17$ A

    Power to 2.0-V battery $= 0.33$ W

    Voltage across 2.0-Ω resistor $= 2.00$ V

    Power consumed by 6.0-Ω resistor $= 0.17$ W

17.22 $R = 1.33$ Ω

17.24 (*a*) Current for $E_1 = 0.55$ A, Current for $E_2 = 9.3$ A

    (*b*) 1.4×10^2 W

    (*c*) 1.2 kW

    (*d*) 89%

17.26 Power delivered by 10-V battery $= 15$ W

    Power delivered by 16-V battery $= 1.0 \times 10^2$ W

    Current through 1-Ω resistor $= 8.0$ A

    Voltage across 0.8-Ω resistor $= 4.4$ V